THE HAMLYN
ENCYCLOPEDIA
OF PLANTS

Illustrated by: V. Choc, E. Demartini, K. Hísek,
J. Kaplická, K. Schmidtová, O. Ušák
Photographs by: B. Evenhuis (chapters 2, 4, 9) and
J. G. Nieuwendijk (chapters 1, 5, 6, 7, 8, 10)

Graphic design by: V. Šmerda
Designed and produced by Artia for
The Hamlyn Publishing Group Limited
London — New York — Sydney — Toronto
Astronaut House, Feltham, Middlesex, England
ISBN 0 600 33545 3
Printed in Czechoslovakia by TSNP Martin
1/12/02/51

The Hamlyn Encyclopedia of Plants

Dr. J. TŘÍSKA

Edited by Helen L. Pursey B.Sc., A. K. C., M. I. Biol.

HAMLYN

LONDON — NEW YORK — SYDNEY — TORONTO

CONTENTS

	PAGE
Below and above the Surface of the Water	7
On the Marshes and on the River Bank	23
Plants of the Seashore	51
Plants of Peat Bogs	69
Plants of Rocky Places	81
Plants of Grassland, Waysides and Sunny Slopes	99
Meadow Plants	133
Plants of Cultivated Fields	155
Plants of Waste Places	183
Woodland Plants	207
How to Use this Book	292
Glossary	292
Index of Scientific Names	295
Index of Common Names	297

FOREWORD

It is probably true to say that never before has man been so conscious of the part he plays in the environment today. The terms 'ecology' and 'conservation' have come to have real meaning for those who are genuinely concerned for the well-being of all living things, and not just for man. However it is not enough simply to consider plants and animals in general and, since they encompass an immense and sometimes bewildering variety of species, some effort is required for the layman to recognise and appreciate at least the more common types.

Today more people than ever before travel abroad and many of them take a great interest in the unfamiliar plants — and animals — which they come across in their travels. It is always helpful to have an illustration, preferably in colour, to which reference may be made and this volume attempts to include the wide range of plants, and not solely flowering plants, which may be found in Europe.

A number of these plants have a fascinating history since many are well-established herbal plants or have played some part in folklore. This is often reflected in their common names. Some details have therefore been given of the less familiar background of these plants and, where they are still in use today, brief reference is made concerning their value in agriculture, forestry and pharmacy.

Each plant is described by its family name, except where two or more species of the same genus occur in one chapter. The plants are also grouped and described according to the type of habitat in which they may be found. Obviously many plants are unselective or unspecialised and may be found in several, sometimes rather different, habitats but other plants are more specialised. These may then be restricted to one particular type of habitat. An obvious example is that of the bogmosses *(Sphagnum* spp.*)* which are restricted to acid and generally wet soils and especially bogs. Plants of this more specialised kind are often *indicators* of particular soil types, climatic conditions and other factors affecting plant distribution.

For the purpose of this volume, the plants have been described in their most important or characteristic habitat. Thus it is possible not merely to identify particular plants, but also to note other species with which they are associated and to have some understanding of what is meant by a 'plant community'. Plant ecology is the study of such communities and of their value and importance in the world today.

BELOW
AND
ABOVE
THE
SURFACE
OF
THE
WATER

INTRODUCTION

Water was the cradle of all life on earth and, beginning with plants and ultimately all other living things, it provided a constant environment for the whole basis of life. For many simple as well as higher plants, water has become their only habitat and such aquatic plants are perfectly adapted to their environment, growing and reproducing in lakes, ponds, ditches and rivers and, for some species, also in the sea.

Aquatic plants may grow entirely submerged, some living unattached and others being anchored by buried stems or roots. Others, although anchored, may produce leaves and flowers on the surface of the water; these are often known as floating plants and water-lilies are the most familiar example of this type. Others, similarly rooted, may develop leaves and bloom well above the water level or, as marsh plants, survive at the water's edge, tolerating more varied conditions of alternating periods of dryness and moisture.

Though water gives the plants more support than air, the plants have to withstand strong currents at times in the water, and of course the deeper the water the more pressure on the plant. There is also less light in the lower regions. Water temperature, however, is at all times more constant than the temperature of the air.

Water plants are perfectly adapted to their environment; this can be recognised by their shape (morphology), their physiology, including the way they photosynthesise (i. e. build up starch), respire, reproduce and disperse their seeds.

Carbon dioxide and oxygen are gases required by all plants for the vital functions of photosynthesis and respiration. Water containing small amounts of mineral salts is also essential. Unlike land plants, water and the dissolved gases can be absorbed through the thin walls of the surface cells of submerged plants. Not surprisingly roots are absent from many aquatic plants and, if present, never have root hairs. Stomata (or breathing pores) are also absent from the surface of submerged stems and leaves. Within the tissues, water-conducting elements are either reduced or completely lacking but interconnecting airspaces or chambers are abundant in all parts of the plant. These may also prevent water-logging of the tissues and help the plant to remain floating.

The stems and petioles (leaf-stalks) of water plants are usually long and flexible which makes it possible to adapt easily to movement and variations in water level. The underwater leaves usually have no epidermal pores i. e. stomata and are generally divided into threadlike segments which give the leaf an enlarged surface area and which easily adapt to the movement of the water. Some species have elongated, undivided, twisted leaves; these are similarly adaptable.

Leaves above the surface of the water, however, have a tough almost leathery texture and a circular shape which enables them to float easily and not be damaged by water movement.

8

They also have a number of pores in the upper epidermis of the leaves which is usually covered with a waxy layer. This gives mechanical strength and also prevents waterlogging and possible sinking of the leaves. Water plants are often heterophyllous. This means they have different kinds of leaves on the same plant. Generally the submerged leaves differ from those borne on or above the water surface. The flowers of plants below water are usually small, very simple and are pollinated by water. The pollination of flowers above water usually takes place by insects or sometimes by small molluscs.

The seeds of water plants are mostly furnished with various 'swimming' devices; others stick, with the aid of mucus or simply mud, to the feet, legs, beaks or feathers of water birds and are spread in this way. Other seeds are carried by fish and eaten, but they are not destroyed by the digestive system of the animal, and may actually germinate more rapidly.

Water plants basically rely on vegetative reproduction through various buds, including winter buds, or by the breaking off of pieces of stem. Many water plants are capable of adapting in another way should the water level sink considerably or even disappear altogether, by becoming marsh plants or land plants and living through periods of little or no water. Many will even flower under these conditions but may not actually produce fruits.

Water plants are perfectly adapted to their environment but they also change and influence these surroundings themselves. Through their growth they form an organic mass (humus) after the plants are dead. This is indispensable for the continuation of life in the water. They produce oxygen and thus aerate the water; they become a food source for other creatures living in water and they provide an environment necessary for many small organisms. These in turn become food for other animals, in particular fish. They provide a safe hiding place for fish and are often used as spawning grounds. Some water plants (chiefly sea-weeds) can be used by man as fodder for livestock and also as fertiliser.

Unfortunately, since water plants reproduce easily and quickly, they are capable of covering the surface of the water, thus keeping out light and warmth. They also restrict the movement of fish and, as the plants decay, make the water cloudy and putrid. The decaying parts of the plants may accelerate the growth of lake margins and reduce the area of open water; they can block locks and outlets, damage technical installations, hinder fishing and fish farming and, in extreme cases, even impede shipping.

Many single-celled and multi-celled small microscopic plants live in water and form a community with other small organisms of the sea and fresh water; these together are known as plankton. Besides bacteria *(Schizomycetes)* and simple fungi *(Phycomycetes)*, the algae are by far the most common form of life found in water. The blue-green algae *(Cyanophyceae)*, the diatoms *(Bacillariophyceae)* and the green algae *(Chlorophyceae)* are abundant in both fresh and sea water. Diatoms are especially important as they form the chief basis for life in water; they are eaten by animals which in turn are eaten by larger ones — and these 'food chains' culminate in man himself. The red algae *(Rhodophyceae)* and brown algae *(Phaeophyceae)* are essentially marine and some of the latter may reach enormous lengths.

9

WHITE WATER-LILY
Nymphaea alba L.
Family: *Nymphaeaceae*

The White Water-lily has a stout, creeping under-water rhizome of up to 7 cm. in thickness and 1 m. in length. It is a perennial plant and produces only floating leaves.

The floating leaves, with their long stalks, are rounded or heart-shaped with a deep triangular incision at the base. They often have a reddish tinge beneath. The smooth upper surface of the leaves permits rapid run-off of water and this also helps to prevent blocking of the stomata.

There is a thick wax deposit on the leaves which acts as a waterproofing agent. The young leaves, which form under water, are rolled. The stalks of the leaves are basically cylindrical and pliable, and have nume-rous air spaces and chambers. These make the stalks of the Water-lily light in weight and provide air sto-rage.

The flowers, which are often more than 10 cm. across, open during the day. They have four green sepals and many white petals which become smaller towards the middle of the flower as they merge with the stamens. The petals and stamens are actually attached to the ovary which bears a flattened disc of radiating rays — the stigmatic surfaces — and this is internally subdivided. Fertilisation is carried out by insects, mainly flies and beetles.

The fruit is a capsule shaped like a half-ball which sinks below the surface and falls off. The capsule then breaks, and the buoyant seeds are carried in a slimy mass, appearing in large numbers on the surface of the water. The slime eventually dissolves and the freed seeds sink to the bottom of the water or are carried further away by water birds, thus ensuring a wide dispersal.

The flowers of the Water-lily open at about 7.0 a.m. on sunny days and close up again in the late afternoon. This particular Water-lily grows in ponds or sluggish tributaries, but varieties are often cultivated as decorative plants on lakes in parks or gardens and may then have pink, red or yellow blooms. It grows anywhere in Europe and is known even in the Cau-casus.

Nymphaea alba

Nuphar lutea

SMALL WATER-LILY
Nymphaea alba ssp. *occidentalis* Ostenf.

This species is found in similar places and under similar conditions to the White Water-lily, but it is a rarer specimen. The stamens are found only on the lower part of the ovary. This Water-lily grows in Central and northern Europe as far as Lake Baikal in Russia. Both species of Water-lilies are often crossed and it is difficult to distinguish one from the other.

The Water-lily has always played an important role in legends and superstition. In almost all folklore, right across the world, the Water-lily is connected with mermaids and water nymphs. The Frisian people thought that if they displayed the Water-lily on their coat of arms it would be impossible to defeat the bearer. The ancient Slavic people used the Water-lily to scare away ghosts. It was also used as a good-luck charm, particularly for long journeys. The root stock would be carried right round a herd of cattle to protect them from being attacked by wild animals. The root stock of the Water-lily has a starch content of up to 40 percent and was often dried and ground to make flour. At times it was even used to tan leather.

13

YELLOW WATER-LILY, BRANDY-BOTTLE
Nuphar lutea L.
Family: *Nymphaeaceae*

This plant has a thick branched rhizome often more than 3 m. long and up to 10 cm. thick from which arise both leaves and flowers. As in the White Water-lily, long stalks carry the floating leaves to the surface. These leaves are oval with wide, deep, almost heart-shaped notches. They grow up to 40 cm. long and 30 cm. wide and are thick and leathery with forking veins. The Yellow Water-lily also forms submerged leaves. These are short-stalked, wrinkled and almost transparent and are produced throughout the summer. The stalks of the leaves are almost triangular in section; they are pliable and readily adapt to changes in the water level. Internally they contain air-spaces. Yellow flowers appear between June and August; they are between 4—6 cm. in size and have an alcoholic smell. They grow above the water surface and have five large yellowish sepals and numerous smaller yellow petals. The ovary is flask-shaped with a flat top bearing the radiating stigmas. After fertilisation, the fruit develops with many small compartments containing sticky seeds. On ripening the fruit bursts and small spongy segments containing numerous seeds break free and float away. The Yellow Water-lily also propagates through its rhizome, parts of which break off and grow into new plants.

This plant grows in still or slow-moving waters, often near the White Water-lily, and at depths of up to 3 m. This contrasts with the White Water-lily which does not grow below 2 m. The two types may be distinguished quite readily by the leaf differences. The leaves often shade the surface of the water which is basically undesirable. However, the undersides of the leaves provide plenty of nourishment for fish. They also often create marshy conditions through their decaying foliage.

The distilled flowers of this plant are made into a drink called *pufer cicegi* in Turkey. Sometimes parts of the rhizome are sold in markets as medicines to cure certain illnesses, though in fact their healing qualities are doubtful. The seller will often insist that the rhizome is an ancient Chinese drug (called *ging-seng* or *ching-seng*, or *nin-sin* in Japan).

COMMON WATER CROWFOOT
Ranunculus aquatilis L.
Family: *Ranunculaceae*

This plant has a rhizome from which branched stems of between 1—2 m. in length develop. It has two different types of leaf. The submerged leaves are finely dissected into thread-like segments which remain undamaged by water currents. They resemble a paint-brush when pulled out of the water. By contrast, the floating leaves have long stalks and are deeply lobed into broad wedge-shaped segments. Intermediate forms between the two types are common. Occasionally floating leaves may be absent. There are considerable variations in both submerged and floating leaves.

The white flowers are between 1—2 cm. in size and grow on long stalks above the water surface. When young they are protected by sepals which may later fall off. The 5 petals each have a rounded nectary at the base and enclose numerous stamens. The flowers submerge after fertilisation and the small beaked fruitlets form in little clusters. The submerged flowers remain closed and fruitlets are produced without fertilisation.

Water Crowfoot forms large colonies in either still or slow-flowing waters. It is widespread in Europe, Central and East Asia, tropical regions of South Africa as well as in North America.

AMPHIBIOUS BISTORT
Polygonum amphibium L.
Family: *Polygonaceae*

This plant can live both in water and on land but the two forms differ in vegetative features. The aquatic type has a long branched rhizome bearing floating stems of up to 1 m. with oval or heart-shaped, dark green floating leaves. It can be confused in appearance with other related species.

Between June and August pink or red flowers appear at the end of the stems in dense, cylindrical, terminal spikes. The fruit is a small shiny nut.

The plant grows in still or slow-flowing water as well as at the marshy water's edge. It usually develops into large colonies covering the surface with its leaves.

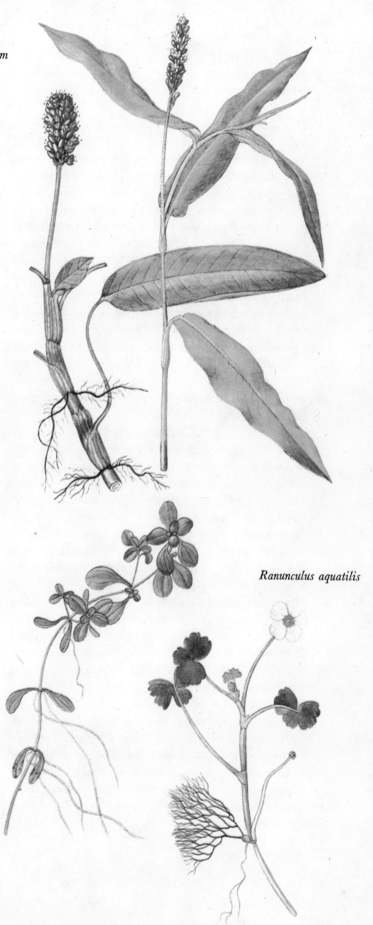

Polygonum amphibium

On dry land it is capable of surviving prolonged dry periods and has therefore adapted to ponds, as well as reservoirs, which have marshy margins and changing water levels.

Terrestrial plants have more or less erect stems with rough, hairy, oblong leaves. Flower spikes are less abundant than in aquatic forms. Colonies of the plant will often include both the water and land-growing varieties with some of the stems in water and some on land. It grows throughout Europe, Central Asia, South Africa and Mexico. Propagation occurs commonly through broken-off pieces of rhizomes or stems. A mixture made from the rhizomes is used as a household remedy for skin diseases.

STARWORT
Callitriche palustris L.
Family: *Callitrichaceae*

This small variable plant has slender weak stems more or less submerged and bears small paired leaves. The stems are anchored by small roots. The submerged leaves, covered with star-shaped hairs, are narrow and pointed but the shape of the leaves varies according to whether they grow in still or flowing water. It is an adaptable plant and when growing in mud, it develops elliptical leaves and the plant behaves as an annual.

Small flowers of different sexes appear during the summer months in the axils of the leaves. The male flower has a single stamen, while the female flower has an ovary with two thin styles.

The plant grows in clear, still or slow-moving water, and even in mud. The plant attracts attention because of its fresh green colour and the fact that it often stays green during the winter months, even beneath a sheet of ice. It is widespread, being found almost anywhere in the world, and is valuable as an oxygenator and as a source of food for fish.

Ranunculus aquatilis

Callitriche palustris

WATER CHESTNUT
Trapa natans L.
Family: *Trapaceae*

This annual or perennial plant has a stalk of up to 150 cm. in length, floating or anchored, and bearing numerous multi-branched roots. Submerged leaves have narrow blades, but floating leaves are rhomboid and, at the end of the stem, form broad rosettes. These latter are dark green, leathery and covered with brown hairs; their leaf stalks are long and have spindle-shaped swellings below the blade during the period of flowering. They carry both the plant and its fruit on the water surface.

Between June and August numerous solitary, white, long-stemmed flowers grow in the axils of the leaves which are above water. The fruit is one-seeded and a peculiar shape; it is turnip-shaped with a hard, stony inner wall and 2—4 stout, horn-like outer spines. The ripe fruits are 3 cm. across and hang in the water from the floating rosettes, from where they then become dislodged and sink.

The following spring, on germination, the root appears first, growing upwards and then bending over to anchor itself in the mud. The spines of the fruit (or nut) at first hold the sprouting plant firmly to the ground, but the mature plants break away and in May float to the surface of the water. The empty black nuts (or fruits) are often washed on to sandbanks in great numbers. The plant is thus unusual both in the type of fruit it bears and in its subsequent germination.

The plant grows in shallow water and on muddy ground in Central and South East Europe, Asia and China and originally this plant grew almost anywhere in the world. Fossils of the Water Chestnut have been found in chalk layers even in America where this plant is now extinct.

The white stone of the nut is tasty and nourishing since it contains much protein, fat and more than 50 percent of starch. The Water Chestnut has been used by man for food since Neolithic days. This has been proved through discoveries of prehistoric settlements. It is a delicacy today in many regions; it can be eaten raw or cooked, or it may be ground into flour.

The plant is cultivated in India including Kashmir, Japan, China, South Africa and Ceylon, and provides a valuable and necessary source of iron in the diet. Some lake-dwelling communities rely on it as a source of starch. The plant grows and spreads quickly under favourable conditions and will transform the surface of ponds into green meadows. In some areas it is used as pig food; elsewhere pendants, necklaces and bracelets are made from the nut.

WHORLED WATER-MILFOIL
Myriophyllum verticillatum L.
Family: *Haloragaceae*

This submerged plant has a long rhizome from which grow brittle, 3 m. long branched stems with leaves dissected into numerous hair-like segments. The overlapping whorls, each of which have 5 leaves and are about 5 cm. long, make a decorative pattern in the water.

Spikes of minute greenish flowers borne in whorls of 5, grow above the surface of the water during the summer. The flowers grow in the axils of bracts of variable length, with bisexual or female flowers in the lower part of the spike, and male flowers in the upper part. The fruits split into 4 small nutlets. Water-milfoil also propagates from the roots or stems which break off and grow into new plants. At the ends of the stems special ('winter') buds are formed in autumn; these enable the plant to overwinter.

As several buds are formed from each plant, vegetative reproduction thus takes place.

Whorled Water-milfoil grows in still and slow-moving waters, particularly in waters with a high calcium content, all over Europe, in Asia and North America. The Spiked Water-milfoil (*Myriophyllum spicatum* L.) is very similar with red, short stalks and smaller leaves in whorls of 4. The spikes of flowers are also shorter, and the lowest whorl of flowers has dissected bracts which are longer and larger than the flowers. It grows particularly well in calcium-rich waters and a deposit of lime can often be observed on the stalks or leaves. The plant grows all over Europe, and is also found in Asia, India, China, Japan, North Africa and North America; it appears even in Greenland.

16

Trapa natans

WATER VIOLET
Hottonia palustris L.
Family: *Primulaceae*

This plant floats in water and has a stem which may also float, or is sometimes anchored in the ground. The stem is between 20—60 cm. long with thin, white roots growing from the nodes in whorls. The submerged leaves are very fragile, pinnate and much dissected. Stems and leaves may be coloured red by small glandular nodules; these glands sometimes bear white hairs.

Between May and June the stem divides immediately below the surface of the water into a number of whorled inflorescences which grow above the water. Each whorl consists of 3—8 lilac flowers with flower parts in fives. While in bloom the plant is very conspicuous above the water surface but submerges again after a short period. The flowers actually submerge after fertilisation and then the fruits ripen into capsules. The Water Violet also propagates intensively through buds which are formed at the tips of the stems.

Water Violet grows in shallow, muddy waters, canals or ponds throughout Europe, in Eastern Siberia and Asia Minor. The plant was named after the botanist Peter Hotton of Leyden (1648—1709).

FRINGED WATER-LILY
Nymphoides peltata O. Kuntze
Family: *Menyanthaceae*

This plant has a long, slender, much branched rhizome which is anchored in the mud. The long, cylindrical stems bear rounded or oval leaves which are heart-shaped and deeply cleft at the base, and which are approximately 10 cm. long. They float on the water surface. The spring leaves are light green but later become dark green and shiny. The upper surface of the leaves may be purple and blotched, and the lower surface becomes purplish in colour.

Between June and July flowers of about 3 cm. in diameter grow above the surface of the water. The

Myriophyllum verticillatum

Hottonia palustris

17

Nymphoides peltata

flowers are golden-yellow and have 5 corolla lobes fringed with long hairs. The fruits ripen under water and release seeds which float to the surface. This plant also propagates by broken-off pieces of stem.

It grows in still and slow-flowing waters, forming large colonies, and is a plant of warmer regions. The Fringed Water-lily is found in Central Europe and across Europe and Asia to China and Japan. If the water level sinks, the plant survives in the mud but then rarely flowers.

GREATER BLADDERWORT
Utricularia vulgaris L.
Family: *Lentibulariaceae*

This submerged aquatic plant has long (up to 45 cm.) thin, sparingly branched stems. The leaves are much divided into thin segments and are about 3 cm. long. They bear small pear-shaped or rounded bladders. These trap small aquatic animals since the plant is carnivorous. The opening of each bladder is ringed with long sensitive hairs and is covered by a membrane which acts as a trapdoor. Lining each bladder are small glands which absorb water and thus lower the water pressure within. When any small aquatic animal, such as a water-flea, touches the hairs or the membrane, the latter suddenly opens and the animal is swept inside the bladder. There it dies and decays, possibly helped by digestive enzymes secreted into the bladder. Eventually the soluble break-down products, especially nitrogenous compounds, are absorbed by the wall and gland cells and are subsequently built up into the plant's proteins.

A long-stalked cluster of about 3—12 flowers appears above the water between June and August. The flowers have a reddish calyx and a yellow spurred corolla. The fruits are capsules. The Bladderwort propagates mostly through buds which survive the winter at the bottom of the pond, but also by the

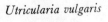

Utricularia vulgaris

Hydrocharis morsus-ranae

growth of new plants from broken-off pieces of stem. It grows in the warmer regions, in still waters rich in small animal life, and can be found in Europe, North Africa, North America and the temperate zones of Asia. Also growing in similar conditions are the Bladderworts *Utricularia neglecta* Lehm, *Utricularia minor* L. (Lesser Bladderwort), and *Utricularia intermedia* Hayne.

FROGBIT
Hydrocharis morsus-ranae L.
Family: *Hydrocharitaceae*

This aquatic plant has a short slender stem from which rosettes of floating leaves, and also roots, arise at the nodes. Each leaf is rounded or kidney-shaped with a smooth upper surface and a lower surface which is often violet in colour. The petiole (leaf-stalk) is long and has a pair of thin, papery stipules at its base. This is the sole member of the family with floating leaves.

At the base of every leaf-stalk (i. e. in its axil) grows a new cluster of leaves. These are therefore produced in abundance and thus the water is often covered with interconnected leaf rosettes. Buds, rich in starch, also develop in the leaf axils in the autumn. These fall off and pass the winter at the bottom of the pond or lake. The buds open in spring and appear as new plants on the surface of the water.

Frogbit flowers during summer. The flowers (1—2 cm. in diameter) grow in long stalks from the leaf axils and are unisexual. Each has 3 white-rimmed sepals and 3 crumpled white petals with basal yellow blotches. Male flowers contain 12 stamens. The female flowers are smaller, whiter and have longer stalks. Frogbit flowers in sunny places but hardly ever in shady positions. It grows in still waters, lakes, bays and ponds in all northern temperate regions.

WATER SOLDIER
Stratiotes aloides L.
Family: *Hydrocharitaceae*

Also known as Crab's Claw or Water-aloe, this aquatic plant has a short rhizome anchored in the mud, from which grow submerged rosettes of leaves 40 cm. long. These leaves are stiff and sword-shaped and have edges with spiny teeth. The leaves appear above the water during flowering time.

The plants, either male or female, bear white flowers in summer on stout flattened stems. The male flower has twelve stamens and often grows in clusters on a long stout stem. The female flower is smaller, solitary, and grows on a shorter stem. The fruit is a leathery berry and the seeds are covered by tissue. Since the plant is unisexual and also capable of vegetative reproduction, by forming rooted runners which in turn form new leaf rosettes, it is possible to come across areas populated by male plants only or by female plants only. Such fruits as may be produced are generally sterile. The rosettes, both young and old, sink to the bottom of the pond or lake just before winter begins. There they take root and thus survive the winter. The Water Soldier also forms egg-shaped winter buds.

It grows in still, muddy waters and often propagates to such an extent that a pond or part of a canal may become overgrown and eventually silted up. It may also be swept away from sheltered areas by currents of wind or water and may then establish itself elsewhere. The plant is well known in Central Europe, rare in North and Southern Europe but appears also in the Caucasus and in Siberia.

Stratiotes aloides

Elodea canadensis

Potamogeton natans

formed in the axils of the leaves. Mainly female plants are known in Europe and the plant reproduces vegetatively either through short, brittle shoots or through broken off pieces of the stem. Reproduction can be rapid and the plant can cover a pond or canal in a very short period of time.

The Canadian Pondweed originated in Canada, and only in 1836 did it appear in a pond in Ireland, possibly having been introduced by a botanist. A few years later it spread to England and Scotland. At one time it was thought that the plant would hinder canal boats and even cause flooding as it rapidly became abundant. A Berlin botanist brought the Pondweed into Germany during 1854—1860 and it has since spread right across Europe. It can be difficult to control since any single, broken-off piece can form a new plant and ultimately a large colony.

A heavy growth of Canadian Pondweed tends to shade the water and to hinder the movement of fish. When the plants decay the water becomes foul and low in oxygen content and may then be unfit for animal life. At times carp have been put into affected water. By disturbing the mud and so clouding the water, the light intensity is reduced so that the plants die off. In some areas it is used as food for pigs since it is similar in nourishment to clover. It is also used as a fertiliser.

BROAD-LEAVED PONDWEED
Potamogeton natans L.
Family: *Potamogetonaceae*

This robust plant has a rhizome with branches from which grow stems of over 2 cm. in length. Long thin leaf-like phyllodes appear in spring and were originally thought to be submerged leaves, but are actually flattened leaf-stalks. Floating leaves appear later and are longstalked, leathery and heart-shaped. The length of the leaf-stalk depends on the depth of the water as do other vegetative characteristics. Hybridisation with other species also produces a range of differing features and makes accurate identification more difficult.

Small spikes appear above the water surface during summer. They carry many tiny simple flowers with 4 stamens in a cup-shaped perianth. The pollen

In some areas it is used to feed pigs or as a fertiliser, and is a protected plant in some countries. At one time it had a reputation for healing wounds. The generic name comes from the Greek *stratiotese* meaning 'sword leaves', referring both to their shape, and stiff texture. *Aloides* means 'similar to the aloe'.

CANADIAN PONDWEED
Elodea canadensis Michx.
Family: *Hydrocharitaceae*

This aquatic, submerged plant has a rather long, slender stalk (sometimes over 1 m.), is densely bushy, and either floats or is anchored at the bottom of the water. The stems are covered with numerous overlapping, shiny, dark green leaves. These are finely-toothed and are generally borne in whorls of three.

The plants are unisexual. The small flowers appear on long stalks between May and August and are collects in the perianth and is carried by wind. The flowers submerge after fertilisation.

This plant forms extensive colonies in slow-flowing and stagnant waters. It is the most common form of Pondweed and grows in temperate and tropical regions all over the world.

SHINING PONDWEED
Potamogeton lucens L.

This plant has a yellowish-brown, mottled, creeping rhizome about 2 m. long with numerous oblong, lance-shaped leaves (10—20 cm.). All leaves are submerged, thin, shining light green and with 10—13 conspicuous veins. The leaves have practically no stalks and have minute teeth along the margins.

During the summer a stalk up to 6 cm. long, stout, and with its thick end upwards appears above the water. The small green and brown flowers are crowded together. Pollen is carried by the wind. The flowers submerge below water after fertilisation and green, 3—4 mm. long, narrow, beak-like fruits are formed. The plant reproduces vegetatively from broken-off pieces of the rhizome and the stem, and also forms numerous winter-buds.

It grows in still or slow-flowing water and often forms a submerged 'meadow'. It is known all over Europe, in North and West Asia as well as in North America. It makes rare appearances in South America.

PERFOLIATE PONDWEED
Potamogeton perfoliatus L.

This is another submerged species with a creeping rhizome. Stems branch off this and are densely covered with leaves. These clasp the stem with their heart-shaped lobes. The leaves are 2—6 cm. thick, shining and almost transparent and with 5—7 conspicuous veins. The leaves shine because the cells of the upper part of the leaf contain drops of oil. A 2—3 cm. long spike appears above the water during June and July covered by small flowers. The fruits are beak-like. The species does not survive if the water level falls as it is essentially a deep water plant.

The Perfoliate Pondweed grows in still, slow-flowing water in warm regions and can tolerate polluted water. It is known all over Europe — but not in Mediterranean countries — and is common in Algeria, Asia, North America and Australia. Because of the similarity of their leaves, *Groenlandia densa* (L.) tends to resemble the Perfoliate Pondweed and was formerly classified as a *Potamogeton*. This species is rare but may be distinguished by the leaves forming in opposite pairs along the stem.

Potamogeton lucens

Potamogeton perfoliatus

21

Potamogeton crispus

CURLED PONDWEED
Potamogeton crispus L.

This submerged species has a creeping rhizome bearing thin, four-angled stems, and is furrowed when mature. These stems are up to 2 m. long and are repeatedly branched. The leaves have wavy edges, are narrow, lance-shaped and are shiny and translucent. They often have rough teeth along the margin and are light green, brown or reddish. The colour depends on the depth of the water and the amount of available light.

The flower spike is short, thick and bears a few flowers only. The fruit is long and beak-like. During the summer, the winter-buds form short, dense, horny outgrowths on the stem. These buds break off easily and are washed ashore in great numbers. The Curled Pondweed oxidises the water and is used by trout as a hiding place. It is food both for fish such as carp and also crustacea.

The plant grows in still and slow-flowing water in temperate and tropical regions. It prefers water with a high nitrogen content and also grows at depths of more than 10 m. It is known all over Europe, Africa, North America and Australia but is not present in South America.

22

ON
THE
MARSHES
AND
ON
THE
RIVER
BANK

INTRODUCTION

The margins of lakes and rivers are rich in humus from dead plants and in the moist soil a luxuriant growth of marsh plants occurs. The environment is unstable, since the mud is soft and the water level tends to rise and fall. Despite these changes there is always a certain amount of free-standing water and the soil never dries out completely. However, marsh plants must be able to resist these changes and generally have spreading, well-branched rhizomes with numerous roots which anchor the plants. Internally, the plants develop numerous air-containing cavities. Growth of the plants is rapid and vigorous since there is a steadily replenished supply of humus in the soil.

A number of marsh plants have long firm stems with elongated sword-like or lanceolate leaves. The elasticity together with the firmness of the stems, prevents the plants from being torn out of the ground by strong winds. The long stems permit the leaves to stand well above the water level.

Marsh plants spread rapidly and their rhizomes give firmness to the ground since the mud settles around them and new growth is thus encouraged each year. Death and decay of the plants gradually causes the level of the ground to rise. In the process the water disappears and a transition zone is formed; the marsh plants are gradually replaced by different plants which thrive on the now drier ground. The marsh plants are then confined to the edge of the shallow water and retreat from the once marshy land which is now being transformed into dry land. Because of these changes ponds which are used for fishing have to be dredged from time to time and the roots of the marsh plants have to be removed, to prevent the pond being filled in. For successful pond management a good stock of marsh plants including reeds and so-called bulrushes is preserved, to encourage the nesting of various water birds.

Very near the water, but on already solid ground such as the banks of a river, brook, pond or lake are to be found a variety of bank or shore plants. They consist mainly of tall, dense, sometimes sprawling or creeping plants, which together form a distinct vegetation zone around the water. This is sometimes so dense it may form thickets. The continued growth of these plants is controlled both by the water content of the soil and also by the activities of man, who tends to grub out the plants and to build cement or stone dams in which rock plants may gradually take hold.

Along the riverbanks a range of trees and shrubs is found, especially different varieties of willow, poplar and alder.

The plants in the marsh contribute to the consolidation of the ground and the plants on the riverbanks help to protect the banks by their long roots and stems. They protect the ground from erosion by preventing the soil from being washed away. The long roots of the alder tree are especially valuable over a period of time as well as contributing to a more picturesque landscape.

MARSH MARIGOLD
Caltha palustris L.
Family: *Ranunculaceae*

This is a long-lived plant with stout, creeping rhizomes from which arise prostrate or erect stems 15—60 cm. long. These are smooth and hollow. The lower leaves are toothed, kidney-shaped, long-stalked, shiny and dark green. The upper leaves are fewer and smaller and are more triangular in shape. They are virtually stalkless. Marsh Marigold shows considerable variation in size and form.

The Marsh Marigold starts to flower early in spring with yolk-yellow shiny flowers up to 5 cm. in diameter, 5—8 petals and numerous stamens. The carpels are typically beaked or curved and develop into follicles which open before becoming dry in the fruit. The plant thrives in marshy, damp surroundings from the plains to upland regions all over Europe, as well as in some parts of Asia and North America. In mountainous areas it is dwarf and creeping.

The plant is poisonous and animals avoid it. Hay containing Marigold leaves in large quantities is of very poor value and leads to intestinal trouble in cows.

GREATER SPEARWORT
Ranunculus lingua L.
Family: *Ranunculaceae*

This is a perennial plant (50—120 cm.) with a thick, hollow rhizome. Smooth erect stems bear basal leaves in the autumn and these are long-stalked but often submerged. The upper leaves are long, lanceolate and short-stalked. They are borne in two rows and nearer the ground, they may clasp the stems.

In June and July appear large, yellow, glossy-petalled flowers up to 4 cm. in diameter. After pollination, the cone-shaped receptacle bears beaked achenes (small nutlike fruitlets) with a minutely pitted surface. The plant usually grows in marshes or shallow water and often in association with so-called bulrushes. It may be virtually submerged or may develop as a robust land-form. The Greater Spearwort appears in marshes, especially in the lowlands of Europe, in Siberia and also in India. It is never abundant.

Despite its widespread distribution in Europe it is rare in the Mediterranean region.

FINE-LEAVED WATER DROPWORT
Oenanthe aquatica (L.) Poiret
Family: *Umbelliferae*

This is a stout and stately plant with perennial rhizomes. The thick hollow stems grow up to 1.5 m.

Oenanthe aquatica

Ranunculus lingua

Caltha palustris

Sometimes the stem grows along the surface of the ground and it then roots at the nodes. Aerial leaves are much divided into small deeply lobed segments, and the submerged leaves are thread-like. Small white flowers compacted into numerous flat compound umbels, 2—5 cm. in diameter, appear in June and July. The umbels are opposite the leaves and at the ends of the stems. The fruits are small (3—4 mm.), egg-shaped or slightly angular.

The plant grows in shallow places near the water's edge, in slow-moving rivers and muddy bays. In almost dry fen ditches it may sometimes be found attaining a great size and may be difficult to eradicate. The plant grows from the plains to the hills all over Europe (except in northern Europe), in the western part of Asia and also in America. It was formerly cultivated for herbal use.

The plant is highly poisonous and contains substances which cause inflammation and colic in the digestive system. It has a strong and highly unpleasant odour. At one time it was used in pulverised form, on the tongue, as a remedy for coughs, kidney-trouble and even tuberculosis, but it has now been superseded by modern drugs.

COWBANE
Cicuta virosa L.
Family: *Umbelliferae*

Cowbane is a stout perennial plant (30—120 cm.). It has a thick rhizome with a sweet taste, smelling of celeriac and containing a yellow juice. The upright stems are hollow and bear 2—3 pinnate leaves up to 30 cm. long. Each leaf is divided into deeply serrate leaflets; the lower leaves have a long hollow petiole whereas the upper leaves are short-petioled and less divided. The umbels consist of numerous small white flowers produced from July to September. Fruits are ovoid (2—3 mm.).

The plant is found in muddy waters and marshes from the plains to the hills all over the northern part of the world. If uprooted by floodwaters the plants may take root again elsewhere. The most favourable habitat is rather acid marshy ground where the plant will spread and may rapidly take over the area.

Cowbane is extremely poisonous, probably the most poisonous of all the *Umbelliferae*. All parts of the plant contain poisonous alkaloids which are most concentrated in spring in the rhizomes. In addition an ethereal oil which is not poisonous is also present in the plant. The alkaloids react on the nervous system especially the brain. If swallowed, the poison causes vomiting, headaches, damage to the heart and brain, and eventual death. For this reason, in ancient Greece an extract of Cowbane was used as a method of killing convicted prisoners. Cowbane is closely related to Hemlock which has similar properties.

BOGBEAN
Menyanthes trifoliata L.
Family: *Menyanthaceae*

A perennial plant with creeping rhizomes, partially or totally submerged, the Bogbean bears trifoliate leaves above the water surface. The leaf-stalks have long sheathing bases and the leaflets are up to 7 cm. long with slightly toothed margins.

The flowering stems are leafless, erect and 12—35 cm. tall and bear pinkish-white flowers in a pyramidal cluster. The flowers are about 15 mm. wide, with sepals, petals and stamens in fives. The corolla is funnel-shaped with long white hairs inside; the anthers are violet. The ovary is globular and when ripe opens into two valves.

As a rule the plant grows semi-submerged in marshes, in transition-zones on river banks and on peaty ground from plains to upland areas. It is found over the whole of the northern part of the globe; in Europe as far as Iceland, in Asia as far as Japan and in North America as far south as California.

Bogbean, although widely distributed, has almost died out in some places because of drainage and widespread reclamation of ponds and marshes. In some countries it is now a protected plant. In other places, Bogbean was once used as a substitute for hops in brewing beer.

All parts of the plant contain a bitter-tasting substance together with iodine and iron compounds, and these have made it useful as a medicinal plant. Although very bitter, for a long time Bogbean has been used as a herbal remedy for medicinal purposes. The leaves are dried and made into a tea which is supposed to

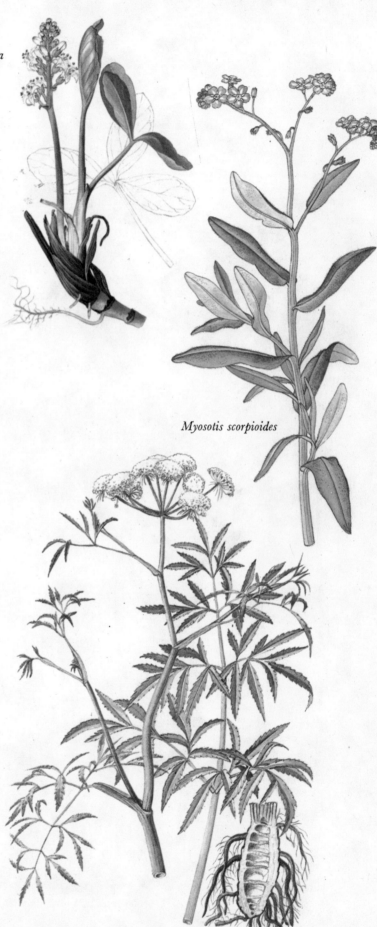

Menyanthes trifoliata

act both as a tonic and as a medicine in fevers and
stomach upsets.

WATER FORGET-ME-NOT
Myosotis scorpioides L.
Family: *Boraginaceae*

Water Forget-me-not is a perennial plant with 15—
45 cm. stems which are erect or creeping. These are
angular and bear stalkless, almost hairless, oblong
leaves. The flowers are cobalt blue (0.5—1 cm.) with
a yellow eye, but are occasionally pink or white. The
fruits are four shiny black nutlets.

This is a very common plant growing in marshy
grounds, woods and on the flat margins of standing
or slow-flowing waters, and is found all over Europe
(and some parts of Asia) from the plains to the mountains. It is also sometimes found on the Pacific side
of North America. It is a very hardy plant and can
also grow submerged in water.

Myosotis scorpioides

BROOKLIME
Veronica beccabunga L.
Family: *Scrophulariaceae*

Brooklime is a perennial plant with stems up to .5 m.
in length. These are often prostrate and may root
at the nodes. The leaves are paired, oval, shiny and
short-stalked. The deep blue flowers (5—7 mm.)
have four unequal corolla lobes, are long-stalked and
grow in open clusters at the upper part of the stem,
10—30 flowers in a cluster. Flowering time is from
about May to August. The fruits are smooth and
rounded.

Brooklime grows mostly in large clumps in shallow
brooks, marshes and ditches with clear water. The
plant grows sometimes half or fully submerged and
may also develop as a land-form. The submerged
plant will sometimes stay green throughout a mild
winter. The plant grows in Europe, in West and
North Asia as far as the Himalayas and also in North

Cicuta virosa

Veronica beccabunga

America. Brooklime is a common and widely distributed marsh plant. It is somewhat fleshy and the leaves and sap were formerly made up into a herbal remedy for a variety of ailments including jaundice and other liver complaints, asthma and even tuberculosis.

FLOWERING RUSH
Butomus umbellatus L.
Family: *Butomaceae*

A perennial marsh plant, the Flowering Rush has a fleshy rhizome up to 1 cm. in thickness. The leaves, which grow from a rosette-shaped base, are 1 m. long, rush-like, triangular in section and with a sheathing base. Erect smooth leafless stems grow out of the rosette and bear terminal umbels of flowers, which are 2.5—3 cm. across and open in succession. Beneath each umbel there are 2—4 pointed papery bracts. The flowers have 6 petal-like segments which are pink with darker veins. There are 6—9 red stamens. The plant flowers between June and August. The fruit consists of 6—9 follicles surrounded by the persistent perianth. Each follicle is purple when ripe and contains many seeds. These are distributed by water. In deeper moving water the plant forms leaves over 2 m. long but does not flower.

The family to which the Flowering Rush belongs is a small one and this plant is the only European member. It is found all over Europe and Asia, but is never common. The plant grows in ditches, ponds and canals, and at margins of rivers.

The strongly bitter-tasting rhizome contains more than 50 percent starch, also protein and fat. In some parts of the East the plant was often used for food. Even today the rhizomes are used dried, baked or ground. The rhizomes when roasted can be used as a coffee substitute.

Butomus umbellatus

ARROWHEAD
Sagittaria sagittifolia L.
Family: *Alismataceae*

This is a perennial plant with large, long-stalked, arrow-shaped leaves arising from a thick, short rhizome, which also develops a number of runners. The leaves develop as a basal rosette and are usually of 3 different types. Below water there are ribbon-shaped translucent leaves; floating leaves are oval or lance-shaped and the aerial leaves (blade 5—20 cm.) are characteristically arrow-shaped and long-stalked. The flower stems are 30—90 cm. in length and three-sided. They bear whorls of 3—5 unisexual flowers, each encircled by 1 or 2 bracts, which open between June and August. The lower whorls of the inflorescence bear the female flowers, the upper whorls bearing the male flowers. All flowers are about 2 cm. across and have 6 white perianth segments — the inner segments with a dark violet patch at the base. Male flowers have long stalks (about 20 mm.) and numerous stamens, while female flowers have stalks about 5 mm. long and numerous flattened carpels spirally arranged on a large receptacle. The fruit is a rounded cluster (1.5 cm.) of one-seeded nutlets.

Arrowhead is widespread in shallow marshy margins of ponds, canals and slow-flowing rivers. The plant thrives in Europe as well as in Asia, the Himalayas, Japan and on the island of Formosa.

The plant forms bluish corm-like buds, especially in autumn, and these contain starch and protein. In fact they contain more protein than potatoes. Fresh capsules taste like nuts and in China they are boiled like peas and are also cooked in an open fire like potatoes.

WATER-PLANTAIN
Alisma plantago-aquatica L.
Family: *Alismataceae*

This is a perennial plant with erect stems up to 100 cm. in height. These are smooth and unbranched and develop long-stalked basal leaves. Water and land forms of the plant have different types of leaf. Floating leaves are elongated but aerial leaves have oval blades (8—20 cm.) with heart-shaped bases. The stems bear, from July to September, terminal branched and py-

ramid-shaped inflorescences. The flowers are pale lilac and 1 cm. across. They are long-stalked with six stamens and six petal-like perianth segments, the outer oblong, the inner rounded. The flowers open only in the afternoon. The fruit is a cluster of flattened nutlets.

The leaves and rhizomes of the plant contain toxic compounds but these are rendered harmless when the plant is dried. The rhizomes contain starch and are eaten dried in some parts of Russia. Here, too, Water-plantain was formerly used against rabies and in Sweden the juice may still be used as a compress for headaches.

The Water-plantain grows in muddy ground beside streams and in marshes all over the northern half of the globe, often in association with Arrowhead and Flowering Rush.

Sagittaria sagittifolia

Alisma plantago-aquatica

FLOATING WATER-PLANTAIN
Luronium natans (L.) Raf.
Family: *Alismataceae*

This is a slender herb with stems which are 50 cm. or more long and which are floating but rooted at the base. The lower leaves are totally submerged and are reduced to flattened translucent petioles about 2 mm. wide and up to 10 cm. long. The upper leaves are floating, with long petioles and elliptical blades up to 2.5 cm. across.

The few flowers are 1—1.5 cm. across and are white with a central yellow spot. They are produced in July and August. The fruit is a hemispherical cluster of 10—12 nutlets.

This perennial plant is native to Britain but is uncommon. It grows in lakes and canals with acid waters and is said to be on the increase. It is found in most of western Europe as well as southern Norway, Poland and Bulgaria.

LESSER WATER-PLANTAIN
Baldellia ranunculoides (L.) Parl.
Family: *Alismataceae*

This is a very variable plant between 5 and 20 cm. high. It is a smooth perennial herb with erect leafless stems bearing terminal umbels of pink or purplish flowers which appear between May and August. The narrow lance-shaped leaves grow in a basal rosette. The flowers are up to 1.5 cm. across and open in succession. The fruit is a dense globular head of nutlets. A widely distributed native British plant, *Baldellia* is locally common in damp margins of streams, lakes and ditches. It is absent from the extreme north of Scotland but is generally distributed in Europe to 60° north in western Norway and is also found in North Africa.

POLICEMAN'S HELMET, HIMALAYAN BALSAM
Impatiens glandulifera Royle
Family: *Balsaminaceae*

This is a handsome plant, a native of the Himalayas as the common name implies; it is planted in gardens

whence it has escaped to waste places and river-banks so that it has now become quite naturalised.

It is a smooth robust annual herb 1—2 m. high with stout reddish stems which are ribbed and hollow and which bear toothed pointed leaves in pairs or in threes. At the base of each leaf stalk is a pair of stalked glands. The leaves may grow up to 15 cm. long.

The purplish-pink (rarely white) flowers are large and handsome, 2.5—4 cm. long, and bilaterally symmetrical with a large upper petal and the other 4 joined in pairs to form a lower lip. The lowest of the 3 coloured sepals is large, pouched and spurred.

There are 5 stamens. These distinctive flowers are borne on long stalks in spikes of 5—10 which develop in the axils of upper leaves and are produced between June and October. The flowers are pollinated by bumble-bees and the fruits are capsules which split explosively when touched into 5 segments.

YELLOW FLAG
Iris pseudacorus L.
Family: *Iridaceae*

A plant with a stout (3—4 cm. diameter) branched rhizome from which develop broad, sword-shaped leaves and flattened, branched flowering stems. Leaves and stems are 40—150 cm. high. The flowers are large (8—10 cm.), yellow to orange in colour and in clusters of 2—3. Each is enclosed when in bud by 2 leafy bracts with papery margins. There are 6 petal-like perianth segments which are fused at the base into a short tube.

Like all Irises, the 3 outer perianth members *(falls)* are larger and often purple-veined, while the inner ones are shorter, more slender and straight. There are 3 stamens partly hidden by the 3 petal-like styles. The fruit is a 3-sided capsule containing numerous brown seeds.

The plant is abundant and is found in marshes, swampy woods, ditches and watersides over the whole of Europe, North America and northern Asia. The rhizome contains tannin which was formerly used in tanneries, combined with sulphate of iron, to give a black dye.

At one time the rhizome was used medicinally. The leaves and roots are poisonous to livestock.

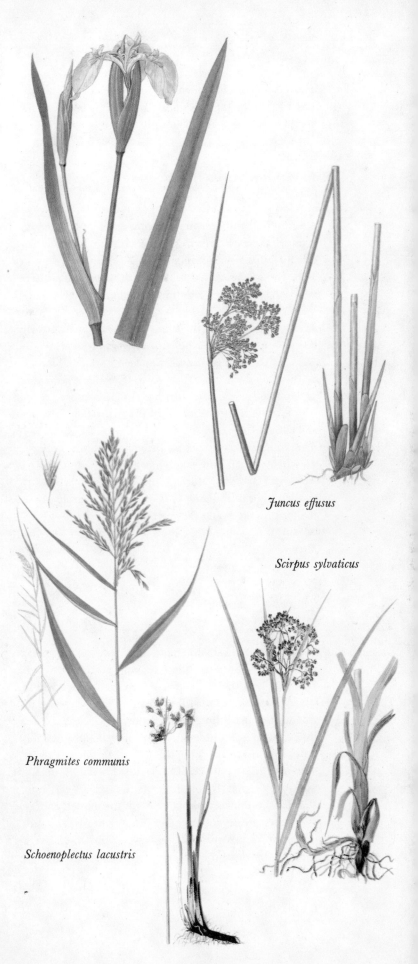

Iris pseudacorus

WOOD CLUB-RUSH
Scirpus sylvaticus L.
Family: *Cyperaceae*

A stout perennial herb 30—100 cm. in height, the
Wood Club-rush has creeping rhizomes. The stems
are smooth, three-sided and leafy; leaves are long,
2 cm. wide, flat, grass-like and rough-edged. The
inflorescences are large (15 cm.), terminal, spreading
and branched.

The plant flowers from May to August. Individual
flowers are tiny with a perianth of 1—6 bristles, 3
stamens and an ovary bearing 3 stigmas. The fruit is
a small (1 mm.) three-sided nutlet.

Wood Club-rush is widespread but not common and
may be found in shallow water at the edges of ponds,
in damp meadows and woods over virtually the whole
of Europe (except the extreme north and south),
Siberia and North America. In spring the plants are
a conspicuous bright yellow-green.

Wood Club-rush is a large rather handsome plant.
Many of the related types formerly grouped with it
have been reclassified. For example, the Bulrush
(Schoenoplectus lacustris) was formerly *Scirpus lacustris*.
This splitting into different genera is usually based
on rather minor features.

SOFT RUSH
Juncus effusus L.
Family: *Juncaceae*

Soft Rush is a perennial plant 30—150 cm. in height.
The stems are yellowish-green and filled with a white
spongy pith.

Small, split scale-like leaves sheathe the base of the
stems. The inflorescence is rounded or spreading,
borne to one side and one third of the distance below
the top of the stem.

The fruits are yellowish brown capsules. Soft Rush

Juncus effusus

Scirpus sylvaticus

Phragmites communis

Schoenoplectus lacustris

is always to be found in wet pastures, damp woods and bogs from the lowlands to the hills, both in the northern and southern hemispheres.

BULRUSH
Schoenoplectus lacustris (L.) Palla.
Family: *Cyperaceae*

A perennial with creeping rhizomes and long, smooth, cylindrical, dark green, 2 m. stems, the Bulrush has tufts of submerged leaves.

The stems have a rush-like texture and are often used for basket making and thatching. Paper is made from the pith.

At the upper end of the stems are the reddish-brown flower spikelets. The Bulrush flowers from June to August, the flowers and fruits being rather similar to those of the Club Wood-rush. The plant seems to prefer a silty substrate and has spread almost everywhere in Europe, also into Asia, Australia, North and Central America.

The abundant rhizomes and stems may form a dense growth at river and pond margins so that the free water surface is reduced. In spring the rhizomes contain starch and sugar; if ground and dried these make a sweet flour. A sweet syrup is produced by boiling the rhizomes of Bulrush and condensing the juice.

COMMON REED
Phragmites communis Trin.
Family: *Poaceae (Gramineae)*

A strong bamboo-like perennial, grey-green in colour which grows 1—3 m., the Common Reed can reach 10 m. in height. It is found in marshy ground where it forms dense clumps like thickets. The leaves, flat, smooth and with long-pointed tips, grow up to .5 m. long and 10—20 mm. wide. They have long sheathing bases and these are loose so that all the leaves point one way in the wind. The leaves break off in the autumn so that the leafless stems and flowerheads stand bare during the winter. At the upper end of the stems grow soft, feathery flowerheads (15—40 cm.) with spikelets of 3—7 flowers, brown-violet in colour. Between the flowers are silky hairs which,

after the plant has flowered, grow longer so that the plant appears silver-haired. The ovary is small and two-styled and develops into a nutlet.

The Reed spreads extensively by means of its creeping rhizomes. These lengthen in the mud and quickly produce new stems. These in turn may develop roots at the nodes, thus establishing new clumps of plants. In this way the Reed can grow out into deeper water and thus reduce the water area. In time it will fill in the pond or ditch in which it is growing.

The plant thrives at the edges of still waters, in marshes and peaty ground and in wet meadows. It indicates the presence of water below ground and is considered a weed which is difficult to eradicate. Reeds are found all over the world except for a few tropical regions such as the River Amazon in South America. The plant is also absent where the soil is very poor or acid.

The young shoots of Reed contain up to 5 percent sugar. In former days when times were hard, the rhizomes were eaten raw, or baked and ground into flour, and were also roasted as a coffee substitute. The uses of Reed are manifold, e. g. for thatching, basket-making and as insulation between walls. In some areas Reed is used for litter in stables. Today the straw is used to produce artificial silk and cellulose. Glycerine and tannin are also found in the plant.

REED-GRASS
Phalaris arundinacea L.
Family: *Poaceae (Gramineae)*

A perennial plant not unlike Small Reed *(Calamagrostis arundinacea)*, the Reed-grass grows up to 2 m. in height. It spreads by creeping, underground rhizomes with clumps of erect smooth stout stems. The leaves are long and flat, 1—2 cm. wide. The flowerhead (panicle) is lobed, pale green or purplish and spreading. The plant flowers from June to July, growing in marshes and by watersides all over Europe, in North, East and West Asia, in North America and in South Africa.

The plant is used in much the same way as the Reed; it is also harvested as a good feed stuff for stock. In some places the plant is cultivated as a forage grass and can be cropped three times a year.

SWEET FLAG
Acorus calamus L.
Family: *Araceae*

This is a sparse perennial plant which grows up to
1 m. in height and which has a stout (3 cm.) creeping
rhizome which is spongy, and white or pink inside.
Leaves are swordlike with a wavy margin, up to 1 m.
tall and with a thick midrib. They smell sweet when
crushed. The flowering stems are three-sided with
a long, leafy tip.

The small, often unisexual, yellowish-green flowers
are produced between May and July and grow as
a tightly packed club-shaped mass on a thick stem
(spadix). This is usually 8 cm. long and grows at one
side of the flowering stem about two thirds of the length
from the base, projecting at an angle of 45 degrees.

The fruits are oblong red berries which form only
in East Asia — not in Europe. Sweet Flag is native to
Asia and America but was brought to Europe as
a medicinal herb. It is now found in Central and
Eastern Europe, northern Italy, the Balkans and
throughout the tropical and subtropical parts of Asia.
Sweet Flag was said to have been introduced to Vienna
in 1574. It was given to the botanist Clusius who
cultivated it in the botanical gardens. Other reports
say it first found its way to Prague in 1557. Later, it
was planted out in the open.

Sweet Flag smells sweetly aromatic, not unlike a
tangerine. From it is obtained Oil of Calamus which
is used for flavouring. The rhizome also contains
starch. The rhizome was known to the Indians, Arabs,
Greeks and Romans and was greatly valued by them
as medicine; the extract was used to cleanse wounds
— also for stomach troubles and other ailments. It was
thought to aid the digestion and was added to bath-
water for nervous disorders. Chewing the rhizome
was thought to provide immunity from infectious
diseases. The prepared rhizome of the Sweet Flag can
be used in the production of alcoholic beverages. Even
today, together with other herbs, Sweet Flag is used
in the making of Benedictine liqueur. The aromatic
rhizomes have recently been used in the production
of toothpaste, perfume and sweets. In Turkey candied
Sweet Flag is a speciality.

Phalaris arundinacea

Acorus calamus

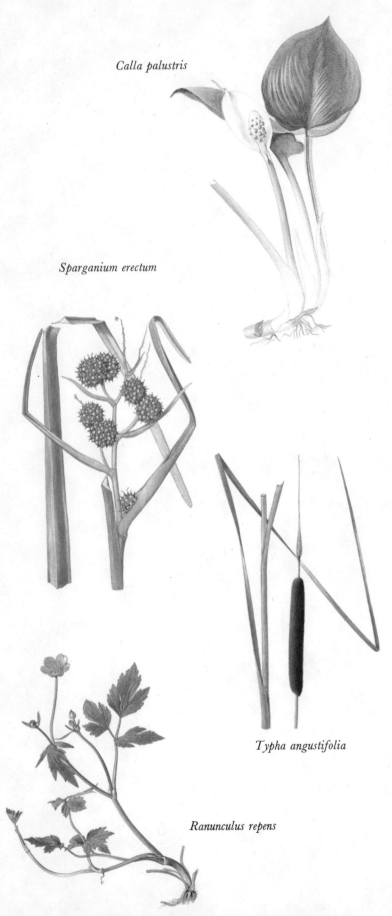

Calla palustris

Sparganium erectum

Typha angustifolia

Ranunculus repens

BOG ARUM
Calla palustris L.
Family: *Araceae*

Bog Arum is a perennial plant (15—30 cm.) with a stout underwater rhizome from which grow long-stalked, shiny, heart-shaped leaves with pointed tips. They are 4—11 cm. wide. The leafless flower stems develop directly from the rhizome and form a 6—7 cm. flower sheath, flat and oval, green on the outside, white inside. Within this is a short, stout stem *(spadix)* with small, densely clustered, unisexual flowers.
The fruits are red, bitter berries with violet seeds surrounded by a transparent jelly; they are spread by birds and water.
The plant is to be found in marshes and lakes in northern and Central Europe (except Switzerland) and in northern Asia. It was introduced in Britain in 1861. The fresh rhizomes are poisonous but when dried are harmless and were formerly ground up for flour in northern countries.

BRANCHED BUR-REED
Sparganium erectum L.
Family: *Sparganiaceae*

An aquatic perennial (30—200 cm. in height), Branched Bur-reed has erect, sword-shaped leaves, 10—15 mm. wide, keeled and triangular in section. Flowers are small, unisexual and greenish, in stalkless round clusters arranged in somewhat leafy branched spikes. The male clusters are at the top, the female at the bottom. Flowering time is from June until August and pollination is by the wind. After pollination the flowers swell into bur-like heads of beaked fruits.
The plant grows freely in marshes, shallow waters and by the margins of slow-moving rivers, especially in lowlands, in Europe and Asia, in the Arctic Circle and eastwards to Japan.

REEDMACE, FALSE BULRUSH
Typha latifolia L.
Family: *Typhaceae*

This is a robust perennial plant, up to 3 m. high, with characteristic dense brown cylindrical spikes. It has long creeping yellow-brown rhizomes and thrives in marshy ground. The lanceolate leaves are longer than the stems and are borne in two rows. The leaves have long sheaths and are 10—20 mm. wide. They are stiff and fleshy and the bases are often partly submerged.

The inflorescence consists of two cigar-like flower spikes, 10—30 cm. long, borne immediately above each other. Each contains a number of small unisexual flowers. The male flowers are uppermost and they drop off after the pollen is shed, leaving a slender terminal spike. The female flowers, surrounded by soft hairs, form the familiar 'bulrush'. The fruits are cotton-tufted nutlets spread by the wind. The plant flowers from June to July.

The Reedmace grows, like the Common Reed, in marshy ground especially in reed swamps rich in silt or organic matter. It also grows in ponds, canals, slow-flowing rivers and by lake margins generally in lowlands. It is found over the whole of Europe and to 30 degrees south from the Arctic Circle as well as in parts of the tropics; it is also found in Australia and Polynesia. It is not found in Central or South Africa.

LESSER REEDMACE
Typha angustifolia L.

This is not unlike the Reedmace described above but the leaves are narrower — only 3—10 mm. wide. The male and female spikes are separated by a gap of 1—3 cm. The plant has a similar distribution to that of the Reedmace, but is not found south of Louisiana in America. It is usually much less common.

The rhizomes are rich in starch and protein. In Asia, North America and some other countries they were used as food, e. g. as a coffee substitute, boiled as asparagus and ground as flour for baking. They were also fed to pigs. Today the chief use of the leaves is for making mats, hats and bags and also as a roofing material.

PLANTS OF MARSH AND MOIST PLACES

Marshland and shallow muddy waters are usually the transitional stage between water and dry land and it is here that the marsh flora is found, benefiting from the rich supply of humus in the soil and from the mineral salts released by plant decay into the water. Such plants can also tolerate the oxygen deficiency of water-logged soils.

Despite the challenges of this unstable environment, a characteristic population of plants is found but, as the marsh begins to dry out, other plants take their place. Such plants rarely show features associated with the more aquatic species, for example, different types of leaf on the same plant, but they thrive in moist places although they may well be found in other habitats also. A much wider range of plants comes into this category and includes trees and shrubs in addition to herbaceous plants.

CREEPING BUTTERCUP
Ranunculus repens L.
Family: *Ranunculaceae*

This is a perennial herb with long, creeping stems reaching .5 m.

The basal leaves and lower stem-leaves have 3 lobes, the central lobe being long-stalked and the other lobes cut into 3 toothed segments. Upper leaves have thin, usually entire, segments.

The typical glossy yellow buttercup flowers appear between May and August but the plant often continues to flower until late autumn. The carpels are somewhat flattened, bordered and they have a rather short but conspicuous beak.

Creeping Buttercup is very variable and adaptable. The creeping stems root easily at the nodes.

The plant is well known all over Europe, in Siberia as far as the Kamchatka, as well as in North Africa. It has also been introduced into North, Central and South America, and New Zealand. The plant flourishes on riverbanks, in damp meadows, in woods and beside paths. It can also be found in dune-slacks and on gravel heaps and as a garden weed.

HORSERADISH
Armoracia rusticana Gaertn. Mey and Scherb.
Family: *Cruciferae*

This robust perennial herb has thick fleshy roots and much-branched flowering stems up to 125 cm. long. At the base of these is a rosette of large leaves. These leaves are long-stalked, 30—50 cm. long, and oval with a toothed margin. The leaves on the flowering stems are smaller, with the lower ones often pinnate, the upper leaves being shorter and often only slightly lobed, or even entire.

Small (8 mm.) white flowers appear in May and June and form dense clusters which later elongate. The 4 petals are twice as long as the sepals. There are 6 stamens. Fruits are rarely produced on plants found growing in Europe, and so here the Horseradish plant spreads very successfully through broken-off pieces of root.

Horseradish grows near water, mainly as a wild plant. It was brought originally from eastern Europe and the borders of West Asia. It spread across the whole world and is cultivated both as a popular mustard-like condiment and formerly as a medicinal plant. It is because of this widespread use that the plant now also grows wild along banks of streams and near lakes.

It is known that Horseradish has been cultivated since the 12th century. The fleshy roots are said to contain twice as much vitamin C as lemons. In addition, pungent oils and other compounds are present which not only give the root (and other parts of the plant) its sharp flavour but also, because of their extremely irritant nature, make the plant poisonous to livestock.

Besides its popular use as a condiment with meat, Horseradish is also used as a medicine. It is used to stimulate the appetite and was formerly valued for its high vitamin C content, being used as a tonic. A syrup is made from the ground root; this loosens coughs and helps to relieve inflammation of the mucous membranes. The practice of applying Horseradish paste as a poultice to parts of the body to increase circulation is still well known in some parts of the world, as is its use in bringing relief in rheumatic illnesses.

SOAPWORT (BOUNCING BETT)
Saponaria officinalis L.
Family: *Caryophyllaceae*

Soapwort is a stout perennial with many erect flowering stems (30—90 cm.). The leaves are elliptic or oval, three-veined, and 5—10 cm. in length. The flowers are borne in dense terminal inflorescences and, in cultivated forms, are often double. These flowers (2.5—3 cm.) appear in the leaf axils and usually have a hairy, reddish calyx surrounding 5 pink or flesh-coloured shallowly notched petals. Each petal bears 2 scales. Flowers appear between June and September and are sweet-scented, especially at night. They are pollinated mainly by hawkmoths. The fruit is egg-shaped with black seeds.

Soapwort grows almost anywhere, from low ground to hillsides. It prefers, however, situations such as the banks of rivers and lakes, also damp woods. The plant is well known in Central and southern Europe, in Asia Minor, Siberia and Japan. It also appears in North America where it was introduced from Europe. The plant is cultivated in some countries including Austria, Hungary and Germany, where it grows in gardens and fields. It is harvested and used for medical and other purposes.

All parts of the plant, but in particular the roots contain saponins which are poisonous. Saponins form suds like soap when mixed with water and the prepared roots are used for washing and cleaning delicate tapestries and woollen materials which might be damaged by ordinary soap or washing powders. The saponins are removed when the plant is used medicinally and it is still regarded as a useful herbal remedy for gout and rheumatism. Soapwort leaves are still used as a herbal tea. Other extracts are made from the roots and used for easing coughs. The plant has also been used to treat boils and skin diseases.

MEADOWSWEET, DROPWORT
Filipendula ulmaria (L.) Maxim.
Family: *Rosaceae*

This hardy herbaceous plant may reach 120 cm. The leaves are both basal and also on the stems. They are pinnate with 8—20 pairs of large leaflets and many

Armoracia rusticana

small ones; they are oval and dentate, usually dark green on the upper side, white and woolly beneath. The numerous small flowers appear in flat-topped terminal clusters, creamy white and smelling of bitter almonds. The stamens protrude beyond the petals. The plant flowers between June and August, in damp meadows and woods, swamps, marshes and ditches. It is absent from acid peat. Because of the light coloured flowers and rich aromatic scent, it is a familiar and conspicuous plant. After fertilisation, the 6—10 green carpels develop into 2 mm. fruits which later become brown and spirally twisted. Meadowsweet occurs all over Europe and in northern Asia as far east as Mongolia.

The plant contains tannins, small quantities of vanilla and various other substances. The leaves and flowers of Meadowsweet can be collected, dried and made into herbal tea. In Portugal the roots are gathered and used to treat kidney and gall bladder trouble. Formerly, it was used to ease the pain caused by gout and was also thought to be efficacious against snake poisoning. The flowers have been used in Scandinavia to flavour beer and wine.

WATER AVENS
Geum rivale L.
Family: *Rosaceae*

Filipendula ulmaria

This is a perennial herb with a short, thick rhizome and reddish, hairy stems 20—60 cm. high. The basal leaves are pinnate, toothed, hairy and large, with 3—6 pairs of small oval leaflets and a large terminal one 2—6 cm. long. The flowers are nodding and bell-shaped and appear from May to September. The calyx is purplish and hairy, the petals 1 cm. long, pink or yellowish. The carpels later become hooked. The fruit is a kind of bur and is animal-dispersed. Water Avens grows along banks and in marshy places, also in wet fields, especially where it is shady.

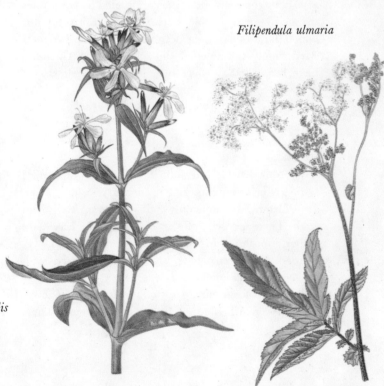

Saponaria officinalis

It is found in cool and temperate zones of Europe, Asia and North America.

PURPLE LOOSESTRIFE
Lythrum salicaria L.
Family: *Lythraceae*

This is an erect perennial, 60—120 cm., with a woody rhizome. The stems are downy, four-angled or with 4 raised lines. They are sparingly branched. The leaves are 4—7 cm., mostly opposite or in whorls of 3 and are stalkless. They are oval or lance-shaped and have an entire margin. The heart-shaped base half clasps the stem. The leaves on the upper part of the stem may be alternate. The inflorescences are long (up to 30 cm.), dense, cylindrical and leafy and borne at the ends of the stems. They contain numerous flowers, bright rosy-purple and they appear from June to September.

The flowers (1—1.5 cm.) are in whorls and are found in three forms on different plants — varying in length of styles and stamens, and in the size of the pollen grains. Such variations tend to encourage cross-pollination and thus produce more vigorous daughter plants.

The plant has been used for a variety of purposes, e. g. the flowers produce a dye used in making sweets, also both rhizome and leaves are boiled as vegetables in some areas. Purple Loosestrife contains tannins which in times past have been used for tanning leather. Medicinally, extracts of both leaves and rhizomes have been used to check bleeding and diarrhoea.

YELLOW LOOSESTRIFE
Lysimachia vulgaris L.
Family: *Primulaceae*

This is a hardy and robust herbaceous perennial with a long, creeping and branched rhizome. From the rhizome develop softly hairy stems up to 1.5 m. high. These are generally unbranched. The leaves are either opposite or in whorls of 3 or 4. They are lance-shaped, 5—12 cm. long, stalkless and dotted with orange or black glands.

The flowers form open pyramidal clusters, their lower branches growing out from the leafy bracts. These flowers (1.5—2 cm.) have 5 joined sepals with hairy, reddish-orange margins and a bell-shaped deeply lobed corolla, golden-yellow in colour. The 5 stamens are red. The fruit is a globular capsule (5 mm. in diameter) containing numerous seeds.

Yellow Loosestrife flowers between June and August and can be found in large colonies along lakesides, and in swamps, fens and marshes. It is found across virtually the whole of the temperate zones of Europe and Asia, from Great Britain to Japan, but is absent from most of the Mediterranean.

The plant is still used in some areas to treat boils and high fevers, as well to stop bleeding. A yellow dye can be extracted from the flowers and a brown dye from the rhizomes. Yellow and Purple Loosestrife are in no way related.

COMFREY
Symphytum officinale L.
Family: *Boraginaceae*

All parts of this robust herbaceous perennial are conspicuously hairy. The stems are winged, branched, and up to 120 cm. The oval or lance-shaped leaves are 5—20 cm. long. The upper ones are stalkless but have bases which continue downwards forming wings on the stems; the lower leaves are longer and stalked. The short-stalked, pendant flowers grow in one-sided inflorescences. These are coiled at first but lengthen as the flowers open. The corolla is tubular with purple, pink or yellowish-white petals. The corolla segments are joined and have 5 very short, erect lobes. At the throat there are 5 triangular scales. Comfrey flowers from May to July. The fruits are shiny black nutlets.

Comfrey grows by watersides, in marshes, fens and damp meadows. It is found in hilly or flat regions all over Europe — eastwards to Asia Minor and in western parts of Siberia. In the north it is found in Scandinavia and in the south in central Italy and central Spain. The plant is probably not native in northern Britain or in Ireland.

Comfrey has, for centuries, been used as a medicine. From the roots was made a kind of gum and this was used to treat wool before spinning. Tannins were extracted for tanning leather. Alkaloids and volatile

Geum rivale

Lythrum salicaria

Lysimachia vulgaris   *Symphytum officinale*

oils are also present. The roots (black on the outside and white inside) were formerly made into extracts, distillates or powders which were then taken to treat diarrhoea and coughs, as well as being used as a pain killer for stomach ulcers. It was thought to stimulate the circulation and to control blood pressure. Comfrey root was usually applied externally, i. e. as a poultice for bruises and varicose veins and for any kind of badly healing wounds.

The root was particularly popular during the Middle Ages and formed one of the most important constituents of all ointments, especially those used for broken bones and arthritis. The plant is still collected and its medical properties are now being scientifically investigated. Comfrey is used even today in a variety of herbal medicines.

BITTERSWEET, WOODY NIGHTSHADE
Solanum dulcamara L.
Family: *Solanaceae*

This is a hardy, scrambling perennial, 30—200 cm. long. The smooth or downy stems are either climbing or prostrate and their bases become woody. This is a well-known plant found in a variety of habitats including waste places. It is conspicuous because of its unusual purple and yellow flowers and bright red berries.

The leaves are up to 8 cm. long — either oval and undivided or with 1—4 deep lobes. The lower leaves are often divided, with 2 small basal leaflets. The purple (rarely white) flowers are formed in open branched clusters opposite the leaves. The petals are lance-shaped and widespreading, and later they bend backwards. Towards the petal tips are 2 green spots. The large anthers are a bright golden-yellow and form a conspicuous cone in the centre of the flowers; they open by apical pores. The flowers appear between June and September. The fruits are at first yellow and then change to a bright red when ripe.

Bittersweet grows along river and canal banks, in woods and hedgerows and even on shingle beaches and sand dunes. It is found all over Europe, Asia including China and Japan, as well as in Africa and North America.

This is a poisonous plant; the poisonous alkaloid

solanin, together with other alkaloids, is particularly abundant in the young shoots and leaves of the plant. Solanin is also present in the berries. All parts of the plant taste bitter at first, then sweet. This is due to the action of saliva in the mouth. It is because of this characteristic that the plant received its specific name *dulcamara* — which is a combination of the Latin *dulcis* meaning sweet, and *amarus* meaning bitter. The herbal properties of Bittersweet have been known since the times of the Greeks and it has long been used for chest complaints, skin diseases, jaundice and rheumatism.

SNEEZEWORT
Achillea ptarmica L.
Family: *Compositae (Asteraceae)*

This hardy perennial grows to between 20—60 cm. with simple or branched, erect angular stems which are smooth below but hairy above. The leaves (1.5—8 cm.) are stalkless, linear or lance-shaped with a fine serrated margin. The 'flowers' (12—18 mm.), like those of all members of the family, are actually inflorescences with an involucre of papery bracts and they are borne in open flat-topped clusters. Each 'flower' has 8—13 white ray florets and greenish-white disc florets.

The plant flowers between July and September and grows beside water, in damp meadows and marshes and in shady places. It thrives in flat regions as well as on higher ground. At times it can even be found amongst the reeds bordering a lake or river. One also finds this plant further cultivated in gardens with larger and denser flowers known as 'Bachelors' Buttons'. Sneezewort can be found all over Europe from the northern Balkans, to north Italy and from Spain to Scandinavia. It grows in the Caucasian mountains, in Siberia, Asia Minor, Armenia and in North America (where is has been introduced). This plant is well known everywhere because it is used both as an ornamental plant as well as a household remedy; it is therefore cultivated to a large extent.

The plant was known in the Middle Ages, although that is the earliest record of it. In Europe it has been known since the 16th century. The powdered leaves make a sneezing powder. Leaves and flowers were used

in early medicinal preparations, yielding an essential oil.

TRIPARTITE BUR-MARIGOLD
Bidens tripartita L.
Family: *Compositae*

This is an annual herb with erect, 10—90 cm. long branched stems. The dark green leaves (5—15 cm.) are opposite and divided into 3—5 coarsely toothed, lance-shaped lobes. The middle lobe is often broader and divided into 3. The leaves narrow towards the stalk which becomes winged.

The globular, erect flowerheads (15—25 mm.) appear at the ends of the stems. They have outer and inner involucral bracts and are often without ray florets. The plant flowers between July and late autumn. The fruits are usually flattened, brownish-green and with 2—5 (generally 3) barbed bristles. The fruit is sometimes carried off unknowingly by animals and is spread in this way. The bristly fruit becomes entangled in the animals' coats.

Tripartite Bur-marigold is mostly found on river banks, watersides, in marshes and in other wet places. It prefers dried-out lakes or ponds and also grows on their shores. The plant is known almost everywhere in Europe, in North and West Asia and has also been brought to Australia.

Tripartite Bur-marigold is closely related to *Bidens cernua* but is distinguished by the three-lobed leaves (from which the plant takes its name) and the upright habit of the flowerheads.

NODDING BUR-MARIGOLD
Bidens cernua L.

This resembles *Bidens tripartita* but differs in having simple sessile leaves and drooping flowerheads. The variety *radiata* DC, has golden-yellow ray florets 1—1.5 cm. long which make the flowerheads very conspicuous.

The plant grows on banks and shores of rivers and lakes all over Europe, in the Caucasian mountains, North Asia and North America (where it has been introduced). Nodding Bur-marigold is often found in similar habitats to those of *Bidens tripartita* but tends to grow where there is standing water in winter.

CABBAGE THISTLE
Cirsium oleraceum (L.) Scop.
Family: *Compositae*

This robust perennial herb is conspicuously yellowish-green. The stem (50—120 cm.) is hollow and grooved and occasionally branched at the top. Unlike some thistles, the stems are not winged.

All leaves are large, light green, fleshy, oval to lance-shaped and with a margin of soft spines. The basal leaves are deeply pinnate. The leaves on the upper part of the stem have clasping heart-shaped lobes and are undivided, with a pointed tip. There is no compact basal rosette.

The large flowerheads (2.5—4 cm.) are borne at the top of the stem and are densely clustered, yellowish-white or sometimes reddish in colour. They are surrounded and partly concealed by light, yellow-green, bract-like leaves. The fruits are 4 mm. achenes, pale grey and angled. Each fruit has a pappus of many rows of simple hairs. The flowers attract a species of butterfly which has the same yellow-green colour as the upper bract leaves of the Cabbage Thistle. In fact, if such a butterfly is placed on the flower of this plant, its wings look like erect upper-bract leaves — an example of protective coloration.

Cabbage Thistles grow by watersides, in marshes and damp meadows. This large and conspicuously coloured plant indicates the presence of water or damp ground. It can be found all over Europe and Asia as far as Siberia.

The genera *Cirsium* and *Carduus* include the majority of thistles found in Britain. All are characteristically spiny, annual or perennial herbs which usually have a stout taproot, and which bear stems terminated in more or less globular purple or whitish flowerheads. There are about 120 species of *Cirsium* in the northern hemisphere of which 9 species grow in Britain. A number of hybrids have also been recognised.

Although often thought of as weeds and plants of

Solanum dulcamara

Achillea ptarmica

Bidens tripartita

waste places, some thistles grow in wet places such as marshes or fens, along streamsides and in damp woods. Examples include the Marsh Thistle *(Cirsium palustre* (L.) Scop.*)* and the Cabbage Thistle *(Cirsium oleraceum* (L.) Scop.). Others may grow in much drier habitats such as chalk downs and hilly pastures e. g. Tuberous Thistle *(Cirsium tuberosum* (L.) All.*)*.

As weeds of cultivated places, thistles are often difficult to eradicate. Seeds are produced in abundance and

45

each is carried by the slightest air current on a characteristic plumed parachute (formed by the hairy pappus).

BUTTERBUR
Petasites hybridus (L.) Gaertn., Mey. and Scherb.
Family: *Compositae*

This robust herbaceous perennial has a stout and extensive rhizome. In March and April flower stems grow up and appear above ground before the leaves. These flower stems carry large dense clusters of either male or female pinkish-violet flowerheads. The stems are stout, 10—40 cm. tall, purplish at the base and covered with greenish lanceolate scales and cobwebby hairs. The stems elongate markedly — to 80 cm. — after flowering. Female flowerheads (3—6 mm.) contain about 100 florets; male flowerheads (7—12 mm.) contain, in addition, a number of sterile hermaphrodite flowers and these secrete nectar which is attractive to bees. The achenes (2—3 mm.) are yellowish-brown with a white pappus.

During and after flowering long-stalked leaves grow from the rhizome; they are heart-shaped, shallow angled and irregularly toothed. The young leaves have downy white hairs on both surfaces, but those on the upper surface disappear at maturity. The leaves grow fast and can reach a diameter of 10—90 cm; they have long stout petioles. All parts of the plant give out an unpleasant odour.

Butterbur grows in colonies beside rivers, or in damp meadows and marshes in both lowland and hilly areas. It is found all over Europe and North and West Asia and has been introduced in North America.

This plant was formerly used medicinally and during the Middle Ages was used against plague, cholera, epilepsy and fevers. The leaves were stewed and taken for a variety of minor ailments. The pulped leaves were, and in some places still are, applied as a poultice on boils and badly healing wounds. There are still a few areas in which the plant is collected and made into herbal remedies. The related Winter Heliotrope *(Petasites fragrans)* has strongly vanilla-scented flowerheads. It is a native of the west Mediterranean region and is a garden escape in Great Britain.

WHITE BUTTERBUR
Petasites albus (L.) Gaertn.

This species resembles *P. hybridus* but both stems and leaves are smaller (the maximum height is 70 cm. and the leaf size 10—30 cm.). The flowerheads are whitish-yellow, and the male heads larger and more globular. The scales on the flower stems are pale green. The leaves are broadly heart-shaped and are thus more rounded than those of *P. hybridus*.
The plant is well known on hills and mountainsides, but is found only rarely in lowland areas.

ALDER
Alnus glutinosa (L.) Gaertn.
Family: *Betulaceae*

This is a medium-sized tree, 20, and sometimes even 40 m. high, with a dark brown bark. The branches at first grow upright but later become pendant. The young branches are usually sticky with short-stalked buds which are violet. The leaves (3—9 cm.) are short-stalked, sticky when young, and rounded with a notched apex and a doubly toothed margin.

The tree bears both male and female catkins which appear in the autumn but elongate in February—April. The male catkins (2—6 cm.) are in groups of 4—6 at the ends of the twigs. The female catkins are short, upright and cylindrical and the fused bracts become woody, changing during maturity into rounded cones. These cones, at first green, become black after pollination by wind, and stay on the tree until the following year, even after the seeds have fallen out. The cones resemble small (1.5 cm.) pine cones, but are different botanically. The fruits are small, flattened nutlets with a loosely woven margin which enables them to float in water.

Coral-like outgrowths form on the roots in clusters. These contain symbiotic bacteria which absorb nitrogen from the air and convert it into nitrogenous compounds. These are subsequently absorbed by the cells of the Alder.

The Alder needs constantly moist ground and therefore it is found mainly alongside rivers or lakes, and in fens and marshes. This tree is most frequently found in flooded areas and, in marshy regions, groves of

Cirsium oleraceum

Petasites albus

Petasites hybridus

Alnus glutinosa

Alders can be seen. In very wet areas the Alder often develops stilt-like roots which give the tree greater stability. The Alder can be found anywhere between the mountainous regions of southern Spain, northwards to Finland and eastwards as far as Sicily and the Ural and Caucasian mountains. It also occurs in North Africa. The wood of the Alder is soft, light and easy to split. Originally white, it changes its colour quickly to red if exposed to the air. The wood is rich in tannic acid and therefore resistant to water; it is often used in constructions which are placed in or near water. The wood is also used for woodcuts, pencils, ornamental boxes and bowls. Charcoal from the wood is used in the manufacture of gunpowder.

In Britain, besides *Alnus glutinosa*, the Grey Alder (*Alnus incana* (L.) Moench) may also be found. It is not a native, but although it is sometimes planted on poor or wet soils it is also occasionally found growing wild. Both species are planted either for timber or to form shelter belts. The Grey Alder may be identified by it smooth grey bark, and leaves which have pointed tips and are greyish or bluish-green beneath. When young the lower leaf surface bears reddish hairs.

Ornamental varieties of the Grey Alder are also grown. These include one form with pendulous branches, another with deeply dissected toothed leaves, and another with yellowish young shoots and foliage and reddish catkins.

Also on wet soils, a familiar feature of the British landscape is the range of native willows *(Salix ssp.)*. In parks and gardens the most handsome and best known species is the Weeping Willow *(Salix babylonica* L.). This is believed to be Chinese in origin.

Nowadays a number of hybrids with other species have been produced and are actually more frequently planted than the true Weeping Willow.

The genus is large and highly complex and consists of about 300 species together with a number of hybrids. The great majority of these are native to the north temperate and arctic regions but some occur in south temperate and tropical areas. These, however, are never found growing naturally in the East Indies or in Australasia.

Willows reproduce easily by cuttings. Twigs or branches root readily in moist soil or even in water. Fence-posts of willow (providing they have not been allowed to dry out) have been known to root, sprout and grow into trees.

The following are among the better known species of *Salix:*

Salix alba

WHITE WILLOW
Salix alba L.
Family: *Salicaceae*

This is a tree which reaches 25 m. in height. The young twigs are silky, hairy, and pliable, though not fragile.
Both sides of the leaves are covered in soft hairs which give a shining white appearance. Like all willows, male and female plants are separate.
The White Willow grows beside rivers all over Europe, in temperate regions of Asia and even in North Africa. The tree is cultivated in America and Australia. It is grown and regularly pollarded to provide twigs for basket-making. The Cricket-bat Willow is another variety.
The bark is of value medicinally as it is rich in salicylates and salicine (a substitute for quinine).

CRACK WILLOW
Salix fragilis L.

This is a tree (up to 25 m.) with easily broken olive-green twigs bearing hairless bright green leaves. The tree is known all over Europe, the Caucasus and in the temperate regions of Siberia. Unlike *Salix alba* it is of little commercial use.

PURPLE OSIER
Salix purpurea L.

This is a slender shrub (1.5—5 m.) rarely forming a tree. The branches are thin, flexible, shining and yellow-brown or red.
The leaves are 4—10 cm., lance-shaped to oblong, dull bluish-green and often turn black when dried. As in many willows, the catkins appear before the leaves.
Purple Osier grows along rivers and in damp meadows in fens and swamps, from the lowlands up to the lower slopes of mountains. It is found mainly in South and Central Europe but also grows in the temperate zones of Asia and in North Africa. The twigs are used to make baskets and garden furniture and the tree is therefore cultivated.

COMMON OSIER
Salix viminalis L.

This shrub usually grows 3—4 m. but occasionally reaches 10 m. high. The young branches are greyish, flexible and hairy. The leaves (10—25 cm.) are narrow and lance-shaped, and the underside is strongly veined and covered in white, silky hairs.
The Common Osier grows along rivers and waterways as well as in damp meadows all over Central and southern Europe, in the Caucasus, in Siberia, Japan and in North and South America. The tree is widely cultivated and the twigs, known as withies, are used for basket and furniture making.
The bark is bitter and contains large amounts of salicin as well as 10 percent tannins. Salicin helps to reduce fever and relieves rheumatic pains. Until

Salix fragilis

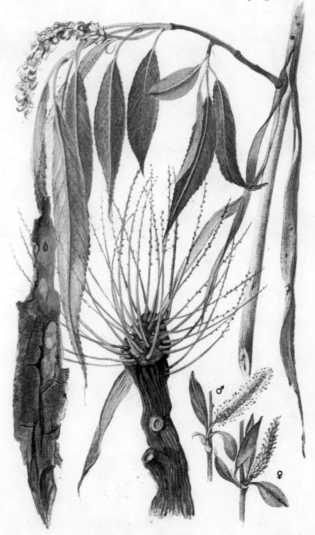

Populus alba

Salix purpurea

recently the bark was the chief source of salicin, but has now been replaced by synthetic compounds. During the Middle Ages the bark was used instead of hops in brewing; later, the leaves were used for the same purpose — particularly since hops, being comparatively scarce, were so expensive.

WHITE POPLAR
Populus alba L.
Family: *Salicaceae*

A wide-spreading tree 30 m. high, the White Poplar has greyish-white bark. The leaves appear after the catkins, are oval with 3—5 toothed lobes and are covered with white, downy hairs beneath.
The trees are unisexual. The male catkins are 4—8 cm. long and cylindrical; the female ones are shorter (2—6 cm.). The anthers are red, later becoming yellow and the stigmas are greenish-yellow. The catkins of the White Poplar appear in March and April. The seeds, with their long, white, downy hairs, are carried off in clusters by the wind.
The wood of the White Poplar is valuable as timber. Both it and the Black Poplar *(Populus nigra* L.*)* are frequently planted beside rivers and waterways in Europe.

PLANTS
OF
THE
SEASHORE

INTRODUCTION

Flat sandy seashores may seem an unusual place for plants to grow in; among the controlling factors here are the salt content of the soil-water, the soil type and its physical properties — especially of sand and shingle. On the seashore we find plants which can tolerate salt i. e. the halophytes and also plants which can survive in sand, the psammophytes. Both types of plant form typical zones on the shore. These zones depend in part on the salt content of the ground, which in turn is dependent on tide levels.

The plants which best tolerate salt grow nearest to the sea and may actually be washed by the tide or by spray. This poses problems of water-uptake by the plants. A variety of special anatomical and physiological features is present in these plants and many of these features are also found in other plants of the seashore. Such features include cell sap (present in the cell vacuoles) with a specially high concentration of mineral salts. The cells thus have a higher osmotic pressure which enables the roots to absorb water from their saline habitat. The stems and leaves are often fleshy and water-storing, and the surface layer may be waxy, which reduces water loss.

Sand and shingle do not retain moisture and are also very unstable, the particles moving easily over each other. There is little or no humus, and in most soils humus is important in helping to retain the soil water. So we find that the plants growing under these conditions have extensive root systems, often very deep-rooting and these serve both to absorb water and also to anchor the plants in the shifting substrate. Such plants can also tolerate being covered by blown sand because they are able to grow through it. A number of these psammophytes are grasses with leaves which, by means of special cells, roll inwards when water is in short supply. This device ensures that a layer of moist air lies over the stomata (or pores) of the leaf and this effect may be supplemented by the presence of epidermal hairs which restrict air flow. Inrolling also effectively reduces the leaf surface and these all serve to reduce the rate of water loss from the plant which is thus able to survive these adverse conditions.

Dunes and sandhills are the characteristics of this ever moving sand. The sand is blown by the wind and will stop if it comes across a sufficient obstacle (e. g. stones or plants). In this way embryo dunes are formed. More sand will heap itself against these dunes and the dune grows. If a plant proves to be the obstacle and is covered by sand, it gradually grows up towards the surface and the new stems give substance to the dune. Slowly the dune moves away from the sea and so retreats from the waves and salt-water. The salt, contained in the sand, is washed away by rainwater and a so-called 'fixed' or 'secondary' dune is formed. This dune contains little salt, is far less mobile, and may be rich in calcium if numerous broken shells have become part of the dune. Other plants can now grow on these dunes which makes them still more stable; humus is formed giving more plants a favourable habitat in which to grow. A little further away still, the 'tertiary' dune is now firmly established and stabilised. Numerous herbs and shrubs grow here and sometimes plants are cultivated on the dunes to assist in stabilisation.

Plants experience saline and sandy conditions not only near the sea, but also in or around salt lakes or deserts, as for instance in parts of Asia or Africa.

SEA ROCKET
Cakile maritima Scop.
Family: *Cruciferae*

This is a bluish-green, fleshy annual, 15—60 cm. tall. The erect stems may become woody at the base. The stems bear smooth, fleshy, slightly to deeply lobed or entire leaves, whereas the basal leaves are even more variable, either entire or deeply divided. All have a marked salty taste.

The sweet-scented flowers are light violet, pink or white. The narrow elongated sepals tightly surround the lower part of the petals, which thus form a tube 3—5 mm. deep and into which nectar is secreted. The flowers are borne in elongated leafless clusters. The fruits, shining and yellowish, are divided into two sections each containing one seed. The shorter lower part is top-shaped whilst the larger upper part resembles a mitre.

The plant flowers from July until October, in coastal areas close to the drift-line and also in saltmarshes. It has migrated inland and flourishes on saline ground, on waste land and along roadsides. Sea Rocket tolerates a range of salt concentrations. The seeds may be dispersed in sea water and appear to be unharmed by it. It grows all along the coasts of Europe except in Belgium and Iceland. It is found also beside the Black Sea and Aegean Sea, and in North Africa from Egypt to Madeira.

Cakile maritima

LESSER SEA SPURREY

Spergularia marina (L.) Griseb.
Family: *Caryophyllaceae*

This is an annual, sometimes biennial plant (20 cm. or more high) with numerous erect or prostrate glandular stems. The fleshy leaves are linear and 2 cm. long. The flowers have 5 pointed petals (2.5 mm.) which are smaller than the sepals and are rose pink with a white base. There are 1—5 stamens.

The fruits are round with yellow-brown seeds. Lesser Sea Spurrey blooms between May and September and grows in muddy and sandy saltmarshes, inland in brackish meadows and sometimes even along the roadside. It is found in coastal areas all over Europe from Sweden to North Africa, in Asia Minor, Siberia

Spergularia marina

and Central Asia as well as throughout South and North America.

ANNUAL SEABLITE
Suaeda maritima (L.) Dumort
Family: *Chenopodiaceae*

Annual Seablite is a variable, prostrate or erect annual with stems 50 cm. or more. It is bluish-green, often with a reddish tinge. The short narrow cylindrical leaves are 3—25 mm. long, fleshy, and flattened on the upper side. The lower leaves are longer and all leaves have pointed tips and are also narrowed at the base. The small flowers have 5 short green or red fleshy perianth segments. They are borne in groups of 1—3 in the leaf axils. The fruits contain shining black seeds with a fine, net-like pattern.
The plant flowers between July and October and grows in large colonies along seashores almost all over the world. Sometimes it is also found inland in saline areas.

PRICKLY SALTWORT
Salsola kali L.
Family: *Chenopodiaceae*

This annual plant grows to almost 1 m. in height. The stems are fleshy and prickly and are usually prostrate. It is grey-green and its stems often have red stripes. The leaves are small (1—4 cm.), cylindrical, and fleshy with a spiny tip. The upper leaves are shorter, broader and almost triangular, with single flowers in their axils. The flowers are small and have 2 spiny-tipped leafy bracteoles. The 4—5 perianth segments are green and pointed. There are 5 stamens and the ovary has 2 styles. The fruit is surrounded by the tough, ridged or winged perianth.
The plant flowers between July and September and is often found on seashores, dunes, and saline areas. It can sometimes be found in sandy fields, beside roads and in waste places. Prickly Saltwort is found in South and Central Europe, southern parts of Scandinavia, Britain and Finland, North Africa, Caucasia and Siberia, in North America and in New Zealand. It often becomes a weed in the prairies of North America. This is a variable plant with a number of

varieties in Europe and in other parts of the world. The plant is burnt and its ash, which contains 25 percent soda, is still used for soap. The ash is called *barilla* in Spain, *rochetta* in Sicily and *blanquette* or *salicor* in France.

GLASSWORT
Salicornia europaea L.
Family: *Chenopodiaceae*

This variable annual has a great preference for salt. The plant has fleshy, erect, jointed and branched stems (up to 30 cm.), which are bright green tinged with red. The leaves are minute, fleshy, and in opposite pairs nearly fused to the stems so that they are almost unnoticeable. The flowers are borne in a fleshy terminal spike and develop in groups of 3, the central one being larger. Each flower is rather angular and contains a single stamen and ovary. The fruits are enclosed by the perianth.
The plant blossoms between July and September and grows usually in vast numbers along the seashore. It may also be found in isolated cases inland, if saline conditions exist.
Glasswort can be found along seashores all over the world but is not found in Australia or extreme northern Europe.
It is typical of a plant flourishing in conditions which are not only extremely rich in salts but also where the plant is, at long intervals, completely submerged by sea water.
Glasswort tastes salty and bitter and has a high soda content which used to be extracted from the ash of the plant. The plant has also been used as a vegetable or eaten raw as a salad mixed with vinegar.

SEA-HOLLY
Eryngium maritimum L.
Family: *Umbelliferae*

This is a stiffly branched perennial 15—60 cm. high with a distinctly bluish tinge to all parts. The roots grow very deep; the smooth stems bear stiff, spiny-edged, holly-like leaves. The thick, grey-blue, rounded and somewhat leathery leaves have cartilaginous edges. The basal leaves are broad, three-lobed and spiny;

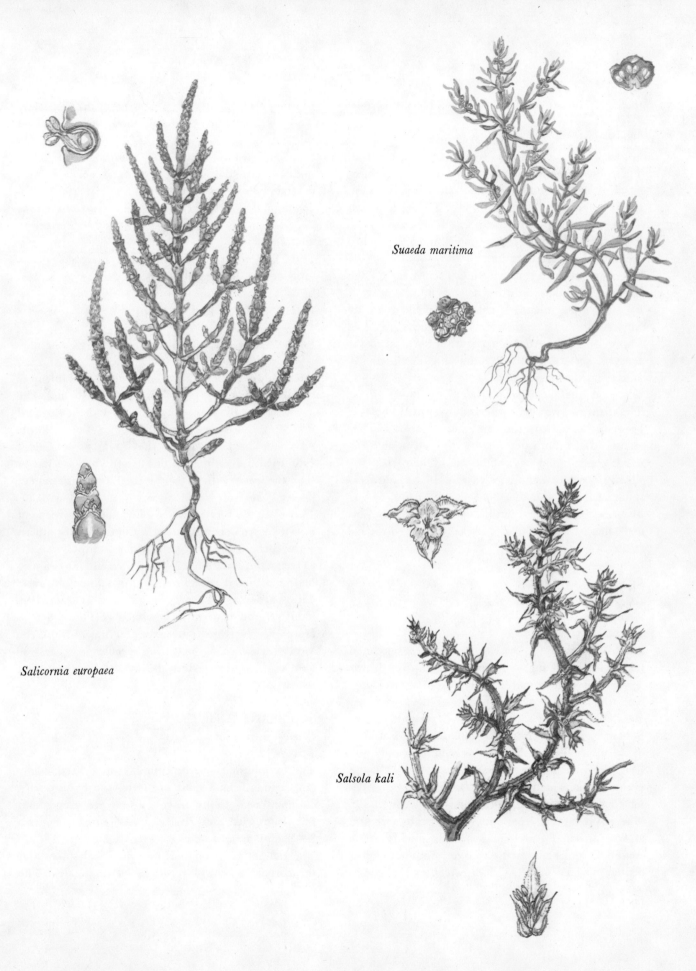

Suaeda maritima

Salicornia europaea

Salsola kali

the stem leaves are palmately lobed and all leaves show conspicuous veins.

The flowers are blue, and occur in dense, globular heads (1.5—2.5 cm. across) which later become oval. These flowerheads are surrounded by an involucre of large, spiny, toothed bracts. Each flower is 8 mm. in diameter with 5 pointed sepals, 5 notched petals and 5 stamens — all parts borne above the ovary. The fruits are crowded, egg-shaped and spiny. They are animal dispersed.

This very attractive plant grows exclusively on the seashore and flowers between June and August; it does not grow inland. It grows along the coasts of Mediterranean countries, from Morocco to Asia Minor, along the Atlantic coast from Portugal to the coast of western Britain, Ireland and the Shetlands, and along the coast of the North Sea and the Baltic as well as the Black Sea.

The plant survives being covered by sand, and this is because the buried stems are able to grow rapidly to the surface. Both stems and roots tend to hold the moving sand and to stabilise it. The root tastes slightly sweet and smells of carrots. In certain areas it has been used as a household remedy against several illnesses. In northern European countries the roots are eaten as a vegetable or boiled in sugar to make sweets.

SEA MILKWORT
Glaux maritima L.
Family: *Primulaceae*

This is a small (5—30 cm.) grey-green perennial herb with spreading and rooting stems. These bear 4 ranks of simple stalkless leaves 4—12 mm. long. The small fleshy leaves are oval and the lower ones grow opposite each other while the upper ones do not. Solitary small flowers can be found in the leaf axils of the upper leaves. The calyx is reddish or pink and has 5 deep lobes. The stamens too are reddish. There are no petals. The fruits consist of five-valved capsules which burst when ripe, releasing 5—11 seeds.

The plant flowers from May until September and grows particularly well in sandy or muddy saline conditions along the coast. Often one finds large areas densely covered with the plant, which stands up well

to being covered either by sea water or drifting sands. This plant sometimes, but only rarely, appears inland in damp saline conditions.

Sea Milkwort is found along the coasts of North and western Europe, in north and north western coastal areas of Spain, the Near East, Siberia, China, Japan and Tibet as well as in North and South America, but is much rarer along the Mediterranean coast.

Sea Milkwort is one of the most successful plants growing in salt-rich habitats.

BUCK'S-HORN PLANTAIN
Plantago coronopus L.
Family: *Plantaginaceae*

Buck's-horn Plantain is a hairy annual or biennial plant which grows to a height of 5—40 cm. The leaves of the basal rosette are long and slender and usually toothed or deeply cut into linear lobes. From the basal rosette of the leaves grow slender cylindrical spikes up to 4 cm. long. They are longer than the leaves with numerous small brownish papery flowers. The fruit is a four-seeded capsule.

The plant flowers between May and October and is well known in coastal areas in Central and southern Europe, the Azores, in North Africa and the Far East, as well as in Australia and New Zealand. It can also be found inland beside roads or in saline-rich areas. This particular Plantain has a very characteristic habit of growth when in flower, since the numerous flower spikes curve outwards and upwards in the form of a crown — hence the specific name. It was used as a herbal remedy and is today sometimes eaten in salads.

SEA PLANTAIN
Plantago maritima L.

This is a bluish coloured perennial (up to 40 cm. high) and, arising from a stout woody base, it has a rosette of long linear fleshy leaves. These are grey-green, flat or grooved and generally 2—6 mm. wide with 3—5 faint parallel veins.

The flowers grow on narrow cylindrical spikes and the corolla is brownish with a leathery calyx. The

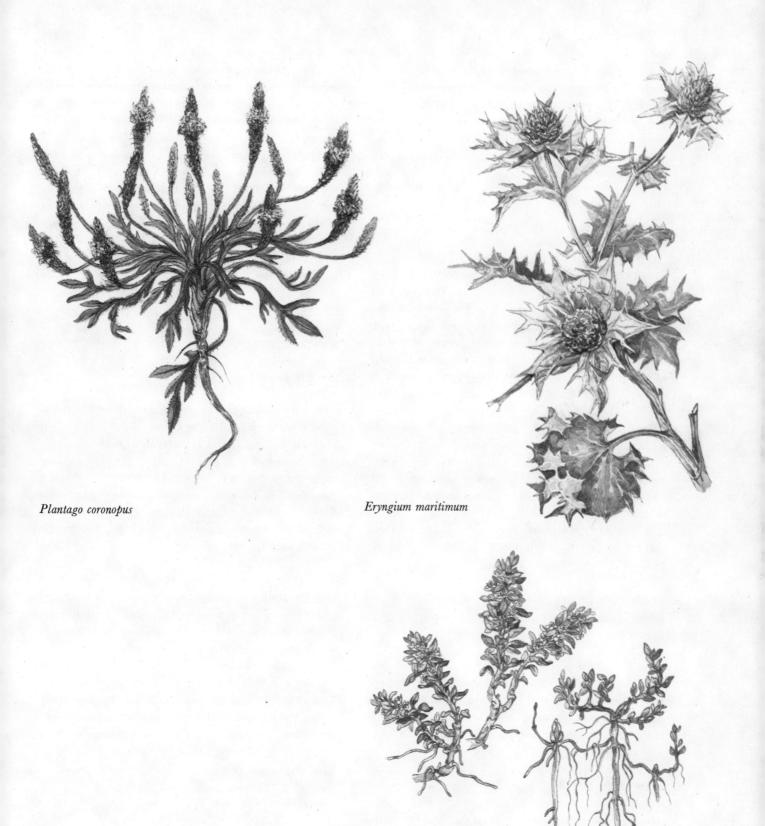

Plantago coronopus

Eryngium maritimum

Glaux maritima

fruits consist of egg-shaped capsules which contain seeds. The plant flowers between June and September and is well known along the coasts of the North Sea and the Baltic; a mountain form is found inland and grows in Europe, Asia, South Africa and America, not only in saline conditions but also in areas where the salt content is low.

SEA ASTER
Aster tripolium L.
Family: *Compositae (Asteraceae)*

Sea Aster is a distinctive short-lived perennial (15—100 cm. high) with a short swollen rhizome and smooth well-branched stems. The leaves are oblong to lance-shaped, 7—12 cm. long and fleshy; the basal leaves are long-stalked. Open clusters of flower-heads, which are 1—3 cm. across, appear at the top of the stem. The disc florets are orange-yellow and the ray florets bluish-purple or sometimes whitish. The involucral bracts are blunt; the inner ones are papery. The fruits are small brown achenes with a brownish pappus. Flowering is from July to October and the plant grows on seashores where it prefers damp, sandy and muddy ground. It can also be found inland in saline conditions, or near mineral springs, but this is rare.
The Sea Aster is known along the coasts of Europe, and the Caspian Sea but also in inland areas in Central Europe, Central Asia and Siberia.

SEA CLUB-RUSH
Scirpus maritimus L.
Family: *Cyperaceae*

This is a robust perennial herb growing 30—100 cm. high. It has a rhizome which produces short runners which are tuberous at the tip. The stems are three-sided and are rough towards the top. The leaves have blades about 10 mm. wide, with a pronounced keel. The margins are rough.
The florets are borne in spikelets in dense, much-branched, rather flat-topped inflorescences which are terminal on the stems and are about 5 cm. across. The associated bracts vary from leaf-like to hair-like, and are usually much longer than the inflorescen-

ce. The reddish-brown spikelets are rather few in number, 1—2 cm. across, and are single or in groups of 2—5 at the ends of the inflorescence branches. Each floret has a perianth of 1—6 rough bristles and 3 stamens with flattened filaments. The fruit is a wedge-shaped shiny brown nutlet 3 mm. across. The plant flowers in July and August and the fruits develop in August and September. It is essentially a coastal plant, rarely found inland, and' grows in ditches and ponds near the sea and along the muddy margins of tidal rivers. The plant is native to Britain and may be locally abundant, growing all round the coast as far north as Ross, in Scotland. It is a cosmopolitan plant, found everywhere except in arctic regions.

SAND SEDGE
Carex arenaria L.
Family: *Cyperaceae*

This is a spreading creeping perennial with a branched rhizome several metres long. Erect aerial stems (10—40 cm. high) grow at intervals from the rhizome. The three-angled stems are longer than or as long as the leaves during flowering. The dense inflorescence has 5—12 spikes and is oval-oblong in shape. Male flowers are found only in the upper spikes, both male and female flowers appear in the middle, and female flowers only appear in the lower spikes of the inflorescence.
The fruits are ovoid and ribbed; the upper half and the beak are broadly winged and toothed. The plant flowers between May and August and appears in clusters on dunes along the seashore, sometimes in sandy places on heaths or pine woods inland.
Sand Sedge grows along the coasts of Europe and the Black Sea, in Siberia and North America.
The long rhizomes spread quickly through the sandy dunes and it is often cultivated to ensure the stability of the dunes. The rhizomes have also been used herbally.

MARRAM GRASS
Ammophila (Psamma) arenaria (L.) Link
Family: *Gramineae (Poaceae)*

This is a robust erect perennial 60—120 cm. high.

Scirpus maritimus

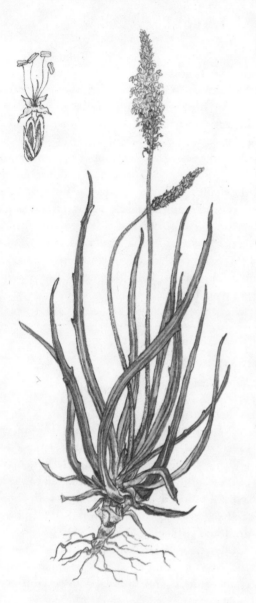

Aster tripolium

Plantago maritima

Carex arenaria

From long creeping and rooting stems arise tufts of erect stems bearing long, stiff, grey-green, sharply pointed leaves. These are ribbed and tightly inrolled. The inflorescences (7—22 cm.) are whitish spikes with flattened, overlapping spikelets.

The grass flowers between May and August and grows abundantly on dunes and sand along the seashore. It is known along the coasts of Europe, the Mediterranean and, introduced, in North America. This is a kind of grass which is often cultivated, together with others, to stabilise sand-dunes.

SAND COUCH-GRASS
Agropyron junceiforme (A. and D. Löve) A. and D. Löve
Family: *Gramineae*

Sand Couch-grass is a spreading bluish perennial, 25—50 cm. tall. The flowering stems are erect, the others mainly prostrate, and both arise from the abundant creeping rhizomes. The leaf-blade or lamina is about 8 mm. wide and 60 cm. long. Later it becomes more or less inrolled, and covered with short soft hairs on the upper surface. The spikelets have between 5—8 florets and are fragile and very easily broken off. They are borne in 2 opposite rows.

The grass flowers between June and August and grows in great profusion on dunes and sand along the seashores. It is related to the troublesome weed Couch-grass or Twitch *(Agropyron repens)*. It is known all along the coasts of Europe, as well as in West Africa and in Asia Minor. Sand Couch-grass is also cultivated, since its long rhizomes hold down the sand and therefore provide a firm substrate in which other plants can take root.

LYME-GRASS
Elymus arenarius L.
Family: *Gramineae*

This is a robust bluish perennial with large tufts of erect stems 1—2 m. high, arising from creeping underground rhizomes. The pungent leaves are broad (8—20 mm. wide), tough and sharply pointed; when dry they become inrolled. They have short hairs along the ribs of the upper surface. The flowerheads are cylindrical, 15—35 cm., and dense.

The large hairy spikelets grow in clusters of twos or threes arising from each joint of the axis and are placed broadside on to it. The plant flowers between June and August.

Originally this grass grew wild on dunes and sandy coastal areas along the North Sea and the Baltic. It was later cultivated and planted inland to further the cultivation of sandy areas. However, it acclimatised in only a very few places and disappeared again in most others. It grows along the coasts of western and northern Europe, in Siberia and North America. It is unknown in Portugal, however. Lyme Grass is still cultivated on dunes and in Iceland its seeds, in the form of grain, were formerly used to make bread.

SEA MEADOW-GRASS
Puccinellia maritima (Huds.) Parl.
Family: *Gramineae*

This is a rather tufted perennial grass 10—80 cm. high. Erect stems arise from creeping stems. The leaves are smooth, narrow and generally flat, blunt-tipped with slightly rough edges. The flowerheads are heavily branched and spreading, with many spikelets. Each spikelet has between 5 to 9 flowers which are usually tinged violet.

The plant flowers between June and August. It grows along the seashore and flourishes in mud-flats; it stabilises the ground and so is used to reclaim land. Sea Meadow-grass is known along the coasts of the Atlantic Ocean, the North Sea and the Baltic, in Greenland and North America. The plant is still used in some areas to feed livestock.

SAND CAT'S-TAIL
Phleum arenarium L.
Family: *Gramineae*

Sand Cat's-tail is a small annual grass 3—15 (sometimes 30) cm. high. The stems are solitary or clustered,

Elymus arenarius

64

Ammophila arenaria

Agropyron junceiforme

Elymus arenarius

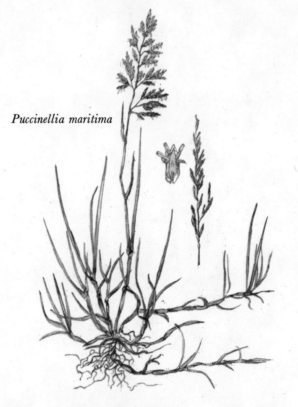

Puccinellia maritima

with short smooth leaves up to 4 mm. wide. The uppermost leaf sheath is markedly inflated.

The inflorescence is a dense spike (.5—5 cm. long of numerous small whitish or pale green spikelets. Each of these is stalkless and flattened and has only 1 fertile floret which has narrow hairy bracts. The plant flowers between May and July and is found on dunes, the seashore and in sandy fields. It is well known in western Europe and also grows from southern Sweden to the Mediterranean.

TOWNSEND'S CORD-GRASS
Spartina townsendii H. and J. Groves
Family: *Gramineae*

This is a robust grass with creeping, wide-spreading rhizomes. The plant appeared in Southampton Water in 1870 as a hybrid between two other species *(Spartina alternifolia* and *S. maritima)*. The plant spreads rapidly forming clumps or even meadows.

The stems (0.5—1.5 m.) bear smooth, stiff and often purplish leaves about 8 mm. wide and 20—40 cm. long. These are ribbed on the upper surface, and flat or rolled upwards. The inflorescence resembles a dense cluster 10—30 cm. long, but is actually made up to 3—6 erect spikes, each with 2 rows of numerous overlapping spikelets.

The grass flowers between June and September and grows only in salt marshes and mud-flats along North Sea coasts. There it stands up well to being flooded by seawater. Townsend Cord-grass is often planted to stabilise coastal mud-flats and to reclaim land in many parts of the world.

SEA BUCKTHORN
Hippophaë rhamnoides L.
Family: *Elaeagnaceae*

A thorny shrub or small tree 3 m. or more high, the Sea Buckthorn produces many suckers and thus

Phleum arenarium

becomes bushy. The leaves are simple, elongated (1—8 cm.), and bear silvery, scale-like hairs. The twigs are also scaly. The plant is unisexual and flowers before the leaves appear. The male flowers have two sepals and 4 stamens. They form small clusters in the leaf axils. The female flowers are elongated with two very small sepals and are borne singly. All the flowers lack petals.

This shrub flowers between March and May and grows wild on dunes and sea cliffs, as well as along sandy or shingly river banks. It is known from western and northern Europe to southern Siberia and West Asia.

Sea Buckthorn grows on established 'secondary' dunes and in the 'dune slacks' between them. Its roots stabilise the sand and for this reason the plant is often cultivated. There are numerous fruits, orange coloured with brown dots, which are rich in vitamin C but are acid and poisonous.

Hippophaë rhamnoides

PLANTS OF PEAT BOGS

INTRODUCTION

Peat bogs are easily recognisable areas of poorly drained acid soils where water (from springs or rain) readily accumulates. A bog is, therefore, almost always formed in large, shallow, basin-shaped areas, both in lowlands and also on hills, or in hollows on mountain sides. Peat bogs can also form around springs, rivers or more stagnant waters but the basis for their formation must always be an acid, i. e. calcium-free soil.

A particular kind of moss is found here — the bog moss *(Sphagnum)*. This grows in large quantities, covering vast areas and resembling soft cushions. It is often partially submerged in the water and in addition, its stems and leaves retain absorbed water. Whilst the bogmoss is continually growing at the tops of the stems, the basal parts die off. These lower parts become compressed and in time a black-brown mass forms, which may be several metres deep. This is peat. Peat bogs range in size from the very small to those of many square kilometres, and the depth also varies considerably. 'Living' peat bogs can be compared to enormous sponges, soaked in water, forming a soft carpet and breaking up easily if walked upon. It has long been known that animals and persons who have strayed on to bogs have slowly sunk into the brown clinging mass unless rescued in time. In Britain, bogs tend to be found in the wetter western areas.

Bogs represent a very wet, poorly aerated, cool, acid environment which contains undecayed humus and is therefore low in nutrients. Under these conditions very few species can exist and these will not often be found elsewhere.

Such plants are usually low, creeping and sometimes woody, preferring dampness and low temperatures. Carnivorous, i. e. insectivorous plants, are also found here, since bogs are particularly deficient in essential nitrogenous salts.

Many different kinds of sedges *(Carex)*, cotton grasses *(Eriophorum)* and rushes *(Juncus)* live in bogs. These are plants which may also grow in drier conditions. This may appear to be a contradiction but in fact some plants cannot easily absorb the acid water contained in the peat and therefore exist as if in a dry environment. Peat can therefore, despite its high water content, form a particularly difficult habitat in which plants grow.

Because of its high acid content peat preserves the bodies of both dead plants and animals. It also preserves the pollen and seeds of shrubs and trees, which may have blown there from nearby. The pollen preserved in any one layer, can be accurately determined by pollen-analysis. This means it is possible to determine what kinds of trees and shrubs grew in these areas tens of thousands of years ago, and thus to find out what climatic changes have taken place over long periods. It is almost possible to read these layers of peat like a book and fascinating information can be gained by so doing. This information dates back into the Ice Ages, and facts from those times about climatic conditions and plant evolution and distribution, can be determined with considerable accuracy by modern scientists.

Bogs, particularly on the sides of mountains, form enormous water reservoirs and are important in the origin of mountain springs. Thus the thoughtless process of 'drying out' peat bogs or over-working them can have important environmental repercussions.

Peat bogs which have been drying out, or which have been drained, yield peat which is still, in some areas, dried and used as an inferior type of fuel. More commonly, it is baled and sold as a fertiliser and soil conditioner.

BOG MOSSES
Sphagnum spp.
Family: *Sphagnaceae*

These are mosses which form over a long period of time deep layers of peat by constantly growing at the top and compressing the dead parts below. Bog mosses form green or reddish, 'cushions' with a high water content. There are many different kinds of bog mosses, but they are very difficult to distinguish and identify. The stems are 10—40 cm. high and are usually, but not always, unbranched. The leaves on the stems and branches are varied in shape. The leaf consists of two cell types; some are narrow cells, shaped like an elongated letter 'S' and green in colour. The others are large, colourless and filled only with water. It is because of these large cells that peat bogs hold such enormous amounts of water. Bog moss can absorb 29 times more water than it actually weighs. When dry, the moss loses its green colour, becoming white. *Sphagnum*, like all mosses, reproduces by spores which form in capsules; however, it also spreads vegetatively from broken pieces of stem. Bog moss grows very fast, about 3 cm. a year, but at the same time the basal parts die off.

Among the commonest and best known species of bog mosses are *Sphagnum cuspidatum*, *S. cymbifolium*, *S. papillosum*, *S. plumulosum*, *S. rubellum*, *S. subsecundum* and *S. tenellum*.

COMMON SUNDEW
Drosera rotundifolia L.
Family: *Droseraceae*

This slender perennial grows up to 20 cm. high with flattened rosettes of long-stalked leaves. The leaf blades are circular, conspicuously red, with glandular hairs on the upper surface. The ends of the hairs glisten with small, shining droplets. The young leaves are spirally inrolled. One or more red-tinged stems grow from the middle of each rosette and bear a few white 5 or 6-petalled flowers. The fruits are capsules opening into 3 valves.

The plant flowers between June and August and grows in peat bogs, damp heaths and margins of lakes or ponds. It can be found in Central and north-

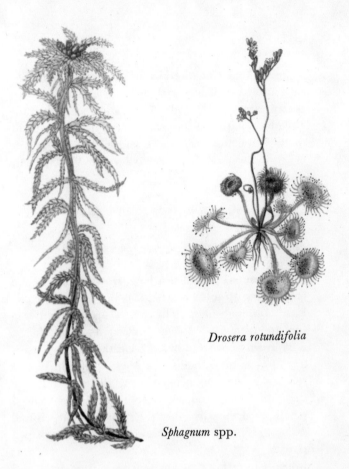

Drosera rotundifolia

Sphagnum spp.

ern Europe, northern Asia, Japan, and in temperate and northern parts of North America and Greenland. The Sundew is an insectivorous plant. When an insect comes to rest on the leaf, it is trapped and held by the long glandular hairs which curve inwards.

The glands secrete protein-digesting enzymes; as in man, enzymes aid the digestion of food. The soft parts of the insect body are digested and the soluble food-substances are absorbed by the leaf. These provide essential nitrogen compounds for the plant. Only the chitinous 'shell' of the insect is left and this is later dispersed by the wind.

It is said that Charles Darwin and his son Francis made some experiments in 1877. They fed the Common Sundew and discovered that the plants which had been fed grew considerably. The plant reacted to raw and fried meat, cheese, sausages, egg white and milk, but showed no response to sugar, starch and vegetable matter.

The Sundew has for a long time been used as a herbal remedy, though its healing powers have often been overestimated. Contained in the plant are quinine-like substances which hinder the growth of bacteria; also present are organic acids and tannins, as well as the already mentioned proteolytic enzymes. Medicine made from this plant was said to relieve muscle cramps, lower the blood sugar level and to alleviate respiratory illnesses.

MARSH CINQUEFOIL
Potentilla palustris (L.) Scop.
Family: *Rosaceae*

This perennial plant has a long, woody rhizome and erect stems up to 45 cm. high. Both stems and leaves bear scattered hairs. The leaves are toothed and pinnate with 5—7 oblong leaflets (3—6 cm. long), dark green above and bluish beneath.

The flowers are produced in May—July and have 5 spreading and long-pointed sepals. These are longer than the petals and are purplish in colour. The 5 petals are deep purple like the numerous carpels and stamens. The fruits are clusters of small egg-shaped nutlets.

Marsh Cinquefoil grows in peat bogs, in marshes and fens, both in lowland areas and mountain regions up to 2,100 metres above sea level. It is found in Central and northern Europe, Greenland, the Caucasus, Siberia, Japan and North America. The plant contains tannins and was often used to work leather. It produced a red dye to colour wool and was also used as a herbal remedy for diarrhoea.

COMMON BUTTERWORT
Pinguicula vulgaris L.
Family: *Lentibulariaceae*

This small plant, 5—15 cm. high, has a basal rosette of 2—8 cm. long and oval, glandular, fleshy leaves, which are bright yellowish-green in colour. The plant overwinters as a rootless bud.

The flowers are 1—1.5 cm. across, violet or lilac, and appear, usually singly, on the erect flower stems. The corolla is two-lipped and spurred, with a white patch in the throat. The spur is up to 7 mm. long, directed backwards and somewhat downwards. The plant flowers between May and July and is known

over almost the whole of Europe as far north as Iceland. It grows in peat bogs, wet heaths and among wet rocks.

Common Butterwort is an insectivorous plant and insects are caught on its fleshy sticky leaves. Glandular hairs develop on the upper surface of the leaves and these exude a sticky, protein-digesting secretion which is retained by the incurved leaf margins. The enzymes digest the soft parts of the insect which are then absorbed into the leaf tissue.

Today the plant is not very common. Formerly its leaves were collected and used medicinally as a purgative, and to relieve cramp and respiratory illnesses. In many countries the Butterwort is protected because of its rarity.

COMMON COTTON-GRASS
Eriophorum angustifolium Honck.
Family: *Cyperaceae*

This is a perennial sedge-like plant with a dark brown creeping, branched rhizome and erect stems 20—60 cm. high. The leaves are narrow, rough in texture and grooved, ending in a three-sided tip. The uppermost leaf has a swollen or funnel-shaped sheath. The stems are round and leafy, and bear terminal inflorescences of 2—7 brownish spikes which are at first erect, but later become pendant. Below the spikes are several leafy bracts.

The flowers are covered with dense, silky or cottony hairs which elongate to 3—4 cm. after fertilisation. The spikes then appear as white, hairy tufts. The fruits are nutlets which are dispersed by the wind and can be carried for considerable distances.

The plant usually grows in large groups in peat bogs, acid meadows and marshes. It is known in lowland areas and on high ground over most of Europe Siberia and North America. The cottony hairs were formerly used for candlewicks.

BROAD-LEAVED COTTON-GRASS
Eriophorum latifolium Hoppe

This species has broad leaves and the uppermost leaf has a close fitting sheath. During flowering between 5 and 12 spikes appear. In comparison with the Common Cotton-Grass the stalks of the spikes are much rougher.

This plant grows over most of Europe, in Asia Minor and the Caucasus area, in Siberia and North America.

COTTON-GRASS, HARE'S-TAIL
Eriophorum vaginatum L.

This species differs from the others in that it forms pronounced tussocks. The stems are smooth, erect, 20—60 cm. high and triangular in section.

The basal leaves are thread-like; the other leaves are borne low down on the stems and are wide, rough, and have cylindrical light brown sheaths all around the stem.

At the end of each stem is a single flowering spike which, unlike the other species, stays erect even during flowering. Like the other species it bears long white hairs. The plant grows in most northern temperate areas.

DWARF BIRCH
Betula nana L.
Family: *Betulaceae*

This is a stiff, low-growing and spreading shrub, rarely more than 1 m. high. The twigs are dark brown or blackish-purple and are covered in soft velvety hairs. The leaves are deciduous, small (0.5—1.5 cm. long), rounded or oval and short-stalked. They are hairy when young, becoming hairless later. Their texture is rather thick.

The shrub bears both male and female unisexual catkins on the same plant. These appear in May, a short time before the leaves. The male catkins are about 8 mm. long, pendant, and consisting of a number of bracts, each with 3 small flowers in the axil. Each male flower has a small perianth and 2 stamens. Pollination is by wind. The female catkins are erect and 5—10 mm. long. They consist of numerous

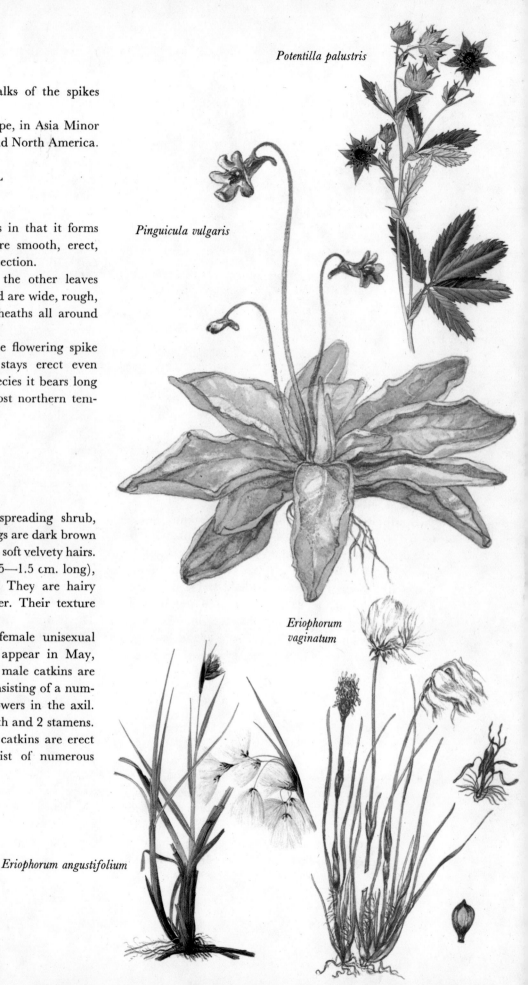

Potentilla palustris

Pinguicula vulgaris

Eriophorum vaginatum

Eriophorum angustifolium

Pinus mugo ssp. *uncinata*

three-lobed scales, each with 3 flowers in its axil and these flowers are reduced to a minute ovary bearing 2 styles, and with no perianth. The fruits are flattened winged nutlets and are wind dispersed.

Dwarf Birch grows in bogs, moorlands and glacial valleys. It is a sub-arctic species which is often found in association with Mountain Avens *(Dryas octopetala)* and Dwarf Willows *(Salix* spp.*)*. It is rare in Britain and occurs only in Northumberland and some of the Scottish mountains. It is found in northern and Central Europe from the Arctic southwards. Probably, in some mountain areas it is a relic of the Ice Age flora. In Lapland the fine roots are used to make blankets.

LEDUM
Ledum palustre L.
Family: *Ericaceae*

This is a dense, branched shrub up to 1 m. high. The simple evergreen leaves are 1—4.5 cm. long, linear or oblong, short-stalked and with an inrolled margin. They are dark green and covered with dense, rust-coloured hairs beneath, although the midribs generally remain visible. Similar hairs are also present on the young stems. The small cream flowers appear in May—July and are borne in terminal umbel-like clusters. They have long stamens which open by apical pores. The fruits are small capsules.

Ledum is an uncommon bog plant which may be found amongst dwarf birches where it forms large colonies. It is occasionally also found in damp, moss-covered crevices, particularly in sandstone. Since this is a very rare plant it is protected in many countries. It grows in bogs in Central and northern Europe, and Central and northern Asia as far as Japan. A closely related species *(L. groenlandicum)* occurs in North America and Greenland.

The plant is poisonous and contains, mainly in its leaves, several glycosides and volatile oils with markedly poisonous properties. Ledum has a strong, overpowering smell and this is due to the activity of small glands on the flowerstalks. When dried the plant is supposed to kill insects.

Both the flowers and leaves of this plant were used in medicine and as household remedies against fever, coughs and bronchitis. The dried leaves were used against insects as already mentioned and also, during the Middle Ages, the leaves were added to mead as a preservative. Towards the end of the 15th century Ledum was used instead of hops in some areas.

MARSH ANDROMEDA
Andromeda polifolia L.
Family: *Ericaceae*

The plant is an evergreen shrub up to 40 cm. high with small linear leaves which have inrolled margins. The leaves (1.5—3.5 cm. long) are dark green above and tinged grey-blue beneath. The flowers are bell-like, pendant and pale pink and borne on 4 cm. long red stalks. They may be self-pollinated or pollinated by bumble-bees and butterflies.

Marsh Andromeda grows in wet heaths, tundras and peat bogs in lowland and mountainous regions. It flowers between May and June. It is a plant which grows well at high altitudes. It is found in northern Europe and northern Asia, eastwards to Japan, and in North America as far south as New York. When growing in peat bogs high up in the mountains it often represents a relic of the Ice Age flora.

Marsh Andromeda is poisonous and also contains much tannin. In some eastern countries the plant was used both to tan leather and also as a black dye for items of clothing.

BOG WHORTLEBERRY
Vaccinium uliginosum L.
Family: *Ericaceae*

Bog Whortleberry is a dense shrub up to 70 cm. high. The stems are bushy, brownish when young, with numerous small oval blue-green leaves. The globular flowers are pale pink and grow singly or in small clusters in the leaf axils. The calyx lobes are short and blunt. The fruits are bluish-black berries which are sweet, and edible in small quantities.

The plant grows in drier bogs, moors and damp conifer woods in lowlands and in mountain areas. It is easily seen from a distance since it grows in abundance and has a grey-blue colouring which is very noticeable. It is found in the northern parts of Europe, in Asia and North America. In the Alps, the Sierra Nevada and other mountain ranges it may reach as high as 3,100 metres above sea level.

The Bog Whortleberry is not poisonous unless eaten in large quantities, when it has a toxic effect and can cause vomiting and headaches. In many Scandinavian countries the fruit was added to intoxicating drinks to improve the flavour.

CRANBERRY
Vaccinium oxycoccos L.

This is a slender creeping shrublet with prostrate stems reaching up to 80 cm. They are thread-like and rooting. The evergreen leaves are tiny, short-stalked and oval with pointed tips. They are dark green above and bluish below.

The pendant flowers are pink, borne on long thin stalks which have two small bracts in the middle. The petals are free almost to the base, with the tips strongly

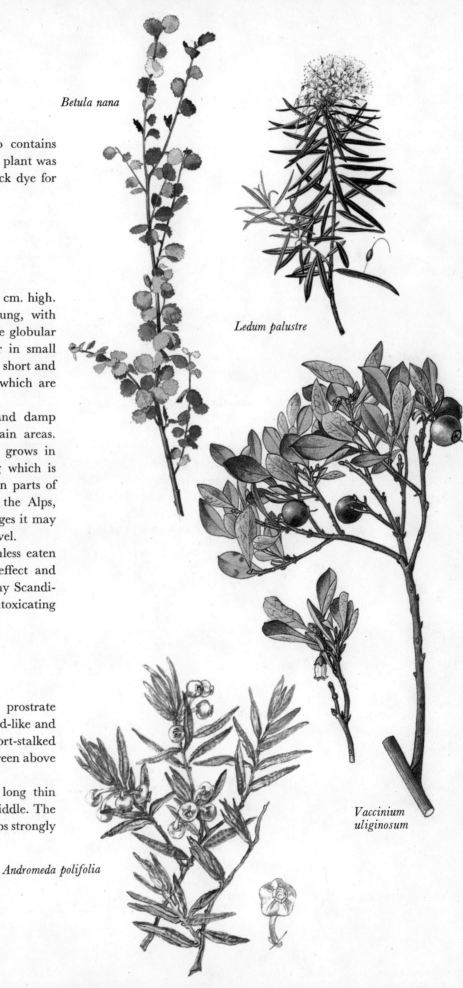

Betula nana

Ledum palustre

Vaccinium uliginosum

Andromeda polifolia

Vaccinium oxycoccos

bent backwards. The stamens have downy red filaments and project well beyond the corolla.

The fruits are berries, light green when young and becoming red (sometimes speckled with brown) when ripe. Cranberries flower between May and August and grow in peat bogs in northern and Central Europe, in the tundras of the northern regions as well as in North America. The berries contain up to 8 percent sugar, as well as organic acids, tannins and a red dye. Cranberries are often gathered and made into a preserve which is eaten as a dessert or sauce.

In the USSR and in Finland, where cranberries grow in abundance, the berries are fermented and made into a refreshing alcoholic drink called *kwass*. The berries used to be made into remedies to treat infections, and a tea was brewed from the leaves.

MOUNTAIN PINE
Pinus mugo ssp. *uncinata* Turra
Family: *Pinaceae*

This particular type of pine is rare and is not found in Britain. It forms either a dense spreading or erect shrub up to 3.5 m. high, or sometimes a small tree with a rather thin crown. The bright green leaves are 3—8 cm. long and in pairs. Mature cones are about 5 cm. long, horizontal or down-turned, and are short-stalked, symmetrical and shining. The young male and female cones appear in May to June. This pine grows naturally in Central and eastern Europe but may be planted in northern Europe. It is found in the mountains, sometimes growing in boggy areas.

PLANTS
OF
ROCKY
PLACES

INTRODUCTION

There are some plants that grow on virtually barren rocks, under extremely difficult conditions, and show an ability to survive and reproduce where many other plants would fail.

Soil, in minute quantities, is found in cracks and crevices of rocks, or in larger amounts, on sloping or terraced ground in mountainous areas. Such soil may survive being washed away by water or blown away by strong winds.

There is no regular supply of water since it runs off the rocks easily and evaporates quickly. This means that the plants often have to survive quite long periods with hardly any water, and sometimes they exist solely by being covered by mist. Further difficulties are presented by the periodic intense sunlight and wind — these factors increase the rate of evaporation of the soil water. By contrast there are, of course, areas which are constantly damp and shady; for example, near waterfalls, springs or in gorges and here we find plant species which flourish particularly well under these more favourable conditions.

Rocks which slope at much more than 40 degrees do not provide a habitat for any great variety of plant life. One finds mostly microscopic blue-green algae, also various species of lichens, liverworts and mosses. These plants can gradually disintegrate the surface of the rocks by both chemical and physical processes, and so prepare the ground for other and larger plants. The dead remains of mosses and lichens then form deposits of humus in the cracks and crevices in which other plants, including eventually shrubs and small trees, are then able to grow. Such a process of change over a period of time is termed *succession*. The algae, lichens and mosses which grow on rocks are termed *lithophytes*. Plants which grow in crevices where small quantities of humus are present — and these would include mosses, small ferns and also certain flowering plants — are termed *chasmophytes*.

Many lithophytes and chasmophytes are arctic-alpine plants. They have long branching roots which find a hold deep in the smallest cracks of the rocks. These plants are usually very low growing, some forming small shrublets and others with rosettes of often fleshy leaves lying close to the rock or soil surface. Many of the plants are very hairy and this may help to reduce the high rate of transpiration from the plant surface which is induced by strong sunshine and wind. Like dune plants, many rock plants roll their leaves, thus reducing transpiration.

These plants have, as a rule, only a short life span. They flower, form seeds quickly and die down, and may often propagate vegetatively e. g. by offsets.

Another important factor governing the growth of plant life can be found in the chemical substances present in the rocky ground. Some plants prefer exclusively limestone or calcium-rich ground; others grow only on rocks rich in silicates. There are, however, a great number of species which are indifferent to, or tolerant of, a range of soil types.

Of the larger plants which are able to colonise crevices in rocks or even in dry stone walls some of the commonest are ferns. Reproduction is by spores produced in sporangia borne on the leaves. The young leaves of ferns are typically spirally inrolled. Mature leaves are commonly pinnately divided and bear the sporangia either on the margins or on the backs of the leaves. Certain genera are highly successful in rocky habitats and some of these ferns are here described. Many of these are in the family *Polypodiaceae*.

The genus *Asplenium* has pinnately divided fronds which, as in most ferns, have sporangia organised in groups *(sori)*. In *Asplenium* the sori are numerous, oval or linear, and borne on the backs of the fronds. Each is directly over a vein and protected by an elongated flap of leaf tissue *(indusium)*. The linear sorus and its flap-like indusium, facilitate identification of *Asplenium*.

FORKED SPLEENWORT
Asplenium septentrionale (L.) Hoffm.
Family: *Polypodiaceae*

This is a small fern with a red-brown, scaly rhizome and tough evergreen fronds which are 5—15 cm. long. The leaf-stalk (petiole) is about three times longer than the leaf blade, and is dark reddish-brown at the base. The frond is divided once or twice into leaflets which are linear to wedge-shaped and toothed at the tips. The sporangia are arranged in linear sori which nearly cover the underside of the blades when mature. This small species grows only in lime-free areas. It is found on damp siliceous rocks — rarely on walls — all over Europe except in the extreme west and south, in the Near East, also in the Caucasian Mountains across to the Himalayas and Japan. It is also known in the Rocky Mountains in North America.

MAIDENHAIR SPLEENWORT
Asplenium trichomanes L.

This small perennial fern has a short rhizome which is covered with dark, narrow, hair-like scales. The fronds are usually 4—20 cm. long and are thick and dark green. Each has a tough, dark reddish-brown or blackish axis with a narrow, pale brown wing. The petiole is less than a quarter of the leaf blade. The leaflets are rounded or oval and toothed, both lower and upper leaflets being smaller than the middle ones. Whitish indusia cover the small elongated sori which merge at maturity. The plant prefers dry conditions and grows on the sunny sides of mainly limestone rocks and on old walls. It is known all over Europe, also in temperate zones and on mountains in tropical parts of Asia, Africa and North and South America.

The leaves, when rubbed together, give off a very unpleasant odour; they were formerly used in household remedies for a variety of ailments. During the Middle Ages the plant was used in witchcraft.

GREEN SPLEENWORT
Asplenium viride Huds.

This species has fronds (usually 5—15 cm. long), each with a bright green wingless axis and reddish-brown

Asplenium septentrionale

Asplenium trichomanes

at the base. The pale green leaflets are rounded, of similar size, with sori near the midribs.

The plant grows on shady and damp limestone rocks and in old and crumbling walls, and is found at heights of up to 2,700 m. above sea level. It is found especially in mountain regions over most of Europe and the Near East, in the Caucasian Mountains, in Siberia and the Himalayas as well as in North America.

WALL-RUE
Asplenium ruta-muraria L.

This is a small fern (maximum height 15 cm.) with a creeping, scaly rhizome. The leaves are long-stalked and dull, dark green in colour; they are bipinnate with subdivided leaflets. The sori are small and linear and borne near the base of each leaf segment. They later merge and cover the whole underside of each leaflet when mature.

This attractive fern grows mainly in cracks and crevices of calcium-rich rocks. It can also be found on walls of castles, in ruins and in rubble. In the Alps the leaves were at one time used as a herbal remedy and were also regarded as an antidote against witchcraft.

The species is common in the British Isles. It is known over most of Europe including the Mediterranean, the Near East to the Himalayas, also in central and eastern parts of North America.

POLYPODY
Polypodium vulgare L.
Family: *Polypodiaceae*

This is a fern with a long creeping rhizome at, or just below, the surface. It is densely covered with brown lanceolate scales. Rather leathery, more or less pinnate fronds arise at intervals. These have blades 5—45 cm. long and petioles one third to as long as the leaf blades. The leaves are lance-shaped with 5—25 segments on each side. These have deeply indented or toothed margins. The circular or elliptical sori occur in two rows on the underside of the leaf segments. They are orange at first, later turning brown, and are naked i. e. unlike the sori of most ferns, they are not protected by indusia.

The plant grows on rocks and walls, often with mosses and, in the wetter parts of Europe and elsewhere, as epiphytes on tree trunks. It is known over all of the northern hemisphere except the extreme north and south, also in South Africa and in western parts of North America.

The rhizome of this fern is very sweet and contains sugars, tannins and oils. The plant was formerly used as a household remedy in cases of apoplexy, and for a variety of digestive and respiratory illnesses, and also for gout.

The fern species described above is one of 3 variable and closely related species of *Polypodium*. They all have a similar distribution and there is some doubt as to how far they should be regarded as distinct species.

BRITTLE BLADDER-FERN
Cystopteris fragilis (L.) Bernh.
Family: *Polypodiaceae*

This is a delicate, quickly-wilting fern, with a short rhizome and tufts of leaves with long, brown, slender stems. The leaf-blades are oval or broadly lance-shaped with single or double, deeply lobed, toothed leaflets. The second lowest pair of leaflets (of which there are up to 15 pairs), is always the longest. The sori are in 2 rows on either side of the midrib, on the underside of the leaflets. The indusia are whitish, oval to lanceolate, sharply pointed and larger than the sori.

The plant grows on damp, shady, generally limestone rocks, in crevices of old walls and sometimes in rocky woods. It is widespread and cosmopolitan although it is confined to mountains in the tropics. It is the most widespread of all ferns.

GOLDEN ALYSSUM
Alyssum saxatile L.
Family: *Cruciferae*

This is a perennial, often woody at the base, with a rosette of basal leaves and erect, slightly leafy stems 10—40 cm. tall. All leaves are grey and hairy, spoon-shaped, entire or lobed. The stems are branched and end in rather dense, flat-topped flower clusters. The flowers are small, golden yellow, with 4 sepals and 4 notched petals. There are 6 stamens. The fruits are flattened and pod-like.

The plant flowers early in spring, between April and June, and is found in stony, rocky places of warmer regions. It is a native of Central Europe but has now spread into South East Europe and across to the southern parts of Russia. There are 3 subspecies with differing distributions. The plant is often cultivated and is a common and familiar rockery plant

Asplenium ruta-muraria

Polypodium vulgare

Cystopteris fragilis

Alyssum saxatile

Alyssum montanum

in Britain. In some countries however, it is rare and therefore protected. In parts of Britain it is sometimes found as a garden escape.

MOUNTAIN ALISON
Alyssum montanum L.

This is a perennial plant, prostrate or erect and up to 20 cm. high, but without the leaf rosette of Golden Alyssum. The stems, as well as the leaves, are coloured grey because of the dense star-shaped hairs. The basal leaves are spoon-shaped, the upper ones linear.
The bright golden-yellow flowers have petals twice as long as the sepals, and quickly lose the calyx and corolla. The flowers are in simple clusters which later elongate. The fruits are rounded and pod-like.
This plant grows on rocks and dry rocky slopes, as well as along the outskirts of dry woods, in both lowland and mountain areas. It grows in Mediterranean countries, in warmer regions of Central Europe, as well as in south and central areas of Russia.
In mountainous regions such as the Alps, and parts of Germany, Portugal and Italy, another species — *Alyssum alpestre* — appears, and can be found at heights of up to 3,100 m. above sea level.

CHEDDAR PINK
Dianthus gratianopolitanus Vill.
Family: *Caryophyllaceae*

A perennial, densely tufted blue-green herb, with firm stems and a woody rhizome. The many prostrate stems are densely covered in tough, pointed, linear leaves. The flowering stems are erect (10—30 cm. high) and have fewer leaves. Each has usually one terminal flower.
The flowers are pale pink or deep rose-pink, toothed and hairy with a reddish calyx. They are strongly clove-scented. The plant flowers between May and

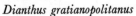

Dianthus gratianopolitanus

July and grows in between rocks and on stony slopes. It prefers limestone but will also grow on other types of rocks. In Britain it is found only in the famous Cheddar Gorge (Somerset). It occurs in western and Central Europe and across to Hungary. Cheddar Pinks are commonly cultivated as rockery plants. The plant is rare and is under protection in some countries.

MOSS CAMPION
Silene acaulis (L.) Jacq.
Family: *Caryophyllaceae*

This perennial plant is only 2—10 cm. high and forms bright green moss-like cushions of densely tufted stems. The leaves are linear, 6—12 mm. long, borne both on the stems and in basal rosettes. The solitary flowers have a bell-shaped calyx and rose-pink or whitish notched petals. The fruits are capsules.
The plant flowers between June and August and grows on damp rocks, stony slopes and screes, often above the tree-line on British mountains, in the Pyrenees, the Alps and Carpathians. It is also found in the mountainous regions of the south-west Balkans, in the Urals, as well as in the Rocky Mountains of North America. It tends to prefer limestone and is essentially a plant of arctic or alpine regions.

HOUSELEEK
Sempervivum tectorum L.
Family: *Crassulaceae*

Houseleek is a perennial plant with a basal 20 cm. wide rosette of fleshy, lance-shaped leaves. These are light green, and reddish above; they have pointed tips and white bristles along the margins.
In June—August, from the centre of the rosette, grows a stout hairy stem up to 15 cm. high. This is covered

Silene acaulis

Sempervivum tectorum

90

in lance-shaped softly hairy leaves and terminates in a much branched cluster of numerous flowers. These are 2—3 cm. across, pink or sometimes purple, and hairy. The flowers usually have 13 pointed petals with the same number of sepals. The stamens have purple filaments and orange anthers. The fruit is a group of follicles.

The plant comes from the southern parts of the Alps, but is also known in the Pyrenees, the Jura mountains, the Apennines, and the northern parts of the Balkans. In many parts it may not be truly wild. In some areas the Houseleek is cultivated but often returns to its wild state.

Where growing wild, it is found among rocks in both lowland and mountain areas but where planted it grows on roofs and old walls and also in garden rockeries. The Houseleek has, since time immemorial, been used as a cure for many diseases. It was used even in the time of Theophrastus (372—287 BC) for burns. The plant was also reputed to protect crops from pests. In the Middle Ages the plant was grown on roofs as a protection against fire and lightning, and on old buildings, particularly those with stone roofs, it may still be seen to this day.

It was also used as a general herbal remedy. For instance, a leaf placed between the teeth was claimed to relieve toothache; the juice of the plant was used for burns and, if mixed with wine and taken orally, it was supposed to relieve fevers and infections. It was even used as a remedy against deafness.

The Houseleek is a very variable plant with a number of subspecies, some probably due to hybridisation. The cultivated form is larger than the type and is often partially sterile, the plant then reproducing by rooted offsets. The name *Sempervivum*, meaning 'ever-living', refers to its ability to survive under extremely dry conditions.

HEN-AND-CHICKEN'S HOUSELEEK
Jovibarba sobolifera (J. Sims) Opiz
Family: *Crassulaceae*

This perennial plant has a basal rosette 2.5—4 cm. in diameter, more or less globular, with fleshy, pale green incurved, red-tipped leaves which clasp and cover the stem. This ends in a dense rounded cluster,

about 7 cm. across, of pale yellow flowers. The leaves, and also the sepals and petals of the flowers, are thickly edged with numerous stiff, glandular hairs. Numerous smaller rosettes surround the main one and grow on slender brittle stolons. They easily break off and take root. The appearance of the main rosette surrounded by the smaller ones, has given rise to the name Hen-and-Chicken's Houseleek.

This species flowers between July and August. It prefers sunny grassy slopes and sandy ground and is better known in lowland regions of Central and northern Europe as well as in Asia. This particular Houseleek was formerly grouped with *Sempervivum* as the habitat is rather similar. The genus *Sempervivum* has many species of which about 80 occur in rocky habitats.

ORPINE, LIVELONG
Sedum telephium L.
Family: *Crassulaceae*

This is a robust perennial with tuberous roots and fleshy, unbranched, blue-green or reddish stems, up to

Sedum telephium

Jovibarba sobolifera

80 cm. high, with numerous flat, fleshy, oblong and slightly toothed leaves. The numerous flowers are reddish-purple, lilac or sometimes whitish, and in dense flat-topped clusters. The fruits are erect follicles. A variable species, Orpine flowers from July until September and grows not only among rocks and rocky slopes, but also in woods and hedges. It is found in Europe, Asia Minor and Siberia.

WHITE STONECROP
Sedum album L.

This small perennial is 5—18 cm. high and has both creeping woody stems forming mats, and also sparsely leaved flowering stems. The leaves (6—12 mm. long) are usally ovoid-cylindrical and reddish. The flowers are white, rarely pink, and have 10 red stamens. They are borne in many-flowered, flat-topped clusters. The fruits are erect pink follicles.

The plant flowers between June and August and grows on rocks and in stony meadows, on walls and on roof tops. It grows in warm regions from the lowlands to hilly areas and is well known in most of Europe (excluding Iceland). In Britain it was almost certainly introduced. It is also found in North Africa and western parts of Asia but is absent from many areas in Russia. The plant is sometimes grown in garden rockeries.

YELLOW STONECROP, WALL-PEPPER
Sedum acre L.

This small, pale yellow herbaceous perennial grows only 2—10 cm. high. It forms mats of short creeping stems. The leaves are small (3—5 mm. long), fleshy, triangular-ovoid and with a small spur at the base. All stems are well clothed with leaves which are particularly abundant on the vegetative stems. Dead leaves become white, soft and papery.

The small (1 cm. diameter) yellow, star-like flowers are shortly stalked. They are borne in clusters of 2—4. The fruits are follicles which open in the wet and the seeds (which need light for germination) are then dispersed.

The plant flowers between June and July and grows in crevices in rocks, on stony slopes in dry meadows, on sandy ground and dunes, and on walls and roofs. Stonecrop is known all over Europe; in the Alps it can be found up to 2,300 m. above sea level. It also grows in the northern parts of Asia and in North Africa.

The plant is naturalised in North America. It is the commonest and smallest of the Yellow Stonecrops, with great variation in form. All parts of the plant, but particularly the leaves, have a bitter, peppery taste (hence the common name of Wall-Pepper). The plant contains vitamin C and can be eaten to prevent scurvy but it is poisonous in large quantities. Irritant substances are also present which cause vomiting, together with inflammation of the mucous membranes.

The plant was formerly a very important herbal medicine and the leaves in particular were commonly used. They were generally dried and made into a powder. Among its other uses, it was applied to the skin for a variety of sores and other conditions. The leaves were also made into a herbal tea which was taken for high blood pressure. The specific name *acre* refers to the bitter acrid taste of the leaves when chewed.

The Stonecrop is an extremely variable plant and the many differences it shows in size, leaf shape and also size of flowers, have led many botanists to believe that a number of separate species or varieties exist. Probably, however, differing forms are merely variations of a basic type.

LIVELONG SAXIFRAGE
Saxifraga azoon Miller
Family: *Saxifragaceae*

This herbaceous perennial has blue-green stiff lime-encrusted leaves, which form basal rosettes 1—3 cm. across. The leaves are strap-shaped and finely toothed. From the rosette of the leaves grows the flower stem (12—30 cm.) bearing a few small, toothed leaves. It branches at the upper end to form small clusters of white, often red-spotted, flowers on glandular, hairy branches. The fruits are round capsules. The plant flowers between June and August. Out of the leaf rosette several small shoots grow. These form their own rosettes which take root very quickly and when

Sedum acre

Sedum album

Saxifraga azoon

Gentiana verna

Gentiana clussii

they break off, form separate plants. As a result colonies build up like mats on the limestone rocks and screes in which the plant lives. Like a number of rock plants this also is a variable species.

Livelong Saxifrage is a species found often on rocks and is known in Central Europe, from Spain eastwards to Greece and Italy. It is absent from Turkey but is found in western Russia. Northwards it occurs in Iceland and in parts of Norway. It is absent from Britain.

STEMLESS TRUMPET GENTIAN
Gentiana clusii Perr. and Song.
Family: *Gentianaceae*

This is a perennial Gentian with flower stems 2—10 cm. high, singly or in pairs, and a basal rosette 5—15 cm. across, of light green leathery elliptical to lance-shaped leaves. The flower stems bear generally 2 pairs of small leaves.

Each stem carries a single, brilliant bright blue flower, 5—6 cm. across. Unlike some species of Gentian, the corolla is not green inside. The calyx is bell-shaped with pointed lobes. There are 4—10 stamens fused to the corolla.

This plant flowers between April and July. It is found on damp limestone rocks and stony slopes on mountains. It is sometimes also found in pastures, and rocky places generally, in the Alps, Carpathians and Apennines. Stemless Trumpet Gentian is a typical mountain plant which—somewhat like Edelweiss — also has a symbolic meaning and is used as a motif on many souvenirs.

SPRING GENTIAN
Gentiana verna L.

Spring Gentian is a small perennial Gentian with flower stems 2—10 cm. high, elongating after flowering. Each bears 1—3 pairs of small leaves and arises from a basal rosette of oval to elliptical leaves. These rosettes are clustered into cushions. Flowers are borne singly, with a brilliant deep blue lobed corolla 1.5—3 cm. across. There is a small scale between each lobe. This beautiful species grows in Central and southern Europe, the Caucasus and also in northern parts of Iran. The plant often starts flowering in March. In lowland areas it is found in stony grassy places. In Britain, it is confined to limestone hills of northern England and western Ireland.

EDELWEISS
Leontopodium alpinum Cass.
Family: *Compositae (Asteraceae)*

This is a famous alpine plant, perennial, sparingly branched and growing 5—20 cm. high. The 'flower' looks like a star, but botanically is a dense flat-topped cluster of flowerheads surrounded by 6—9 elongated leaves of varying lengths, densely covered by white, woolly hairs. Somewhat similar leaves form a rosette at the base of the flower stems. The flowerheads are yellowish, nearly globular in shape and range in number from 2—10 in a cluster. The central florets in each flowerhead are tubular and bisexual, the outer florets being sterile. The fruits are downy nutlets which are wind-dispersed.

Edelweiss flowers between June and September and grows on limestone rocks in the Alps, the Pyrenees, the Carpathians, the mountains of the Balkans, the Pamirs and parts of the Himalayas. Edelweiss is not known in either the Urals or the Caucasus. In the Alps it grows to 3,400 m. above sea level.

Edelweiss has been a symbol of the mountains for a long time now, not only for tourists and climbers, but also for various clubs. The star-shaped flower is worn on uniforms and hats, and is also often used in making flower pictures. Though Edelweiss is protected in many countries, it is still sold here and there. Particularly valuable are flowers with large 'stars'. The inhabitants of the Sacrathal in the Alps in 1891 handed Duke Karl Ludwig an Edelweiss which apparently had 29 supporting leaves and a 'star' 12 cm. in diameter.

Edelweiss was formerly used as a household remedy against rabies and dysentery. Legend has it that the smoke of Edelweiss had mystical powers and would keep away evil spirits and animals. In legend and song, Edelweiss is one of the most famous of flowers.

ALPINE ASTER
Aster alpinus L.
Family: *Compositae*

This is a small hairy perennial herb with erect stems 5—20 cm. high. The lower leaves are three-veined and oval, the upper leaves are one-veined and lance-shaped. The flowerheads are large (3.5—5 cm. across), solitary and showy, with blue-mauve (occasionally pink or white) ray florets and yellow disc florets.

Alpine Aster flowers between July and September and grows in crevices, on rock terraces, as well as in stony meadows and pastures. It is found also on hills and mountains in the Alps, the Pyrenees, the Jura; in Bohemia and the Carpathians, in the Balkans, the Caucasus, Armenia and Iran, as well as in Siberia. It is known to grow up to 3,100 metres above sea level in the Alps. A similar species can be found in the Rocky Mountains and the northern parts of North America. Alpine Asters are often grown in garden rockeries and several varieties have been cultivated.

BLUE MOOR-GRASS
Sesleria coerulea (L.) Ard.
Family: *Gramineae*

This is a tufted perennial grass growing up to 50 cm. high. The leaves are mainly basal, 2—6 mm. wide, keeled beneath and narrowing abruptly to a fine point. The numerous erect thin stems are 10—50 cm. high. They bear single, terminal ovoid inflorescences which resemble small spikes. Each spike has many 2—3 flowered bluish-purple spikelets.

This grass flowers between March and May and grows in between rocks or on stony slopes; it prefers limestone. It grows in Central and South West Europe, in Iceland and Scandinavia and can survive up to 3,000 metres above sea level. Sometimes large colonies are formed and the plant may be locally abundant. In Britain it is quite common in northern England and western Ireland.

This grass was named after the Venetian naturalist,

94

Leontopodium alpinum

Aster alpinus

Sesleria caerulea

Cotoneaster integerrima

scientist and doctor of medicine, Leonhard Sesler, who lived during the 18th century.

Cotoneaster integerrima Medicus
Family: *Rosaceae*

This is a small twisted deciduous shrub, up to 2 m. high, with low spreading branches which are hairy when young. The leaves are rounded or oval, short-stalked, green and hairless above, but densely covered with grey hairs below. The flowers are small, with pink petals about 3 mm. long, and are borne in twos or threes in drooping clusters.
The fruits are small, (6 mm.) red and globular. The shrub flowers between April and June and grows amongst rocks and hill screes. It is known in Central, South and East Europe, in North Wales in Great Britain, in southern Scandinavia and also in Finland. It also grows in Spain, Italy, the Balkans, the Crimea, the Caucasus and in Siberia. This shrub prefers dry, stony places mainly in mountain areas and also prefers limestone rocks.

Cotoneaster niger (Thunb.) Fries.

This shrub has white flowers which later become pink; the fruits are red but change later to bluish-black. It prefers limestone rocks and grows in southern Central Europe right across to Rumania and Macedonia.

Cotoneaster nebrodensis (Guss.) C. Koch.

The lower leaf surfaces, flowerstalks and sepals of *Cotoneaster nebrodensis* are all densely woolly-haired.

WHITEBEAM
Sorbus aria (L.) Crantz
Family: *Rosaceae*

Whitebeam is a shrub or small tree up to 25 m. high, with red-brown branches which have white, downy hairs when young. The short-stalked leaves are 5—12

Sorbus aria

96

Dryas octopetala

cm. long, often oval, double-saw toothed and with a dense, white felt of hairs below. The flowers have 5 white petals and are borne in 10 cm. wide, dense flat clusters. Fruits are rounded or egg-shaped, and scarlet with many lenticels (pores) in the skin.

The shrub flowers from May until June and grows on rocks and stony slopes and in dry woods, particularly in warm and sunny positions. It grows in Central and southern Europe from Ireland and Spain eastwards to the Carpathians, and also in the Himalayas. In Britain it is common in chalk and limestone areas.

This is a striking plant in spring because the white hairy leaves, from a distance, resemble Magnolia flowers. It is an extremely variable species, particularly in its leaves.

MOUNTAIN AVENS
Dryas octopetala L.
Family: *Rosaceae*

This is a much-branched, low growing, creeping shrublet forming mats of several square metres, but it is only about .5 m. high. It is long-lived and may grow for about 100 years.

It is an evergreen; the glossy leaves are oval, .5—2 cm. long, with margins bearing rounded teeth. The upper surface is dark green and the lower surface has a dense white felt of simple woolly hairs. The flowers are white, up to 4 cm. across, and borne singly on erect stalks which are covered with blackish glandular hairs. The calyx has similar hairs. The corolla has 8 (sometimes more) petals and the fruit is a group of feathery-haired nutlets.

This shrublet flowers between May and August and grows on rocky ledges, screes and rocky pastures, preferring limestone rocks. It is an arctic-alpine plant and can grow well above the tree-line. It is found in northern parts of Europe, Asia and North America. In the high mountains of Central and southern Europe it is an Ice Age relic.

Rhododendron ferrugineum

This interesting plant was discovered only in the 16th century during the early mountain-climbing expeditions. In Britain it is rare in the wild but is often cultivated. The leaves used to be dried and made into a kind of tea.

ALPENROSE
Rhododendron ferrugineum L.
Family: *Ericaceae*

This is a small shrub (50—120 cm. high) with shining, evergreen leaves, 2—4 cm. long, with inrolled margins and rusty scales beneath. The flowers are in clusters of 3—8, and when in bud they are covered by large papery bracts. Each flower is deep pinkish-red, bell-shaped and 2 cm. long. The fruits are capsules with extremely small, light seeds (about 0.000025 grams). They are wind-dispersed.

Alpenrose grows in damp crevices of rocks, (generally those with no limestone content), in open woods and in mountain pastures in the Alps, Pyrenees and Apennines. Really an alpine plant, it is occasionally found in adjacent lowlands. It often reaches the snow-line and, in pine woods, there may be enough plants to form a ground cover.

This is a poisonous plant containing several toxic glycosides. It is poisonous to horses, cattle and sheep, and honey from the flowers can be dangerous.

PLANTS OF GRASSLAND, WAYSIDES AND SUNNY SLOPES

INTRODUCTION

Abundant sunshine and a rather dry soil are characteristic of the habitats of those plant species which grow in grassland and also on sunny slopes. Natural grassland forms the ground cover on very thin soils and also on upper mountain slopes above the tree line, both such habitats being incapable of supporting trees and shrubs. The activities of man and of a variety of animals may also prevent the growth of trees and shrubs and this extends the range of grassy habitat.

The most obvious of such habitats is the meadow, which is an artificially created area of grassland and which is considered in another chapter.

Until the advent of myxomatosis in Britain and a number of other countries, rabbits bred prolifically and their regular grazing prevented the growth of seedlings of trees and shrubs. The effect was to restrict the development of scrub or forest even on land which was capable of supporting it. This can be seen today in downland areas, which no longer carry large flocks of sheep nor have a large rabbit population, and so in many parts of the country the downs are reverting to scrub and tree cover. Deer herds in Scotland and other countries may have a similar effect on tree growth.

Paths, roadsides and railway tracks provide a well-drained open habitat for plant growth. Such places, where access may be restricted and plants relatively undisturbed, can act as a kind of nature reserve in miniature. In time, the seeds of many interesting plants are blown or carried there and thus railway and motorway verges have sometimes been called the nature reserves of the future. Here we may find a rich variety of plants, many of them perennial, and not just grasses alone, although these are ofter more conspicuous.

In drier places we find plants which can conserve water and survive on very little moisture. Rock plants will grow on more stony slopes, whereas in sunny places and where there are deposits of humus, one can often find a range of shrubs. Often the plants are selective in the soil type in which they grow, particularly in rocky habitats. Thus we find, for example, that some plants prefer limestone and others may prefer granite.

Although species growing in these conditions are usually untouched by man's activities, some places are at times set on fire in springtime. The burning of areas of grass is, however, not only dangerous but also destroys much plant and animal life. Generally this is done to stop the spreading of weeds, but in fact it often encourages the spread of such plants. Upland pastures and heaths which have been invaded by bracken or heather are the areas most frequently subjected to burning.

SMALL PASQUE FLOWER
Pulsatilla (Anemone) pratensis (L.) Miller
Family: *Ranunculaceae*

This perennial plant has flower stems about 10 cm. high, but after flowering these elongate to 45 cm. The flowers are hairy and grow from a blackish root-like stem. The basal leaves form a rosette. The leaves are thrice pinnately divided, with narrow segments which are very hairy and have a feathery appearance.

The flowers appear in May and are 3—4 cm. in diameter and solitary. They vary in colour from white or greenish-yellow to reddish-purple, and are drooping and more or less cylindrical in shape. There are 6 perianth segments (or sepals) which are softly hairy outside, with slightly outcurved tips. The fruits are a cluster of nutlets with long feathery styles.

This plant prefers limestone, and may be found in sunny meadows in the warmer regions of Central and southern Europe, but it is also found northwards in south east Norway and even in Siberia. It is protected in many countries since it is a fairly rare plant. It is not found in Britain. The Small Pasque Flower is very variable in colour and the deeper coloured forms are found in the northern parts of its range, the paler forms in the southern areas.

The fresh leaves (but not the dried) are poisonous and some people may develop dermatitis, or diarrhoea and vomiting if they are eaten. The dried leaves were formerly used as a herbal remedy for cramp, chest troubles and also skin diseases. When the leaves are dried the poisonous substances cease to be effective, and this is also true for a number of plants of medicinal importance. The flowers were formerly used to dye Easter eggs and hence the old name of Pasque (i. e. Passion of Christ) Flower. This and other kinds of Pasque Flower are often cultivated in rock gardens.

YELLOW PHEASANT'S-EYE
Adonis vernalis L.
Family: *Ranunculaceae*

This handsome perennial is 10—40 cm. high. The stems are erect with scale-like leaves at the base. The upper leaves are without stalks, much-dissected into linear segments and densely clothe the stems.

The solitary flowers grow at the ends of the stems and are shining and golden-yellow, measuring 4—8 cm. across. The corolla has between 3 and 20 elliptical petals; the 5—8 broader hairy sepals are only half as long. The flowers open in sunshine, but stay closed during dull or bad weather.

The fruits are elongate heads of rounded hairy nutlets, with backward curving styles. The plant flowers between April and June, growing on warm sunny hillsides or at the edges of sunny pastures; it prefers limestone.

Yellow Adonis is well known in Central and South East Europe but occurs only rarely in Spain. Surprisingly, it can be found in south east Sweden but is never found wild in Britain. It also grows in Asia and North America.

All parts of the plant contain poisonous substances; nevertheless these are valuable as a heart stimulant and the plant is still used medicinally for this purpose.

Adonis vernalis

Pulsatilla pratensis

In Britain the plant is often grown in gardens for its striking appearance. It looks somewhat like a Buttercup (*Ranunculus*) but lacks the characteristic nectaries.

COMMON ROCKROSE
Helianthemum nummularium (L.) Miller
Family: *Cistaceaceae*

This small perennial shrublet is 5—50 cm. high. The hairy stems are sprawling, often forming a mat, and becoming woody at the base. The leaves are .5—5 mm. long, elliptical and hairy beneath, with linear stipules.
The loose one-sided inflorescences contain 1—12 flowers which are 2 cm. wide and generally bright yellow. The flowers open fully only in bright sunshine, lasting until about midday. It is a variable species with flower colour orange to white.
Common Rockrose flowers between May and September and grows on chalk or limestone rocks in sunny situations. It also grows in mountain pastures and in grassy places generally, on dry hillsides and at the edges of scrubland. It is known over most of Europe except the extreme north, also in Asia.

FIELD MOUSE-EAR CHICKWEED
Cerastium arvense L.
Family: *Caryophyllaceae*

This a rather inconspicuous perennial herb, with long prostrate non-flowering stems which are up to 30 cm. high and which root freely below. It also has more upright flowering stems of the same height. The leaves are up to 2 cm. long, linear to elliptical, and downy.
The flowers are 1—2 cm. across, with 5 hairy sepals and 5 white petals which are twice as long as the sepals and bilobed. There are 10 stamens; the ovary has 5 styles. The fruit is a cylindrical capsule which opens by 10 teeth.
The plant flowers between April and August and grows in dry open places, including meadows and fields, and in both lowland and upland areas.
It grows in most parts of Europe, except the extreme north, also in temperate regions of Asia, in North Africa and in North America.

CARTHUSIAN PINK
Dianthus carthusianorum L.
Family: *Caryophyllaceae*

This is a smooth perennial herb 20—60 cm. high, with short, stiff, leafy stems and longer unbranched flower stems bearing few or numerous flowers. The leaves are linear and pointed, flat and .5—5 mm. wide, and with leaf-sheaths 15 mm. long.
The flowers form in clusters, with a purplish calyx and are surrounded by a short papery epicalyx. The five petals are toothed, and vary in colour from red to pink or purple, though rarely white. The fruits are oblong capsules.
The Carthusian Pink flowers between June and September growing on sunny slopes and dry pastures, as well as on rocks and in sunny woods. It is found in Central, southern and western Europe also further north in Holland and Denmark, and in Asia Minor. It is sometimes cultivated in Britain.
The specific name commemorates two naturalists, Johann and Friedrich Karthäuser, who lived in the 18th century. The genus *Dianthus* is a large one with 120 European species.

MAIDEN PINK
Dianthus deltoides L.

This is a loosely tufted herbaceous perennial with short leafy stems and long (15—45 cm.) flower stems which are sparingly branched or unbranched. The leaves of the basal rosette are blunt tipped and oblong to linear; those of the flower stems are pointed and linear. All leaves are narrow with short hairs on the margins. The flowers have deep pink, or rarely white, toothed petals, with a darker basal band and faint spots. The calyx has an epicalyx of 2 oval pointed bracts.
The plant flowers between June and September and grows in dry often sandy fields and hilly pastures, as well as at the edges of woods. It is known all over Europe including Britain, Norway, Finland and northern Russia, and in temperate zones of Asia. It is rare in the Mediterranean region.
According to an ancient legend the plant grew from the tears of the Madonna as she wept for Jesus when he was on the Cross.

Helianthemum nummularium

Cerastium arvense

Silene vulgaris

Dianthus carthusianorum

Dianthus deltoides

BLADDER CAMPION
Silene vulgaris (Moench) Garcke
Family: *Caryophyllaceae*

This is a tufted perennial plant up to 50 cm. high
and blue-green in colour. All the stems are erect and
flowering, and arise from a basal leaf rosette. The
leaves are lance-shaped to oval, often with wavy
margins. The flowers are conspicuously large because
of the inflated veined calyx which gives the plant its
common name. The flowers form large drooping
clusters and have 5 deeply bilobed white petals. They
are particularly fragrant and are visited by long-
tongued bees and night-flying moths.

The fruits are globular or ovoid capsules. The plant
flowers between June and September on sunny
slopes, in sandy fields and waste places in lowland
and upland areas. It grows all over Europe including
Norway, Lapland and Iceland, in temperate regions
of Asia and Siberia eastwards towards Japan, in the
East Indies and also in North Africa. It is introduced
in North America.

Bladder Campion is common in meadows and is
thought to be very useful in increasing milk production
in cattle. It is a variable species with about 8 subspecies including one which grows on sea cliffs and
shingle and which is often identified as a separate
species *(S. maritima)*.

NOTTINGHAM CATCHFLY
Silene nutans L.

This perennial species is 20—60 cm. high, with a basal
leaf rosette from which grow erect unbranched stems.
Both basal and stem leaves are lance-shaped and
are softly hairy. The fruits are ovoid capsules.

The flowers are drooping, white, pinkish (or sometimes very pale green) and grow on short sticky
stalks in loose, one-sided clusters of 3—7 flowers.
The petals are deeply cleft with inrolled lobes; the
calyx is glandular-hairy with 10 purplish veins and
5 white-edged teeth. The flowers are fragrant and
open at night. They are pollinated by moths. The
flowers may be bisexual or unisexual and are open

for three nights. The stamens ripen during the first two nights, and the styles protrude and are ready for pollination on the third night. When the stamens ripen before the ovary this is known as *protandry*. During the day the flowers are closed.

The plant flowers between May and August and grows on dry, sunny slopes, in field borders, on rocky hillsides and on undisturbed ground. It also grows on shingle and cliff ledges and is found in most of Europe, northern Asia and North Africa.

MEADOW SAXIFRAGE
Saxifraga granulata L.
Family: *Saxifragaceae*

This loosely tufted perennial is up to 50 cm. high, with a basal leaf rosette which is sometimes dead at flowering. The leaves are long stalked, rounded or kidney shaped, with deeply cut teeth and glandular hairs. In the basal leaf axils develop numerous brown subterranean bulbils.

The stem is usually unbranched, glandular and sticky; the very few stem leaves are small, toothed and wedge-shaped. The flowers have oval glandular sepals and white petals 1—1.5 cm. long and three times longer than the calyx. The inflorescence is loose, with 2—12 flowers. The fruits are broadly ovoid capsules.

Meadow Saxifrage flowers between April and June and flourishes in lowland areas in well drained soils in meadows, and pastures, and on grassy slopes, as well as at the edges of woods. It prefers neutral or basic (i. e. alkaline) soils. It is known over much of Europe, from Spain eastwards to Russia, from Scandinavia to Sicily and also in Morocco.

Since all parts of the plant taste very sour, it is not eaten by grazing animals. The bulbils were at one time used as a herbal remedy for stone in the bladder.

AGRIMONY
Agrimonia eupatoria L.
Family: *Rosaceae*

This is a perennial hairy herb growing up to 60 cm. tall. The erect stems are unbranched and bear stipulate pinnate leaves with 3—6 pairs of large, oval saw-toothed leaflets, which alternate with smaller ones.

The numerous flowers are small (5—8 mm. in diameter) and grow in a slender leafless spike up to 20 cm. tall. The lower part of the flower is actually the receptacle, which is deeply grooved and hairy, with spreading hooked bristles above. These become hard when the fruits are ripe. Dispersal is by animals since the bristly hooked fruits easily become entangled in their coats. The plant flowers from June to September and grows in dry sunny pastures, thickets, hedges, wood margins and in grassy places generally. It is often found on limy soils. It is common in the northern half of Europe, in Central Asia and North Africa. Three subspecies are known as it is a very variable plant. These show differences in degree of hairiness, in leaf shape, fruit size, and distribution.

Agrimony contains tannins and resins, various organic acids, essential oils, silicic acid and also a yellow dye. The plant smells faintly of turpentine, and animals — with the exception of sheep and goats— tend to avoid it. It is an old established medicinal plant which has been used for many complaints including liver and kidney troubles, colds, snake bites as well as skin troubles, for which it used to be added to baths. Today Agrimony is grown for use as an astringent, as a tonic and also as a component of some drugs.

SPRING CINQUEFOIL
Potentilla tabernaemontani Ascherson
Family: *Rosaceae*

Formerly known as *P. verna*, this low growing, hairy perennial is from 5 to 20 cm. high. The woody stems root easily at the nodes and often form small leaf rosettes. The hairy basal leaves are long-stalked, with narrow stipules and 5—7 wedge shaped leaflets which are toothed and bear silky hairs. The leaves on the stems have only 3 leaflets and have oval stipules.

The flowers are yellow, with short stalks, and appear early in spring if it is sunny. It flowers between April and June and grows in dry meadows and on sunny rocky hillsides, often on limestone. It is known in Central, western and northern Europe, and eastwards to Siberia and northern China.

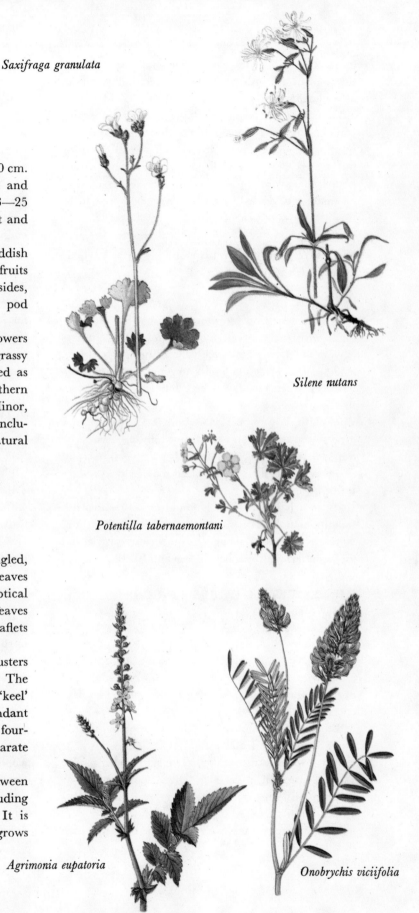

Saxifraga granulata

SAINFOIN
Onobrychis viciifolia Scop.
Family: *Leguminosae (Papilionaceae)*

Sainfoin is a downy herbaceous perennial up to 80 cm.
high. The stems are erect, tough and grooved, and
bear pinnate leaves up to 15 cm. long, with 13—25
linear or oval leaflets. There is a terminal leaflet and
papery stipules on the leaf base.

The flowers are bright pink and have purple or reddish
veins. They form dense, elongate clusters. The fruits
are flat pods with a network of pits on both sides,
shortly spined and with hairs beneath. Every pod
contains only one seed.

The plant prefers limestone ground and flowers
between June and August. It grows on dry, grassy
slopes and roadsides. It is also widely cultivated as
a fodder plant. Sainfoin grows in Central, southern
and eastern Europe, Siberia, Iran, and Asia Minor,
but because it has been so widely introduced (including in North Africa and North America), its natural
distribution is difficult to determine.

CROWN VETCH
Coronilla varia L.
Family: *Leguminosae*

This is a straggling perennial with smooth, angled,
erect or prostrate stems 30—60 cm. long. The leaves
are pinnate with 7—12 pairs of oblong-elliptical
leaflets with a terminal leaflet. At night the leaves
adopt a so called 'sleep position' i. e. with the leaflets
folded together.

The flowers are borne in rounded long-stalked clusters
of 10—20 pinkish-mauve or white flowers. The
'standard' of the flower is lilac or pink and the 'keel'
is pale pink with purple tips. The flowers are pendant
when young. The fruits are erect, oblong and four-
angled pods with 3—6 constrictions which separate
as one-seeded joints.

The plant prefers limestone and flowers between
June and August. It grows in grassy areas including
dry meadows, on hillsides and beside paths. It is
often cultivated as a fodder plant. Crown Vetch grows

Silene nutans

Potentilla tabernaemontani

Agrimonia eupatoria

Onobrychis viciifolia

in Central and southern Europe, but has been naturalised in a number of countries including Britain,
as well as in parts of Asia and America.

All parts of the plant contain a substance which
causes diarrhoea and is somewhat poisonous; an
infusion made from the leaves can act as a strong
purgative. Cattle and sheep eat only very young
plants and avoid the older ones. The leaves used to
be made into a medicine which was supposed to be
useful in cases of heart trouble.

YELLOW (MEADOW BEAKED) MILK-VETCH
Oxytropis pilosa (L.) DC.
Family: *Leguminosae*

This is a hairy low growing perennial, 10—20 cm.
high, with tough erect stems bearing hairy pinnate
leaves. The flowers are pale yellow and are borne on
leafless stems in dense, 5—15 flowered, ovoid clusters.
The fruits are ovoid, 1.5 cm. long and covered in
hairs.

The plant flowers between June and August and
grows in grassland and on sunny hillsides, rarely by
the sea. It tends to grow in rather dry habitats and
the general hairiness of the plant may help to reduce
transpiration.

In Britain it is rare, and is found on a few Scottish
mountains only. It is found in Sweden, Finland and
North Russia and mountainous regions of Central
and southern Europe, North Asia and North America.

KIDNEY-VETCH, LADIES' FINGERS
Anthyllis vulneraria L.
Family: *Leguminosae*

This is a very variable annual, biennial or perennial
plant with spreading stems up to 60 cm. high. All
parts of the plant, particularly the upper half, are
covered with hairs.

Most leaves are pinnate, with the terminal leaflet
much larger than the rest. Lower leaves may be
reduced to only one leaflet. The largest leaves are
14 cm. long. All leaves have either short petioles or
none at all. The fruits are disc or egg-shaped one-
seeded pods.

The flowers are pale yellow, often reddish, with

a calyx covered with white woolly hairs. The flowers
are usually in pairs, in rounded heads which are
half encircled by 2 leafy bracts.

The plant flowers between May and September and
grows in shallow soils on sunny hillsides, in dry
meadows and alpine pastures over the whole of Europe and eastwards to the Caucasus, in East Asia and
in North Africa, in the Sahara Desert and Ethiopia.
Kidney-vetch is quite often cultivated as a fodder
plant since it grows easily on poor soils. It is especially a plant of chalk and limestone areas, generally found on shallow soils and often growing near
the sea.

The plant was formerly used as a herbal remedy for
wounds and stomach upsets. Today it is of interest
for its great variability of form, so much so that the
species is often subdivided into as many as 30 subspecies — some recognised as species — which vary
in size of calyx and of leaves.

BLOODY CRANESBILL
Geranium sanguineum L.
Family: *Geraniaceae*

This is a bushy, hairy perennial up to 40 cm. high,
with a thick creeping rhizome which turns red when
broken. The stems are erect or creeping, branched
and hairy. The basal leaves die off quickly; the stem
leaves have hairy stalks and are divided deeply into
between 5 and 7 narrow lobes which are often further
three-lobed; these latter lobes have a finger-shaped
structure.

The flowers are usually solitary with bright, reddish-
purple, long-stalked flowers, 2.5—3 cm. across, with
5 notched petals and 10 stamens. The slightly hairy
fruits are 4 cm. long, with a long beak formed by the
fused styles, and split at the base into 5 parts, each
containing one seed.

The plant flowers between June and September and
grows in sunny, stony and grassy places and in open
woods and hedgerows. It prefers limy soils. Bloody
Cranesbill is known in almost all parts of Europe
as far as the Crimea and the Caucasus, as well as in
Greece, Italy, Sicily, Spain and Portugal. A somewhat
different variety is found on sand dunes.

Coronilla varia

BURNING BUSH
Dictamnus albus L.
Family: *Rutaceae*

This robust perennial grows 40—80 cm. high and
has a woody rhizome from which grow erect, densely
leafy, downy-haired stems. These bear numerous
black glandular hairs. The leaves are pinnate with
3—6 pairs of lance-shaped leaflets, each 2.5—7.5 cm.
long, dark green, with transparent dots marking
the position of oil glands.

The flowers are irregular, 4 cm. across with a glandular calyx and large, decorative, pink or white petals
with violet veins. The flowers are strongly lemon
scented. The petals are lance-shaped with the 4 upper
ones erect and the lowermost one thrust forwards.
The 10 stamens have green anthers and long purple
filaments. The fruits, which are glandular capsules,
are deeply five-lobed and shrink when ripe, flinging
out the shining black seeds.

The plant flowers between May and June and grows
on warm sunny hills, in dry, rocky, grassy or bushy
places. It is known all over Central and southern
Europe and northwards to Siberia, northern China
and the Himalayan regions.

All parts of this plant contain highly scented aromatic
oils which are particularly obvious on very hot and
sunny days. The oil glands have a strong lemon scent
which is characteristic of the plant, but the secretion
can cause irritation to the skin in some people who
may be allergic to it.

Burning Bush is so called because, on a really hot,
still day, sufficient of the volatile oils is secreted into
the air surrounding the plant, for it to be ignited by
a lit match. The plant was also used as a herbal remedy
against a variety of ailments including boils, festering
wounds and other poisonous conditions.

The original specific name was *fraxinella* which reminds

Oxytropis pilosa

Anthyllis vulneraria

Dictamnus albus

Geranium sanguineum

111

us that the leaves resemble those of the Ash *(Fraxinus spp)*. The plant is grown in gardens in Britain.

CYPRESS SPURGE
Euphorbia cyparissias L.
Family: *Euphorbiaceae*

This is a perennial plant growing up to 50 cm. high, with woody, reddish-tinted underground rhizomes from which grow numerous erect flowering and vegetative stems. The leaves are linear, up to 3 cm. long, and extremely dense on the vegetative stems. Both stems and leaves are smooth and hairless. The fruits are three-angled and three-celled capsules which are warty, and with each cell containing a single seed. As in all Spurges, the 'flowers' are really inflorescences and are borne in compound umbel-like clusters. Each 'flower' consists of conspicuous kidney-shaped opposite bracts surrounding cup-shaped involucres. Each involucre has 4—5 small teeth alternating with 4—5 conspicuous glands and it surrounds several male flowers (each of one stamen) and a single stalked female flower. In *E. cyparissias* the umbel has 9—15 rays (each with either 2—3 flowers or else 2—3 further rays with 1—3 flowers each). The bracts are yellowish to reddish. The glands are sickle-shaped. Cypress Spurge flowers between May and August and grows in grassy places (including chalk grassland), along waysides and on scrub, and on cultivated ground in Central and southern Europe eastwards to the Baikal mountains. The plant spreads quickly because of its underground rhizomes and can become an unwelcome weed on cultivated land.

All parts of the plant contain a milky, bitter and sticky juice called latex. This plant is poisonous if taken internally and its milky juice contains many substances including organic acids, gums, volatile oils and albumen. Cattle tend to avoid the plant but if, however, cattle fodder contains much Cypress Spurge, serious illness can develop because of its irritant qualities.

In Britain, the plant is only doubtfully native and was probably introduced. The latex was formerly used as a herbal remedy in skin complaints such as warts and corns. It was also used to lighten freckles.

The plant has the common name of Cypress Spurge because of the appearance of the vegetative stems. These, because of the dense overlapping greenish-yellow leaves (later turning reddish), resemble a small conifer.

COMMON ST. JOHN'S WORT
Hypericum perforatum L.
Family: *Hypericaceae (Guttiferae)*

This hairless branched perennial, 10—100 cm. high, has a branching rhizome from which grow erect stems. These are woody at the base and have 2 raised ridges. The leaves are oval to linear and have many translucent oil-producing glandular dots.

The flowers are in branched clusters and have golden-yellow petals edged with tiny black dots, and a calyx which is often covered with similar minute black dots. There are up to 80 stamens arranged in 3 bundles. Small dots are also found on the flowerstalks and are scented glands which contain an oily dye and can stain the hands red if the flowers are rubbed between the hands. The fruits are ovoid capsules which also have glandular black dots. The plant flowers between May and September and grows in dry meadows and on grassy banks, also in hedgerows and open woods.

It is known over most of Europe except the extreme north, in West Asia eastwards to China, in North Africa, and on the Canary Islands. It was introduced into the East Indies, North and South America and in Australia.

St. John's Worts characteristically have leaves which, when held up to the light, show the translucent dots which indicate the presence of oil glands. In a few species e. g. Imperforate St. John's Wort *(H. imperforatum)* and Mountain St. John's Wort *(H. montanum)* these glands are few or absent.

The glands produce volatile oils which are released through the leaf epidermis. In addition, some species have either red or black spots. The spots are found on stems, leaves and flower parts — as in *H. perforatum* — and these produce a reddish light-sensitive substance known as hypericin. What function this substance performs in the plant is not clearly understood, nor indeed is the production of volatile oils by the internal glands of *Hypericum* species. It is thought however, that these oils may have some effect in reducing the rate of transpiration.

The name St. John's Wort is a reference to the association of the plant, in Britain and in other countries, with St. John the Baptist. The red juice was said to be the blood of St. John and this juice was used in a variety of 'magic' activities. According to legend, if the plant were picked on the night of St. John, it would protect people from illness. The plant was also credited with 'magical' properties and was hung up in windows and doorways to prevent the entry of evil spirits.

The plant is a herbal remedy, still in use today, for a variety of complaints including asthma, kidney, gallbladder and stomach troubles, burns and fevers. The juice can cause harmful light-sensitization of the skin.

Some of the St. John's Worts make useful garden plants. Probably the best known of these is the Rose of Sharon *(Hypericum calycinum L.)* This grows up to 50 cm. high, with bright green, oval, evergreen leaves and striking solitary flowers about 8 cm. across. It forms dense carpets of foliage particularly in part shade beneath trees. In some parts of Britain it has escaped and become naturalised. Some of the larger shrubby species are also cultivated.

Euphorbia cyparissias

Hypericum perforatum

FIELD ERYNGO
Eryngium campestre L.
Family: *Umbelliferae*

This is a pale yellowish-green perennial, 20—70 cm. high, densely branched and very deep-rooting. The basal leaves are 5—20 cm. long, with long stalks and with 3 spiny-toothed segments. The stem leaves are simpler and smaller and tend to clasp the stems. The flowerstems end in ovoid flowerheads which are 1—1.5 cm. across and which are surrounded by 3—6 spiny bracts.

The flowers are small, whitish-green or purplish in colour. The calyx tips are spiny. The flowers are produced during June to September. The fruits are densely scaly.

The plant grows in dry, grassy places including banks and waysides, and even in stony places. It is rare in Britain, but in the rest of Europe it is found in central and southern areas and especially in Mediterranean countries. It also grows in Iran across to Afghanistan.

The general spiny nature of the plant makes it unpalatable to animals and in some areas it may become a troublesome weed.

In the autumn or the following spring, the stems die off at the base and the rounded clumps are blown about by the wind. Thus those parts of the plant which are above ground are dispersed and the seeds are widely distributed.

Other species of *Eryngium* are better known as Sea Holly and are cultivated in sunny well-drained soils. Like *E. campestre* the flowers lack stalks and are crowded together into ovoid or conical flowerheads. The colour range is limited to white or shades of blue.

LONGLEAF
Falcaria vulgaris Bernh.
Family: *Umbelliferae*

This is a bluish-green biennial or perennial plant 30—80 cm. high, with erect, finely grooved and much branched stems. The lower leaves are ternate (i. e. divided into 3 parts) or twice-ternate with long pointed segments. These leaf segments are elongate, slender and almost sickle shaped, with strongly serrate margins.

The white flowers are produced during July to September in umbels 4 cm. across.

The plant grows in grassy and waste places, including meadows and waysides. In Britain it is a naturalised plant of East Anglia and south east England. It is known all over Central and southern Europe and also in southern Sweden. It also grows in South America where it was introduced.

WILD CARROT
Daucus carota L.
Family: *Umbelliferae*

This is a biennial herb, the ancestor of the cultivated carrot. The plant has a characteristic odour from the production of volatile oils in ducts in the stems and in the roots.

It is an erect hairy plant growing 30—100 cm. high, and has a long thin root.

The stems are solid and ridged and bear thrice-pinnate dissected leaves which are about 50 cm. long and have a rather feathery appearance. The flowers are borne in umbels 3—7 cm. across and open in June, flowering through to autumn. These flowers are white, but the centre one of the umbel is often red or purple. The umbels are grouped, i. e. the inflorescence is a compound umbel.

Below the inflorescence are several feathery bracts and these, together with the saucer shape of the umbels (very noticeable as the fruits mature), make the plant easy to recognise. The fruits are 2.5—4 mm. long, oblong to ovoid in shape, with alternating spiny and hairy ribs.

The plant flowers from June to September and is common in fields, by waysides and in grassy places generally. It may also grow near the sea, and here it becomes much more fleshy and luxuriant in habit. It is known all over Europe, including Britain, from Scandinavia southwards to North Africa and eastwards into Russia and eastern India. It is also naturalised in other temperate and many tropical countries.

Several subspecies are known, of which the most familiar is subspecies *sativus*, the common carrot, which is cultivated throughout Europe.

The carrot was known to the Greeks and Romans as well as some Germanic tribes and has therefore been used as a vegetable for many hundreds of years. Besides being rich in starch and sugar, the carrot contains Vitamin A and also volatile oils which give the plant its characteristic odour. It was formerly used as a herbal remedy for stomach and liver upsets, also for kidney and bladder infections. It was at one time taken for intestinal worms.

BURNET SAXIFRAGE
Pimpinella saxifraga L.
Family: *Umbelliferae*

This plant is a somewhat hairy, rather slender perennial growing up to 60 cm. high, with tough cylindrical, finely ribbed and generally solid stems. The basal leaves are pinnate, with 3—7 pairs of leaflets which may be ovate or pinnately dissected. The upper leaves are much smaller and simpler.

The root has a noticeably unpleasant odour. The plant bears umbels of small whitish flowers in July—September and these are followed by slightly ribbed, broadly ovoid fruits.

It grows in dry grassy places including fields, pastures and waysides, especially on chalky soils. It is found in both lowland and upland areas in most parts of Europe but is absent from much of the south and from Arctic regions.

114

It also grows in Asia Minor and western parts of Siberia and may possibly be native in East Asia. It has long been known and used as a herbal plant and was taken, in the Middle Ages, in wine as a remedy against cholera and the plague. The roots contain volatile oils and tannins which appear to have been effective against diarrhoea and dysentery.

At one time extracts from the plant were added to beer to improve its flavour. The common name of the plant is misleading since the plant is neither a Burnet nor a Saxifrage, but the pinnate leaves somewhat resemble those of Burnet *(Sanguisorba)* and hence the name.

VIPER'S BUGLOSS
Echium vulgare L.
Family: *Boraginaceae*

Viper's Bugloss is a biennial plant growing 30—90 cm. high. The erect unbranched stems bear white-bristled, lance-shaped leaves which also form a basal rosette. The basal leaves are up to 15 cm. long and often die away before flowering time. The upper leaves bear somewhat curved inflorescences in their axils.

The flowers are 1.5—2 cm. across, and are pink in the bud, later changing to bright blue, rarely to white. The stamens are protruding.

The fruits are angular hairy nutlets within a hairy calyx.

The plant flowers between May and September and grows on grassy slopes, in fields, beside railway lines or on waste ground. It may be found on light, dry or chalky soils and may be locally common. It is known almost everywhere in Europe and in Asia Minor. It is naturalised in North America.

Viper's Bugloss is an old herbal remedy which was used for a variety of ailments. Its name derives from its former use in the treatment of snake bites. At one time, in some areas, the young lower leaves were cooked and eaten like spinach.

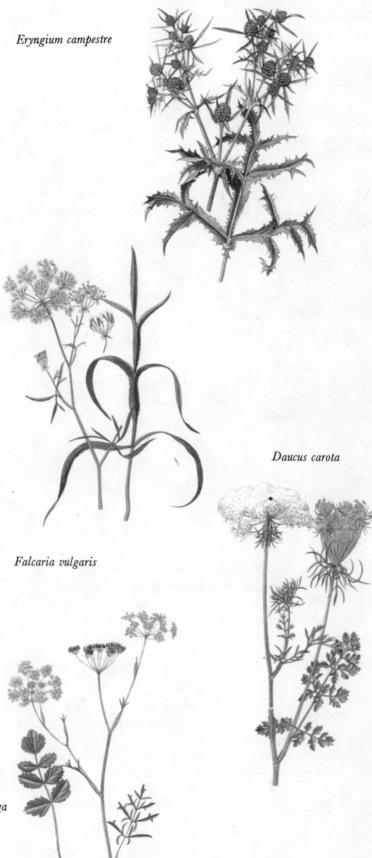

Eryngium campestre

Daucus carota

Falcaria vulgaris

Pimpinella saxifraga

TRUE ALKANET
Anchusa officinalis L.
Family: *Boraginaceae*

This is a biennial or perennial plant growing to about 80 cm. high, with roughly hairy stems and leaves. The leaves are lance-shaped; the basal leaves are long stalked and wither away during the flowering period of the plant. The flowers are reddish becoming bluish-purple, rarely white, and form dense coiled clusters which later elongate. The fruits are ovoid nutlets.

The plant flowers between June and August and grows in fields and grassy places generally, including waste ground and waysides. It is found in both lowland and upland areas where it may grow to a height of up to 2,300 metres above sea level. It prefers warmer regions.

The plant originally came from East Asia but is now found over most of Europe, where it was grown by man as a dye. The dye is red and is obtained from the roots of this and other genera including Alkanet *(Pentaglottis)*.

NONEA
Nonea pulla (L.) DC
Family: *Boraginaceae*

This may be an annual, biennial or perennial herb up to 50 cm. high. The plant is greyish-white in colour because both stems and leaves are covered with dense, fine, glandular hairs. The lower leaves are linear to lance-shaped and may form a basal rosette. The stem leaves are broader and clasp the stems, which branch at their upper ends.

The flowers are short-stalked with a bell-shaped calyx and a brownish-violet, sometimes tinged yellow or white, tubular corolla about 1 cm. in diameter. They are borne in short coiled inflorescences in the upper leaf axils. Fruits are ovoid nutlets with a short lateral beak.

The plant flowers between April and August in dry, grassy (sometimes stony) places including fields and waysides, in lowland and upland regions of the warmer parts of Europe. It originally came from the

grasslands of South East Europe and later it spread to Central Europe.

COMMON BUGLE
Ajuga reptans L.
Family: *Labiatae*

This is a creeping perennial 10—30 cm. high. It has a short rhizome and long, leafy and rooting runners. The stems are erect, unbranched and often tinged bronze. The basal leaves are oval, 4—7 cm. long, often with slightly lobed margins and forming a basal rosette. The upper leaves are shorter and almost stalkless.

The short-stalked flowers grow in the axils of bracts which are often tinted blue; they are borne on the upper parts of the stems. Each flower has a bell-shaped calyx and a blue (rarely pink or white) 2-lipped corolla, the upper lip short and undivided, the lower 3-lobed. Inside is a ring of hairs. There are 4 stamens and the fruits are 4 nutlets. The plant flowers between April and July in damp, grassy places and in damp woodlands.

It is known over all of Europe except Iceland, in South West Asia and Tunisia. The plant was formerly a herbal remedy. This and related species differ from most Labiate flowers in having a much reduced upper lip to the corolla.

WILD THYME
Thymus serpyllum L.
Family: *Labiatae*

This is a spreading, faintly aromatic mat-forming perennial herb, with woody creeping and rooting branches and erect flower stems which are about 5—10 cm. high. These stems are four-sided and hairy all round but the related subspecies known as *T. drucei* Ronn. has stems which are hairy on 2 sides only. The glandular leaves are 5—9 mm. long, oval or elliptical, and hairy at the base.

The flowers are about 3 mm. across, with a bell-shaped calyx and a pink to purple two-lipped corolla. They are borne in terminal rounded or elongate clusters.

Anchusa officinalis

Echium vulgare

Wild Thyme grows in dry grassland, heaths, dunes and screes. It flowers between April and September and is known in Europe, including Iceland and Greenland, also in northern Siberia and in Asia eastwards to the Himalayas, where it grows up to 4,500 metres above sea level. *Thymus drucei* is restricted to western Europe. Both are found in Britain.

Closely related to *Thymus serpyllum* and *Thymus drucei* is the herb plant *Thymus vulgaris*. This is grown in gardens for its leaves, which are used in cooking. It is a small shrublet and is a native of the western Mediterranean region. It too, has the common name of Thyme.

Thyme is an ancient medicinal plant. Extracts from the plant produce a volatile oil which also contains Thymol. This is an antiseptic which is in use today, particularly in mouthwashes and toothpastes. The aromatic oil distilled from the leaves is also used for making soaps and perfumes.

COMMON SELF-HEAL
Prunella vulgaris L.
Family: *Labiatae*

Self-heal is a slightly hairy perennial with short creeping and rooting stems. From these stems arise erect flowering stems, often brownish in colour and 5—30 cm. high.

The leaves are 2—5 cm. long, oval, with either an entire or a slightly toothed margin. The lower leaves have long stalks.

The generally blue-violet flowers are in dense oblong terminal heads with 2 leaves immediately beneath. The corolla (1—1.5 cm. long) is two-lipped, and the upper lip is hooded. The plant flowers between

Nonea pulla

Thymus serpyllum

Ajuga reptans

June and October, producing fruits of 4 nutlets, and grows in grassy places and also on dry ground.

It is known almost everywhere in Europe, in the temperate zones of Asia and in North Africa. It was probably taken by man to East Asia, North America, Chile, Mexico and Australia.

A brew of fresh leaves was formerly used to treat wounds, boils and fevers thus curing people without the aid of a doctor, hence the name 'Self-Heal'.

MEADOW CLARY
Salvia pratensis L.
Family: *Labiatae*

An aromatic perennial 30—100 cm. high, this plant has four-angled stems which are erect and hairy below, and glandular above. The leaves are broad and lance-shaped and somewhat wrinkled (a characteristic of this plant). They are double-toothed and lobed; the lower ones are stalked and the upper ones stalkless.

The bright blue-violet (rarely pink or white) flowers are in whorls in the axils of small bracts, and form a loose spike. The corolla is 1.5—2.5 cm. long — in fact, three times as long as the calyx. Both corolla and calyx are two-lipped, the upper lip of the corolla being hooded. The 2 stamens have an upper fertile anther and a lower sterile anther separated by a long connective, allowing a lever-like action. When an insect enters the flower to suck the nectar, it touches the sterile anther which forms one of the arms of a hinge. This in turn brings the fertile anther down on to the back of the insect, thus facilitating cross-pollination. This lever action is characteristic of all Salvias.

The plant flowers between May and July and grows on chalk grassland and waysides in warmer regions of lowland and upland areas. It is known almost everywhere in Europe (but is rare in Britain), eastwards to the Caucasus and the Crimea, as well as in Morocco.

During the Middle Ages in Germany, this and other aromatic plants were added as flavouring to sour white wine. In other countries it was added to wine or beer to give a more herbal taste.

SAGE
Salvia officinalis L.

This species is a shrub 20—70 cm. high, with hairy branches and wrinkled leaves which contain large amounts of volatile oils.

The leaves are used fresh or dried in cooking, also in cheese and wine making, and to make sage tea which is used medicinally. The flowers are bright blue-purple and the plant makes a handsome addition to the herb garden.

WHORLED CLARY
Salvia verticillata L.

This species is a hairy and strong-smelling perennial 30—80 cm. high. By the time of flowering the basal leaves have already withered. The stem leaves are triangular, heart-shaped and toothed. The plant is often purplish in colour.

The bilobed flowers appear in whorls in the axils of small brown bracts, and have blue-violet (rarely white or pink) corollas and small purplish bristly calyxes. The whorls form a long interrupted leafless spike.

The plant flowers between May and August and is rarely a meadow plant — more a plant of waste places and waysides. It occurs naturally in mountainous parts of southern Europe, from the southern Alps and Carpathians to Spain, Italy and Greece. Originally this plant probably came from Asia Minor, northern Iran and Syria, but today it is known over much of Europe, although it is not often abundant.

MARJORAM
Origanum vulgare L.
Family: *Labiatae*

This hairy and very aromatic perennial is 30—80 cm. high, with a woody rhizome and erect stems which are branched at the top. The short-stalked leaves are 1.5—4.5 cm. long, oval and often toothed. They are dotted with glands on the underside. The dark purple bracts of the flowerheads are similar to the leaves.

Prunella vulgaris

The small (6—8 mm.) rose-purple or white flowers are in dense terminal and axillary clusters forming a much branched terminal inflorescence. The 4 stamens project from the two-lipped corolla. The fruits are brown nutlets.

The plant flowers between July and September and grows on sunny hillsides, in fields, in open woods and in scrub. It prefers dry chalky soils.

It is known in the warmer regions of Europe and in Britain is common in England and Wales, but less so in Scotland.

It also occurs in western Asia, Asia Minor and the Himalayan mountains. It is naturalised in North America.

This highly aromatic plant was known to the ancient Egyptians and was used during the Middle Ages for sprains, bruises and cramp. The dried herb was also used to fumigate rooms.

The herb contains volatile oils and tannins and is still collected today to make a herbal tea. It is also used in perfumery and yields a reddish-brown dye. It is well known as a flavouring agent in cookery and is commonly grown in herb gardens.

AARON'S ROD, COMMON MULLEIN
Verbascum thapsus L.
Family: *Scrophulariaceae*

This is a large biennial plant growing 30—200 cm. high. It has a striking white appearance because both stems and leaves are covered with a dense felt of woolly hairs. During the first year it forms only a basal rosette of large (up to 14 cm. long) lance-shaped, sometimes toothed, leaves. In the second year the tall stem grows out from the rosette, and bears lance-shaped leaves which narrow at the base and grow down the stem as wings.

From June to September the stems develop a long

Salvia pratensis

Salvia verticillata

Origanum vulgare

Verbascum thapsus

Verbascum lychnitis

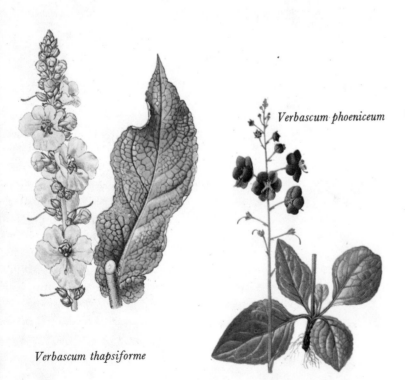

Verbascum thapsiforme

Verbascum phoeniceum

inflorescence of large golden-yellow flowers which are up to 3 cm. across, and which are borne in the axils of bracts. The corolla has a short tube and 5 rounded petal-like lobes. Of the 5 stamens the 2 lower stamens are almost hairless, the 3 upper stamens having white woolly-haired filaments. The fruits are capsules with small seeds.

Common Mullein, like most of the species, grows in dry, sunny, semi-open habitats. These habitats include dry grassland, forest clearings, waysides, waste places and stony slopes, and in such places the plant may be common. It is a species variable in leaf and flower form.

The plant is found in most of Europe except the extreme north, and in much of the Balkan peninsula. It is a well known herbal plant; a soothing tea is made from the flowers and is used for coughs, including whooping cough, as well as infections of the bronchial passages. The leaves have also been used for poultices and as candle wicks. The Romans used to obtain a yellow dye from the flowers. All Mulleins are poisonous to livestock.

Verbascum thapsifome Schrader

This plant is rather like *Verbascum thapsus* but the flower spikes may be branched and its flowers are larger (3—5 cm. across), flat and bright yellow — rarely white — in colour. The leaves are more pointed, coarsely toothed and covered with yellowish-grey downy hairs. They also form wings down the stems.

WHITE MULLEIN
Verbascum lychnitis L.

This species of Mullein is 50—150 cm. high, less densely hairy and with powdery, greyish, angled stems, but here its leaves are dark green above, densely white powdery-haired beneath. The basal leaves are oblong to lance-shaped, 10—30 cm. long, short-stalked; the stem leaves are narrowly oval with pointed tips and stalkless. They do not form wings on the stems.

The flowers grow in clusters of 5—10 in the axils of the bracts. All the stamens have white hairy filaments.

The corolla is white, rarely yellow, 15—20 mm. across.

The plant flowers between June and September and grows in dry, sparsely grassy areas and dry meadows, also in wood clearings, and often on chalky soils. It grows in most of Europe, across to western Siberia and Asia Minor, also in Morocco.

In south eastern Europe the plant is used for making candle wicks.

PURPLE MULLEIN
Verbascum phoeniceum L.

This species is usually perennial, 30—100 cm. high, with a rather bulbous root. The lower part of the plant bears simple hairs; the upper part has glandular hairs.

The long-stalked flowers are solitary in the axils of bracts and are up to 2.5 cm. across. They have a purple or brownish (rarely yellow) corolla. The stamens are violet and hairy.

The plant flowers between May and June on sunny slopes, in dry meadows and pastures, and also in sandy, stony or rocky areas. It is not native to Britain. Purple Mullein is found in Central Europe, southwards into central Italy and eastwards to parts of West Asia. Modern hybrids are grown in English gardens.

COMMON TOADFLAX
Linaria vulgaris Miller
Family: *Scrophulariaceae*

This herbaceous perennial grows 30—80 cm. high. The plant is blue-green in colour and the leaves and stems are smooth and hairless, although sometimes the inflorescence bears glandular hairs. The erect stems are numerous and arise from a creeping rhizome. The leaves are numerous and crowded, linear and 3—8 cm. long.

The many flowers (about 20) are borne in the axils of linear bracts in a long dense inflorescence. The corolla is 15—25 mm. long, strongly two-lipped and looks somewhat like a small yellow *Antirrhinum* but with an almost straight spur nearly as long as the corolla.

Flowers are yellow with orange-spotted lower lips. The fruits are capsules with numerous very small seeds and these, together with the spread of the easily rooting rhizomes, readily allow the plant to become a garden pest.

The plant flowers between June and October and is common in grassy and cultivated fields, hedgerows and waste places. It is found all over Europe except in the far north and in Portugal. It also grows in West Asia and has become naturalised in North America. It is found in both lowland and upland areas.

Interestingly, a different form of the flower may sometimes be seen. In this the corolla is not two-lipped and has five spurs instead of one. The plant was once very important herbally and has also been used for a yellow dye.

GERMANDER SPEEDWELL
Veronica chamaedrys L.
Family: *Scrophulariaceae*

This is a sprawling hairy perennial 7—25 cm. high, with 2 opposite lines of white hairs on the stems. It is a member of a very large genus.

The leaves are 1—2.5 cm. long, almost triangular to oval, stalkless, coarsely toothed and hairy.

The flowers are in an open spike and are deep,

Linaria vulgaris   *Veronica chamaedrys*

bright blue with a white eye. Both calyx and corolla are four-lobed, the petals joined to form a very short tube. There are 2 stamens. The fruits are egg-shaped, hairy capsules. The plant flowers from March to July.

Germander Speedwell is common in meadows, hedges and woods throughout Europe except for the extreme north and south of the continent. It also grows in North and West Asia and is naturalised in North America.

SPIKED SPEEDWELL
Veronica spicata L.

This is a hairy perennial with erect stems 10—60 cm. high. The leaves are 20—80 cm. long, the upper ones linear to lance-shaped, narrowing to the leaf stalk and toothed; the lower leaves are somewhat broader. The flowers are violet-blue with a rather long corolla tube and short flower stalks. They grow in a dense leafy spike about 10 cm. or more in length. The fruits are rounded capsules.

The plant flowers between July and October and grows on dry grassland and rocky slopes, especially on basic soils. It is rare in Britain. It grows in much of Europe but is rare to the west, also in southern parts of Russia and the Balkans, West and Central Asia to China and Japan.

LADY'S BEDSTRAW
Galium verum L.
Family: *Rubiaceae*

This is an erect or spreading perennial 15—100 cm. high, with a slender creeping rhizome with numerous four-angled erect stems. The leaves are in whorls of 8—12, and are linear, hairy beneath, with inrolled margins. They turn black when dried. The bright yellow flowers are small with a four-lobed corolla and are borne in much-branched terminal leafy clusters. The fruits are small (2 mm.), hairless and black. The plant was once used as a herbal remedy and was also used to curdle milk and to colour cheese. The roots give a red dye.

The plant flowers from June to September and grows in dry grassy places on all but the most acid soils. It is

known throughout Europe (except Portugal and Russia), also in Asia Minor and West Asia.

HEDGE BEDSTRAW
Galium mollugo L.

This is a robust perennial growing to a height of 25—120 cm. and with a short, stout rhizome. The four-angled stems may be erect or sprawling and bear linear to oval leaves (green on both sides) in whorls of 6—8. The leaves have stout forward-directed prickles on the margins. This Bedstraw does not turn black when dried. The small white flowers are numerous and they are borne in loose, branched, terminal clusters. The fruits are warty and they turn black when mature.

The plant flowers throughout the summer until autumn and grows on dry grassy slopes, in dry meadows, in hedgerows, scrub and in open woodland. It prefers calcareous soils. It, is a common plant growing over most of Europe, in Asia Minor, the East Indies, Ceylon and Burma. It was formerly a herbal plant. Like other Bedstraws it was frequently used as a kind of bedding. A red dye is obtained from the roots.

CLUSTERED BELLFLOWER
Campanula glomerata L.
Family: *Campanulaceae*

This is a stiff, hairy perennial 5—60 cm. high. The basal leaves are long-stalked, 2—8 cm. long, oval and finely toothed; the stem leaves are smaller, stalkless and half-clasping the stems.

The flowers are bell-shaped, violet or bright blue (rarely white), with a bristly-haired calyx. The flowers are closely encircled at the base by an involucre of leafy bracts. The fruits are capsules opening by apical pores.

The plant flowers between June and September and grows on calcareous soils, particularly in chalk grassland, less often on sea cliffs, by waysides and in open woods. It grows over most of Europe to southern Sweden and eastwards to Japan. It is a rather variable species which develops different forms, including 2 garden varieties.

122

STEMLESS CARLINE THISTLE
Carlina acaulis L.
Family: *Compositae*

This thistle is biennial or perennial, with a very short
unbranched stem growing to a maximum of 10 cm.
The leaves form a large rosette close to the ground.
They are deeply and pinnately spiny-lobed, tough
and either hairless or with a few cobwebby hairs.
In the centre of the rosette develops a large, almost
always solitary flowerhead, 5—13 cm. across. The
outer involucral bracts are leaf-like; the middle ones
are brownish and toothed; the inner ones are linear,
silvery-white on the upperside and yellowish below.
The actual flowerhead is formed by small pink or
white disc florets. The white involucral bracts close
and roll up in bad weather thus protecting the
flowerhead from the rain. During sunshine the flower
re-opens like a star.

The plant flowers between May and September and
grows in poor pastures and in stony and rocky places
in warmer mountain areas. It is known in Central
and southern Europe as well as in central areas of
Russia. It is not found in Britain.

The root is aromatic, tastes bitter and was formerly
much in use as a herbal remedy. It was also known as
a 'magical' plant and was often cultivated in cloister
gardens. In Mediterranean countries it is still cultivated for its fleshy roots, from which a tasty salad can
be made.

The root contains volatile oils, resins and tannins.
These substances affect kidney function and also
improve the appetite. The roots are still in use today
for the manufacture of herbal medicines. Another
use is as a tonic and stimulant for beef cattle. To
improve their appetite and to increase the rate of
fattening, extracts of the root are given to the animals.
The dried flowers are used as a countryman's baro-
meter, the bracts closing together in moist air.

The name *Carlina* may refer to Carl the Great and
legend has it that, when his army was threatened by

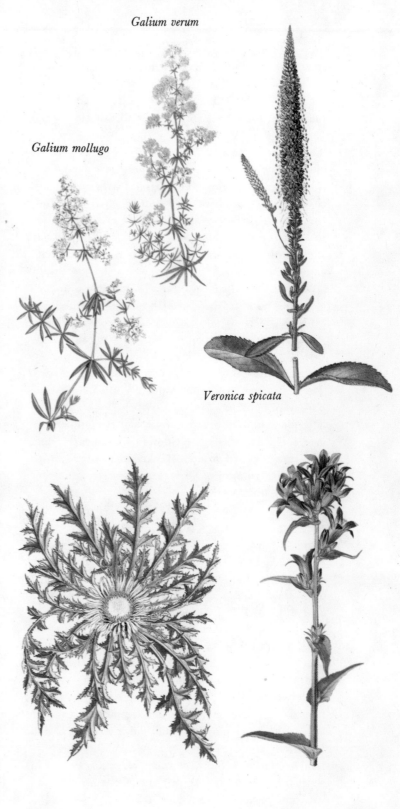

Galium verum

Galium mollugo

Veronica spicata

Carlina acaulis

Campanula glomerata

123

an epidemic of the plague, an angel appeared to Carl the Great telling him to order his men to eat the root.

CARLINE THISTLE
Carlina vulgaris L.

This is a biennial up to 50 cm. high. It forms a rosette of leaves which die off in the first year before the flower stems develop. The basal leaves are lance-shaped, stiff and bristly along the waved margins; the lower side is woolly-hairy. The erect stems are produced in the second year and are stiff, 5—50 cm. high, with leaves which are lance-shaped and half-clasping the stems.

The 2—5 flowerheads appear in a sparsely branched cluster. The outer involucral bracts are leaflike and pinnate, green or purplish; the inner ones are linear, straw-yellowish in colour and open during sunny periods only, looking like ray florets. The disc florets are yellowish-brown and sometimes red at the tips. The fruits are cylindrical nutlets with a long silky pappus of hairs.

The plant flowers between June and September and grows on dry chalky meadows and pastures, and stony uncultivated ground. It is known all over Europe up to southern parts of Norway and Siberia, and in the Caucasus and Asia Minor.

MOUSE-EAR HAWKWEED
Hieracium pilosella L.
Family: *Compositae*

This Hawkweed is a small perennial growing up to 30 cm. high. It has a rosette of simple, lance-shaped leaves, softly hairy beneath and with long, stiff white hairs on both sides. Long leafy runners grow from the rosettes. The upright stems are leafless and woolly and end in solitary flowerheads with pale yellow florets, reddish beneath. The involucral bracts are linear, grey-green and hairy at the margins.

The fruits are purplish-black nutlets with a stiff brownish pappus. It flowers between May and September and grows in dry, grassy places, especially in short turf. It is known throughout the temperate and subarctic parts of Europe and Asia.

This is a very variable species in a very large genus.

BROWN-RAYED KNAPWEED
Centaurea jacea L.
Family: *Compositae*

This is a perennial herb, 15—60 cm. high. which has a branched rhizome with grooved erect stems. The leaves of the basal rosette are oval to lance-shaped, somewhat lobed, toothed and narrowing into the stalk. Upper stem leaves are lance-shaped and stalkless. All the leaves are hairy. Flowerheads are terminal, 10—20 cm. across, and solitary on the branch stems. The florets are reddish-purple, with marginal florets which are usually larger. Involucral bracts have pale brown scaly tips and an irregular whitish margin. The fruits are hairy but lack a pappus.

The plant flowers between June and September and grows in grassland and waste places, also in thickets and in shady areas. It is known over most of Europe, in northern and western parts of Asia, and has also been recorded in North West Africa. It is a very variable species, which grows in dry areas. It is found in Britain although it is rare. Similar areas are inhabited by Greater Knapweed *(Centaurea scabiosa* L.*)*.

YARROW, MILFOIL
Achillea millefolium L.
Family: *Compositae*

Yarrow is an aromatic perennial, 8—50 cm. high, with creeping underground stems. The upright stems are tough, furrowed, woolly and leafy, and branched when flowering. The leaves are 5—15 cm. long, lance-shaped in outline and pinnately divided 2 or 3 times into linear segments.

The small whitish flowerheads are 4—6 mm. across and are in flat-topped compound clusters at the ends of the stems. There are usually 5 ray florets which are white, pink or reddish. The disc florets are white or cream. The plant flowers between May and October and is common on grassy banks, in meadows, by waysides and in waste places on most types of soil. It is found virtually all over Europe, northwards to Iceland, and to Siberia and the Himalayas in the east. It has become naturalised in North America, southern Australia and in New Zealand. Although the wild plant may be a weed in gardens, a crimson-flowered form has been bred which makes a pleasing garden plant, even though somewhat invasive.

The flowerheads contain a volatile oil, 2 alkaloids and also tannins. Somewhat similar oils are found in related species and all of these are used medicinally. This is a very ancient herbal plant. Herbal teas were made from the leaves for a tonic, and to relieve stomach upsets and coughs. The juice of the plant was applied to wounds to combat infection, to stop bleeding and to hasten healing. It was also used as a gargle. The dried leaves were made up into a kind of snuff. In Austria and Switzerland it is still an official medicinal plant.

FIELD WOODRUSH, SWEEP'S BRUSH
Luzula campestris (L.) DC.
Family: *Juncaceae*

This is a loosely tufted perennial with creeping rhizomes and erect stems 10—30 cm. high. The grass-like leaves are up to 15 cm. long, bright green and with a few long white hairs. The flowers are borne in clusters (1 sessile and 3—6 stalked clusters, each of 3—12 flowers) and together these make up a panicle. The six-pointed perianth segments are brown with a transparent margin. The fruits are capsules containing 3 seeds, and each one has a long white basal appendage.

This plant is one of the first to flower in early spring — between March and June — and grows in meadows and grassy places throughout Europe, except in Iceland. It is known all over the world but in tropical regions it is restricted to mountain areas.

Stipa capillata L.
Family: *Gramineae*

This is a densely tufted perennial grass up to 80 cm. high. The nodes of the erect stems are rather swollen.

Centaurea jacea

Carlina vulgaris

Hieracium pilosella

Achillea millefolium

Luzula campestris

Stipa pennata

The leaves are rough, narrow, .5—1 mm. wide, blue-green and with inrolled margins. The inflorescence is compound and 'feathery', because the floral bracts bear long twisted bristles known as *awns*. These are up to 15 cm. long. The spikelets are green and numerous.

The grass flowers between June and November and grows in warm dry exposed places and on rocks. It is common in Mediterranean countries and in the warmer areas of Central Europe. It is also found in Siberia, northern Iran, and the Caucasus. It is absent from Britain. *Stipa capillata* covers large areas in places that suit it, particularly so in southern and south eastern Europe.

FEATHER GRASS
Stipa pennata L.

This is very similar in appearance to *Stipa capillata* but has far longer 'feathery' awns. These are up to 35 cm. long and bear long, spreading hairs, thus forming a kind of plume. It is a densely tufted blue-green perennial up to 60 cm. high. The spikelets are yellowish-green.

It is found in dry grassland and stony places in Central and South East Europe.

BARBERRY
Berberis vulgaris L.
Family: *Berberidaceae*

This is a bushy shrub, 1.5—3 m. high, with a smooth bark and yellowish twigs. These bear pointed three-pronged spines and short-stalked oblong-oval leaves with spiny teeth. The yellow flowers are in pendant clusters and are scented. They have 9 perianth segments. The 6 stamens are sensitive to touch, ensuring

Stipa capillata

successful pollination. In autumn the fruits become light red, two-seeded, cylindrical berries and the leaves turn red.

Barberry flowers between May and June and grows often on limy soils, on rocky banks, in hedges and at the edges of dry woods. It is known in Central, southern and south eastern Europe; it is naturalised in North America. It is uncommon in Britain and is probably introduced.

It is a very variable species. All parts of the Barberry contain an alkaloid which is used in herbal medicine. The fruits also used to be made into medicine. A yellow dye is extracted from the bark and stems. The wood is soft and yellow, and perfect for wood-carving; it is also used to make tooth picks. The berries contain a high percentage of acid and have always been collected and used to make preserves or as a colouring.

Little spotted warts often appear on the leaves which is a sign that the shrub has the disease known as wheat rust *(Puccinia graminis)* which can quickly spread through crops causing great damage. Farmers, therefore, try to keep the shrub away from fields as it is the alternative host for wheat rust.

DOG ROSE
Rosa canina L.
Family: *Rosaceae*

The Dog Rose is a tall spreading shrub 1—5 m. high, with arching branches which have stout curved broad-based thorns. There are 5—7 leaflets, oval or elliptical and toothed, with broad stipules. The flowers are pink or white, up to 6 cm. across, and appear in clusters of 1—4 at the ends of the branches. At the base of the flower is the hollow receptacle containing numerous carpels. After fertilisation it becomes red and fleshy, forming the familiar globular rosehip which contains many small nutlets when ripe. These nutlets are covered with short hairs and stick easily to the skin.

The Dog Rose is one of the most common wild roses known in Europe. It grows on sunny slopes, in hedge-rows bordering fields, in scrub and at the edges of woods. It is known all over Europe, except in the very northern parts, also in South West Asia as well as in North Africa; it is naturalised in North America. The fruits, which contain a large quantity of vitamin C, are collected and made into a tea or syrup. If the syrup is properly made it contains four times as much vitamin C as orange juice. For this reason the Dog Rose is cultivated in some areas and in World War II rose hips were collected for commercial processing. The hips are also used to add to wine. If they have been exposed to frost they make a well-flavoured jam.

GEAN, WILD CHERRY
Prunus avium L.
Family: *Rosaceae*

This is a deciduous tree growing 5—25 m. high, with smooth reddish brown bark which peels off in strips. The leaves are 6—15 cm. long, toothed and light green, with fine hairs beneath. There are 2 round red glands near the top of the stalk. The long-stalked flowers are cup-shaped and white, 1.5—2 cm. across,

Rosa canina

Berberis vulgaris

127

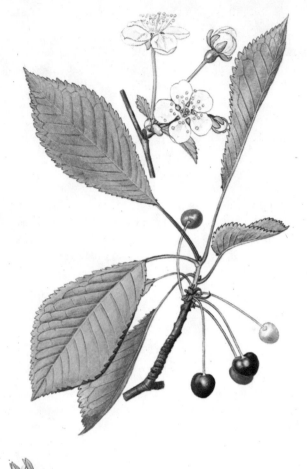

Prunus avium

and in clusters of 2—6 with papery bud scales. The fruits are dark red, round, shining sweet or sour cherries about 1 cm. across.

Birds play a large part in distributing the seeds. They eat the fruits and excrete the undigested stones of the fruits, sometimes several kilometres from the parent tree.

Gean flowers between April and May and grows in hedges bordering meadows and waysides. The plant is also found in woodlands in both lowland and upland areas of most of Europe, North Africa and West Asia.

The ancestor of this cherry tree is a Stone Age variety. Discoveries have brought to light cherry stones from ancient deposits and archaeological remains. The Wild Cherry has been cultivated for a very long time. The edible fruit is used to make jams or alcoholic beverages.

BLACKTHORN, SLOE
Prunus spinosa L.

This is a densely branched thorny shrub, often suckering freely and forming thickets. It is 1—4 m. high, with numerous black or dark brown twigs (hence the common name Blackthorn).

The leaves are oval, 2—4 cm. long, toothed and hairy, and appear after the flowers. The small white flowers smell of bitter almonds and appear singly, or in pairs. They appear early in spring, between March and April, and are produced in abundance. The fruits (Sloes) are globular and blue-black, with a whitish bloom; the flesh is green and they taste bitter-sour, making ones mouth water.

The shrub prefers sunny places on slopes, at the edges of woods, in hedgerows bordering fields, in scrub and at the edges of woods. It is found in most of Europe to Scandinavia in the north, to Iran in the

Prunus spinosa

east and southwards to the Atlas Mountains. It tolerates a variety of soils but not acid peat, nor dense shade.

The bitter fruits contain much vitamin C and are harvested in the autumn or after the first frost. They are made into wine or other alcoholic beverages. In some areas, particularly the north, the fruits are fermented in alcohol; elsewhere a syrup is made from them which is added to herbal medicines. The dried leaves are also used to make certain medicinal preparations because they contain substances which affect the kidneys.

The wood is hard and not easily worked, but tool handles and walking sticks are made from it. Because it branches and suckers so freely, Blackthorn is often planted to make a stock-proof hedge.

MIDLAND HAWTHORN
Crataegus laevigata (C. oxyacanthoides) (Poiret) DC.
Family: *Rosaceae*

This is a thorny shrub or small tree 2—10 m. high. It has reddish brown branches with thorns 6—15 mm. long. The leaves are broadly oval, toothed, with a shallowly 3—5 lobed outline. The stipules are large and leafy. The flowers are white with pink or purple anthers.

The shrub flowers between May and June on sunny slopes, in thickets, in scrub, in woods and in hedgerows. It grows mostly on clay or loam, producing deep red haws in September. It is known over most of Europe and this distribution includes Great Britain. In the north it extends to central Sweden and probably southern Finland; it probably does not occur naturally east of Poland. The leaves, flowers and fruits were formerly used in herbal remedies for high blood pressure, heart trouble and insomnia. The fruits may be fed to pigs as they are quite nutritious.

Crataegus monogyna Jacq. is very similar and grows in much the same areas as *C. laevigata*, often hybridising with it. It differs in having leaves with 3—7 deep triangular lobes. The flowers have 1 style and the fruits have one stone, whereas in *C. laevigata* there are 2 styles and 2 stones in the fruit.

BROOM
Cytisus (Sarothamnus) scoparius (L.) Link
Family: *Leguminosae*

Broom is a much branched generally erect shrub with roots which, like those of most leguminous plants, bear swellings (nodules) which contain symbiotic bacteria. The bacteria absorb nitrogen from the soil air and convert it into soluble nitrogen compounds. The stems are green and five-angled, and bear small short-stalked trifoliate leaves; the leaflets are elliptical and hairy beneath. The leaves often fall early in the year. The flowers are large (about 2 cm. across) and

Crataegus laevigata

Crataegus monogyna

yellow, butterfly-like and borne singly or in pairs. Pollinated flowers show the protruding coiled style. The fruits are black, hairy pods with dark brown seeds. The shrub flowers between May and June and grows (usually on sandy soils) on open grassy ground, on heaths, and in open places in woodland. The seeds take 2 years to germinate but may in fact remain viable for about 25 years.

Broom grows in much of Europe, including Britain, but is absent from Finland, Iceland, Greece, Sicily, Turkey and Bulgaria. It is not found in Asia. The shrub contains poisonous substances; a drug which affects kidney function is obtained from the branch tips, and another drug from both leaves and twigs is used to relieve heart and respiratory conditions. In some countries Broom is an important item in the diet of deer, goats and sheep although it is said to be poisonous to cattle. In some areas the branches are used for thatching and for making brooms (hence the name) and baskets. The roots also provide raw material for cloth and nets, particularly in France; during World Wars I and II, it was added to wool and cotton to make them go further. The bark is used in tanning and for making ropes.

Common Broom is native to western Europe but has

been planted for so many years and has become so much naturalised elsewhere that the extent of its natural range is uncertain.

The wild Broom is one of the most handsome of British native shrubs and is well worth being planted along roadsides and in gardens. The type is bright yellow in colour but garden varieties are reddish-brown, purple, crimson, pink or bi-coloured. The first garden hybrid was produced by cross-pollination at Kew, London, in 1900.

There are about 10 species of *Cytisus (Sarothamnus)* and these grow mostly in Spain and Portugal. They tend to prefer dry, sandy soils and sunny places. Many have now been introduced into gardens in Britain and are strikingly handsome, free-flowering shrubs. All have small simple or trifoliate leaves and green stems with typical pea-like flowers.

Some species are much smaller than the Common Broom; thus *Cytisus ardoinii* Fournier (a native of the Maritime Alps) grows only about 15 cm. high and is usually planted in rock-gardens. *Cytisus decumbens* (Durande) Spach is even smaller and was introduced into Britain from southern Europe as early as 1775. *Cytisus multiflorus* (Ait.) Sweet. is the White Spanish Broom and, although native to Spain and Portugal, grows successfully in gardens in Britain, reaching a height of 3.5 m. Another large Broom is *C. battandieri* Maire which was introduced from the Atlas Mountains, Morocco, in 1922.

Perhaps one of the most interesting Brooms is the Purple Broom *(Cytisus purpureus* Scop.*)*. This is a native of the southern Alps and northern Italy and was introduced into Britain in 1792. It has distinctive purple flowers but is of interest for another reason.

In 1826, in a nursery near Paris, a twig of the Purple Broom was grafted on to the Common Laburnum. The resultant tree was seen to bear small Laburnum-like leaves and small drooping spikes of dull purplish flowers, but also bore some branches of pure yellow Laburnum flowers and, less often, the smaller flowers of the Purple Broom. This plant was named the Purple Laburnum *(Laburnocytisus adami* (Poit.) Schneid.), the specific name referring to the nurseryman who produced it.

The tree is not a true hybrid and its habit of bearing three different types of flower at the same time excited considerable scientific interest. The "mystery" was not solved until the end of the 19th century. When properly investigated, it was discovered that the tissues of one plant had formed a kind of outer "skin" around an inner core derived from the tissues of the other. A plant of this kind is termed a "chimaera" or graft-hybrid. Such a plant differs form a true hybrid which will produce leaves and flowers which are all alike, but which will show differences from the leaves and flowers of the parents. The graft-hybrid also differs from a normal grafted plant. The latter consists of a stock (rooted stem) of one plant type which is beheaded and into the cut surface of which is inserted a bud or twig of another and closely related variety — which is termed the *scion*. Grafting of this type is standard for roses and many orchard and ornamental trees.

Cytisus scoparius　　　　*Ononis spinosa*

SPINY RESTHARROW

Ononis spinosa
Family: *Leguminosae*

This is a dwarf shrub up to 60 cm. high, with a long root and erect branches which become woody. The branches are strongly spiny, with 1 or 2 longitudinal rows of hairs. The plant smells unpleasant. The stipulate trifoliate leaves have oval-toothed leaflets, and the middle leaflets are stalked.

The pea-like flowers are borne on the shorter branches singly or in pairs between June and September. They are purple or pink, 10—15 mm. across; the calyx is hairy. The wings of the corolla are shorter than the keel. The fruits are pods 6—10 mm. long, covered in soft hairs and containing one or a few dark brown seeds.

This small shrub grows in dry meadows and grassy places, especially on dry chalkland, in the more temperate regions of Europe, western Asia and North Africa. It can become a nuisance to cattle because of its spiny thorns.

Spiny Restharrow was for a long time a household remedy. Roots, flowers and leaves are still used as the source of a drug which controls kidney function and also affects gall stones. The roots were collected for a range of herbal preparations; the bark of the root, for example, made a soothing cough mixture because

of the gums and resins present. The young branches yield a dye which can be used to dye wool reddish-brown, yellow or green.

The common name of this and related species comes from the spiny, creeping and rooting stems, which in former times made the process of harrowing fields difficult.

CORNELIAN CHERRY

Cornus mas
Family: *Cornaceae*

This is a deciduous shrub or small tree which grows 2—8 m. high. The twigs are greenish and hairy. The leaves are short-stalked, 4—10 cm. long, pointed, oval or elliptical, and with 3—5 pairs of veins. They are hairy and light green beneath and appear after the flowers. The small yellow flowers are in umbels (about 1 cm. across) which appear between February and April. The fruits are bright shining red, 1 cm. long, oblong in shape and fleshy. They contain 2 hard seeds.

Cornus mas

Cornelian Cherry prefers warmer regions and a limestone soil. It grows in woods and scrub and also in hedges surrounding fields; it will also grow in rocky or stony places. It is known in the warmer regions of Europe, including southern Belgium and central France and southwards to central Italy, also in Asia Minor and in the Caucasus.

The fruits have been known since ancient times, particularly in Mediterranean countries, and were valued for their pleasantly acid flavour. They are still sometimes made into conserves. Today the shrub is cultivated both for its edible fruit and also as an ornamental plant. It was well known in the Middle Ages both as a delicacy as well as a household remedy. Monks in particular used to cultivate the shrub in their gardens.

The fruit is still preserved today, or made into a refreshing drink in some south east European countries; in France it is a sweet, and it is made into a brandy in the Caucasus and the Ukraine (called *dernowka*). The fruits can also be dried and added to dishes; in Slovakia a syrup rich in vitamins is made from the 'cherries', and a sherbet drink is made from it in Turkey.

The wood is hard and is used to make parts of machines and tools. The plant is also a very important nectar plant since it provides bees with food very early in spring.

MEADOW
PLANTS

INTRODUCTION

A meadow is an artificially created and maintained plant habitat and is the product of man's acitivity. The plants growing in it are of great agricultural importance, since they provide both green and dry fodder for domestic animals.

The soil in the meadow is usually good, but may require manuring and liming. The moisture content is important and if too high, drainage may be necessary. The plants are exposed to the light at all times of the year since trees and shrubs are confined to the surrounding hedgerows or may be absent altogether. The plants that make up the meadow are a range of grasses and other plants. These are subject to mowing once, twice or even three times a year and are used either as green fodder, or for the making of hay or silage. Meadows are also regularly grazed by sheep or cattle and are thus manured by urine and animal droppings. Meadow plants are usually herbaceous perennials, often rooting easily, and grasses; all of these must be able to survive being cut or eaten down to just above soil level.

Many of the plants have a rosette-type habit of growth i. e. the leaves develop in a cluster and lie more or less flat, and only the flowerstems grow much above the surface of the soil. Cutting or grazing then tends to do little damage to the vegetative parts of the plants although flowering may be prevented. Grasses are able to grow from the base of the leaves and these again are unharmed by cutting or grazing. All meadow plants tend to flower and set seed in spring or early summer and this has obvious advantages for the plants as cutting for hay takes place later, from midsummer onwards, and the effects of intensive grazing build up only in late summer.

It can be seen that meadows are man-created, since neglect may lead to changes such as invasion by coarse weeds e. g. thistles or ragwort, or a return to wetter or more acid conditions and an invasion by bracken, rushes or horsetails. Such meadows may then return to marshes or swamps. In drier conditions, the seeds of larger plants, and eventually of shrubs and trees, will germinate and grow and thus a return to thicket or scrub, even forest, may take place.

Nowadays meadows may be treated as permanent pasture or may be regarded as temporary — and these are often called leys. A ley is really a field crop — but of grass — and after ploughing and harrowing the land is sown with care fully selected and bred seed mixtures of grasses, clovers and other meadow plants.

Cultivated and partly cultivated meadows occur in lowland and hilly areas in temperate climatic zones. In the tropics they are found at higher, and thus cooler, altitudes.

Natural meadows are formed in river valleys and flood plains, where the high water table in the soil prevents the growth of trees and shrubs. Natural meadow-like growth i. e. different types of grass, is found in the savannahs of Africa and India, and in the less dry parts of Central

134

Australia. Outside the tropics are the vast natural grasslands in various parts of the world e. g. the Asiatic steppes from the Volga and the Caspian Sea to the Gobi desert, the pampas in Argentina and the North American prairies. The actual species of grasses and other plants varies from country to country, but provides a natural 'meadow' for native grazing animals.

MEADOW BUTTERCUP
Ranunculus acris L.
Family: *Ranunculaceae*

This is a perennial herb, with a short erect or creeping rhizome and hollow branched stems which are 30 — 100 cm. high. The basal leaves are long-stalked and palmately lobed with 3—7 lobes. Each lobe is further divided into three-toothed segments. The lower stem leaves are similar; the upper leaves are deeply cut into narrow segments. All leaves are hairy.

The flowers are 1.5—2.5 cm. in diameter, with 5 hairy sepals and 5 shiny usually bright yellow petals which surround numerous stamens and carpels. The petals secrete nectar at the base. The plant flowers abundantly from May onwards throughout the summer, in damp meadows and grassy places on chalky or neutral soils.

The plant is widely distributed in Europe (in the north as far as Greenland) but is not found in Portugal. It also grows in Asia, North and South Africa, and in North America.

Like many ranunculaceous plants the Meadow Buttercup contains the yellow poisonous volatile oil proto-anemonin. The sap of the plant can cause irritation to the skin or even inflammation and blistering. If taken internally it can also cause stomach and kidney upsets.

When it occurs in great quantities in meadows, the plant reduces the quality of the hay, but the poison disappears when it is dried. Experiments have shown that proto-anemonin is a general poison since it kills fish and is harmful to livestock.

GLOBE FLOWER
Trollius europaeus L.
Family: *Ranunculaceae*

This is a perennial herb with a smooth erect stem 10—60 cm. high. It has spirally arranged lobed leaves shaped like a palm, with 3—5 deeply cut lobes. Flowering is from May to August. Flowers are up to 5 cm. across, globular and yellow (sometimes greenish). The 5—15 apparent petals are actually sepals. There are numerous stamens and carpels which, like the sepals, are spirally arranged.

The flowers have 5—15 yellow nectaries. The fruits are beaked follicles. The plant grows usually in mountain areas, in damp pastures and on grassy slopes, but also in scrub and thickets. It becomes locally common, forming colonies. Globe Flower is to be found almost everywhere in Europe, including Britain, and even in Norway and Arctic America. It is also cultivated as a garden plant, often being hybridised with brighter coloured Asiatic species. Globe Flower may still be sold as a flower at markets but is under national protection in some countries to prevent its dying out. The plant also contains proto-anemonin which can poison animals but is harmless when the plant is dried.

LADY'S SMOCK, CUCKOO FLOWER
Cardamine pratensis L.
Family: *Cruciferae*

This is a perennial herb 15—60 cm. high, with a short rhizome and smooth, straight, unbranched hollow stems. A sparse basal rosette has long-stalked irregularly pinnate leaves with 3—7 pairs of oval, toothed leaflets and a larger end leaflet. Short-stalked stem leaves are also pinnate, but with much narrower

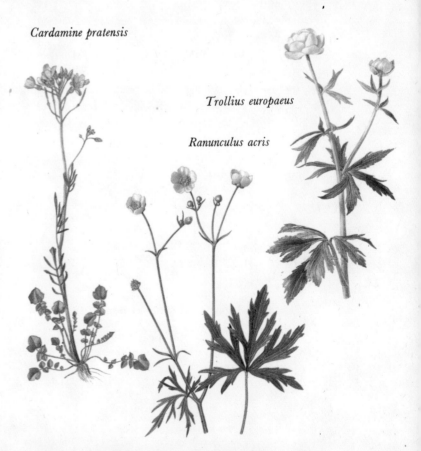

Cardamine pratensis

Trollius europaeus

Ranunculus acris

leaflets. The 7—20 flowers are in dense terminal leafless clusters. The 4 petals are pink, sometimes white, with violet veins and are 3 times as long as the 4 violet-tipped sepals. There are 6 stamens. The fruits are long pods which open by spirally coiled valves.

Flowering time is from April to June, and the plant grows in damp meadows and streamsides in lowlands and in foothills. The plant is widespread in Europe and also in northern Asia and North America.

It is a variable species with differences in leaf size and form and also in habitat — some types preferring coastal areas.

RAGGED ROBIN
Lychnis flos-cuculi L.
Family: *Caryophyllaceae*

This is a perennial herb, with a slender branched rhizome and a sparse basal rosette of long, lanceolate leaves 2—10 cm. long. The flower stems are 20—90 cm. high and are often reddish and sticky below the nodes. Vegetative shoots are much shorter. The few stem leaves are small and narrow.

The flowers are 3—4 cm. across, in open branched inflorescences. The 5 petals are rose-red (sometimes white) and jagged because each is deeply cleft into 4 lobes. The calyx is also reddish. The fruits are egg-shaped capsules.

The plant flowers from May to July in damp meadows, marshes and fens in both lowland and hilly areas. In the lowland areas it is widespread. Ragged Robin grows all over Europe to Norway and Iceland, also in Siberia and the Caucasus. It has been introduced into North America. This is a common meadow plant but is not suitable for fodder. There are two subspecies; the pink form is found all over Europe and a white form is found in the Balkans.

WHITE CAMPION
Silene alba (Mill.) Krause
Family: *Caryophyllaceae*

This is a sticky, hairy annual or perennial herb 30—100 cm. high. The leaves are oval and pointed. It was formerly called *Lychnis* or *Melandrium*. The white flowers are pollinated by moths and open in the late afternoon, emitting a faint scent. There are either male or female flowers i. e. it is a herb with stamens or ovaries. The fruit develops from the female flower as an egg-shaped capsule, surrounded by the calyx. The plant flowers from May to September in meadows and on cultivated land, on banks, waysides and in hedgerows. It is often found in clover fields and used to be a cornfield weed. It grows all over Europe except in Iceland, also in Asia Minor, Siberia, western Asia and North Africa. It is introduced in North America.

COMMON SORREL
Rumex acetosa L.
Family: *Polygonaceae*

This is a perennial herb 20—50 (sometimes 100) cm. high. The leaves are 10 cm. long and arrow-shaped, with downward pointing lobes. The upper leaves clasp the stem. The small greenish-red flowers are unisexual and have a perianth of 6 segments. The inflorescence is loose and sparingly branched. The inner perianth segments surround the fruits but the outer perianth segments bend back after the fruits have ripened.

Common Sorrel flowers from May to August and appears in damp meadows, on field banks, on grassy ground as well as in ditches, in both lowland and upland areas. All parts of the plant taste bitter because it contains oxalic acid. Green fodder containing such plants can have poisonous effects on horses and sheep; the animals produce excessive amounts of mucus and suffer intestinal disorders. In western Europe the leaves of the plant are used in salads and also for making soups.

BISTORT, SNAKE-ROOT
Polygonum bistorta L.
Family: *Polygonaceae*

The name Bistort——meaning 'twice twisted' — is appropriate because of this plant's S-shaped, reddish-brown rhizome. The stem grows 20—100 cm. high and is usually unbranched. Basal leaves are 5—15 cm. long, and narrowly triangular, with hairs on the

Silene alba

underside of the veins. The heart-shaped stem leaves are on winged stalks. All leaves are blue-green on the lower side and spirally arranged along the stem. Where the leaf-stalk is attached to the stem is a brown papery sheath — the *ochrea* — and this feature is characteristic of the family Polygonaceae.

The small bright pink flowers are in close upstanding spikes up to 9 cm. long and 1—1.5 cm. wide. The flowers have a perianth of 5 segments and there are 4—8 stamens. Fruits are three-angled dark brown shiny nutlets.

Bistort grows in clumps, generally in damp meadows and on grassy roadsides, chiefly in mountain areas. It is more common on siliceous (acid) soils. It is found in northern and Central Europe, in Central Asia and in the Arctic regions of North America. It may also be found on moors and heaths.

The plant, especially the rhizome, contains tannins and starch. The leaves contain soluble acids, giving a somewhat bitter taste. The rhizome was used as a medicine for diarrhoea and dysentery and also for snake bites. Both the rhizome and leaves have been used in pharmacy. It is considered a valuable plant for feeding beef cattle when it is present in pastures.

LADY'S MANTLE
Alchemilla vulgaris L.
Family: *Rosaceae*

This perennial herb varies in size from 5—45 cm. high; it is pale green with a woody rhizome which develops a basal leaf rosette. The stalked leaves are rounded, with palmate, toothed lobes. Hairs on the teeth and along the main veins are present on young leaves. The stem leaves are few and small. The small yellow-green flowers are in dense heads at the ends of the stem branches.

The plant flowers from May to September and is

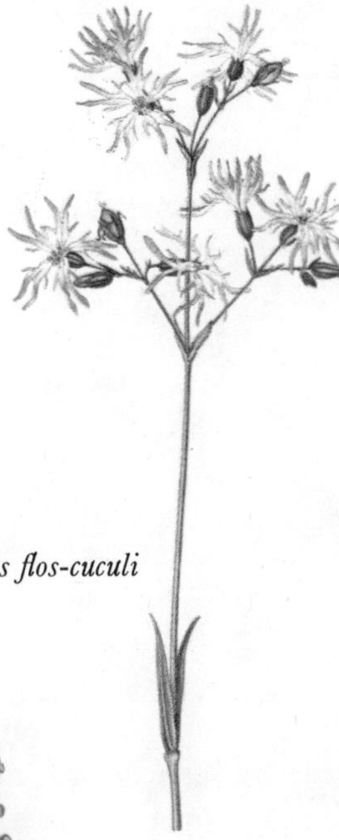

Lychnis flos-cuculi

Rumex acetosa

Polygonum bistorta

Alchemilla vulgaris

widespread in damp meadows and in grassy places, on paths and by river banks, as well as by the edges of forests, in both lowland and hilly areas. The plant is variable, especially in regard to its leaves, and has been considered as forming several different species. It appears almost everywhere in Europe; in North and West Asia from the Caucasus to the Himalayas; in Siberia, Greenland and the eastern side of North America.

The plant contains tannins and organic acids. It has been used for the treatment of diarrhoea and bleeding from kidney stones, for the cleansing of wounds and also as a compress. The leaves are still collected and used dried for a tea, and for the preparation of herbal medicines. Lady's Mantle was used in the Middle Ages for the making of the 'philosopher's stone' by the alchemists, and so gave rise to its Latin name.

GREAT BURNET
Sanguisorba officinalis L.
Family: *Rosaceae*

This is a perennial herb 50—100 cm. high, with erect stems which are straight, grooved and branched at the top. The lower leaves form a basal rosette and are pinnate, oblong-oval and toothed at the edges. The small purplish-red flowers have no corolla and are borne at the ends of the stem branches in dense ovoid flowerheads. The fruits are enclosed by the calyx. The plant flowers from June to September in meadows and in damp grassy places from the plains to the hills. It is found in the temperate zones of Europe and Asia, from Iceland and Scandinavia southwards. It is also found in Japan and China and grows, as an escape, in North America.

The rhizome contains much tannin and also medicinal compounds. The plant was therefore once often collected and a tea made from the green parts. This was used to encourage sweating and to relieve intestinal troubles. It was also used as a mouthwash to cure gum infections. Pulverized rhizomes were used to cure nosebleeds, and crushed leaves as compresses. In some places the young leaves, like those of the related Salad Burnet (*Poterium sanguisorba*), are used as salad or added to soups.

142

WHITE CLOVER, DUTCH CLOVER
Trifolium repens L.
Family: *Leguminosae*

This smooth perennial herb is one of the more familiar clovers. It has low creeping stems which root freely at the nodes. The long-stalked leaves are trifoliate, the leaflets being reversed wedges in shape, slightly notched and finely toothed at the margins, with a whitish mark at the base. The stipules are oval and pointed. The flowers are in clusters of 40—80. They are small, white, greenish, or pinkish, shaped like a minute butterfly with the wings always longer than the keel. The flowers form roundish heads which are borne above the leaves on straight stems and, after flowering, the flowers turn brown.

Flowering continues throughout summer in meadows and grassy places, especially on clay soils, in both lowland and mountain regions.

This species is found all over Europe, in North and West Asia, North Africa, Madeira, in the Azores and in North America. It has been introduced into South America, also in East Asia and South Africa. It is very tolerant of cool climatic conditions.

It is often planted and mixed with grasses for use as fodder. The plant grows quickly and can spread over a large area within a year. In Ireland, the flowerheads were dried in times of trouble or bad harvests, ground and added to flour. In some places the leaves were used instead of spinach.

MEADOW VETCHLING
Lathyrus pratensis L.
Family: *Leguminosae*

This perennial herb grows by means of tendrils and has scrambling, finely hairy angled stems 30—120 cm. long. The leaves have 1—2 pairs of leaflets and end in a tendril. The yellow butterfly-like flowers are in long-stalked clusters of 3—12 flowers. The fruits are pods which are 2.5—3.5 cm. long.

The plant flowers from May to August in meadows, at the edges of forests, in bushes and in thickets, from the plains to the hills. It grows over almost the whole of Europe, in Siberia eastwards to the Himalayas, and in North Africa as far as Ethiopia. Some time ago the plant was imported into North America where it is now common.

TUFTED VETCH
Vicia cracca L.
Family: *Leguminosae*

This is a perennial herb which has scrambling hairy stems 60—200 cm. high. The pinnate leaves have 6—12 pairs of lanceolate leaflets and end in a branched tendril.

The flowers, bluish to reddish-violet (sometimes white), are in spikes, 2—10 cm. long, of 20—30 flowers. The flowers are small, clustered and pea-like and are borne to one side of the axis. The fruits are flattened, hairless pods. Flowering time is from June to August. It grows in meadows, on sunny slopes, at the edges of forests and in hedgerows, and is usually common.

Tufted Vetch is a very old apparently cultivated plant discovered in settlements of the early Stone Age and Bronze Age. Natural distribution is difficult to determine as it has been artificially planted. It appears all over northern Europe including Sweden and Norway. The sailors of these countries introduced Tufted Vetch into Iceland and Greenland. It also grows in West and northern Asia to Japan.

In some places different varieties are planted as fodder as, like those of all legumes, the seeds are rich in protein as well as carbohydrate, and thus form a valuable feed stuff for animals.

BUSH VETCH
Vicia sepium L.

This is a climbing or trailing perennial with angled stems 30—100 cm. high. The pinnate leaves are 1—3 cm. long and end in branched tendrils. The

Sanguisorba officinalis

Trifolium repens

Lathyrus pratensis

Vicia cracca

5—9 pairs of downy leaflets are oval with a slightly pointed tip. The stipules are more or less arrow-shaped and sometimes toothed.

The 3 — 6 flowers are borne in short-stalked spikes which arise in the leaf axils. They have pale violet or yellow corollas and black, hairless seed-pods.

Bush Vetch flowers from May to August in meadows and fields, on grassy slopes at the edges of woods and in bushes and scrub, from the plains to the hills. It is found in most parts of Europe including Iceland and Scandinavia, also in the Caucasus, Siberia and in Kashmir, but is seldom found in Greece, Corsica or Sardinia. In some areas Bush Vetch is planted as fodder.

BIRDSFOOT-TREFOIL
Lotus corniculatus L.
Family: *Leguminosae*

This perennial herb has a stout rhizome and 10—40 cm. long stems which are partly prostrate. The leaves can either be regarded as trifoliate, with a pair of stipules, or pinnate with 5 leaflets. The flowers, which are yellow and sometimes slightly red on the outside, are in umbels growing in the leaf axils. Flowering time is from May to September, in meadows and in fields, also by waysides and in grassy places generally, from the plains to the hills.

It is found in Europe (except in the extreme north), in temperate zones in Asia (including India), in North and East Africa and in Australia. It is a useful fodder plant in pastures. The common name of Birdsfoot derives from the resemblance of each cluster of elongate pods to a bird's foot.

Birdsfoot-trefoil has very deep roots which enable it to grow on dry or wet ground and for a small plant it is surprisingly long-lived, growing for 20 years or so.

HOGWEED, COW PARSNIP
Heracleum sphondylium L.
Family: *Umbelliferae*

Hogweed is a coarse biennial 50—200 cm. in height, having thick ridged hollow stems which are usually roughly hairy. All parts of the plant emit a strong unpleasant odour. The large leaves (15—60 cm. long) are variable in form; the lower ones are stalked and the upper ones stalkless. The leaves are pinnate with broad irregularly shaped segments which are lobed or toothed. The leaf base is expanded to form a sheathing base with marked ridges.

The small flowers are white, sometimes slightly pink, and grow in large umbels. The fruits are rounded and whitish. The plant flowers from June to September, growing in damp meadows, on river-banks, by rubbish-dumps, in clearings and at the edges of forests near waysides, and, as can be seen, in a wide range of habitats. It is found in most of Europe, in West and North Asia, and in the western part of North Africa. It was introduced into North America, and grows there, along the East Coast.

Touching the plant can cause inflammation of the hands, for the juice causes unpleasant blisters. The leaves are edible and provide a valuable green fodder for grazing animals, although it is never planted for this purposes.

YELLOW-RATTLE
Rhinanthus minor L.
Family: *Scrophulariaceae*

Yellow-rattle is a hairy annual 15—50 cm. in height. The stems are pale green and usually black-spotted, simple or branched. The leaves are lanceolate and stalkless, with toothed margins. They are borne in opposite pairs.

The flowers have a yellow corolla with violet or whitish teeth on the upper lobe. They are in loose spikes mixed with large, green, toothed, triangular, leaf-like bracts. The calyx is inflated and pale, with white hairs.

The flat fruits contain a few large, usually winged, seeds and are capsules. Flowering time is from May to August. The plant grows in meadows and cornfields, also by roadsides, often preferring a calcium-rich ground. It is found in almost all of Europe from Iceland and Scandinavia to central Spain and central Italy, also West Siberia, Greenland and Newfoundland.

Like other plants of this variety Yellow-rattle is semi-parasitic, growing on the roots of grasses. A variable plant, this is considered to include at least four different subspecies.

RIBWORT PLANTAIN
Plantago lanceolata L.
Family: *Plantaginaceae*

This perennial plant has a short rhizome and a basal rosette of long, slightly toothed, stalked lanceolate leaves. On the lamina there are strongly defined nerves (veins). Out of the leaf rosette grow one or more furrowed stems bearing egg-shaped or cylindrical flower spikes. The flowers consist of dry, persistent calyxes and brownish corollas. The yellow anthers grow on long filaments from the corolla tube. The fruits are capsules with lids and contain two seeds each.

Like all Plantains, the species is common and well-known, in fact it is one of the most common plants of the world. Ribwort Plantain is widespread in meadows, in grassy and waste places from the plains to the mountains. It appears all over Europe, in North and Central Asia and has been introduced into most other temperate countries.

This is a medicinal plant which was formerly used to make a number of herbal medicines. It contains a glycoside and also mucous substances. The leaves were used as a tea for coughs, laryngitis and whooping-cough, as well as stomach-upsets. The leaves were made up into poultices, and the juice made up into cough sweets. The seed heads are used as a laxative.

SPREADING BELLFLOWER
Campanula patula L.
Family: *Campanulaceae*

This biennial or perennial herb, 20—60 cm. in height, has slender angular stems. The basal leaves are oval or rounded; the lower stem leaves are short-stalked and lanceolate. The upper ones are linear.
The flowers are purple, sometimes white, and bell-

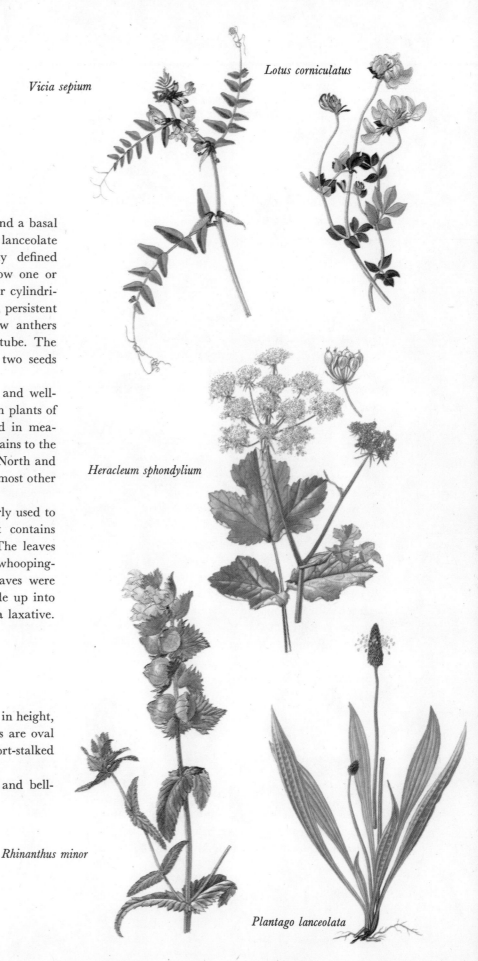

Vicia sepium

Lotus corniculatus

Heracleum sphondylium

Rhinanthus minor

Plantago lanceolata

shaped. They have a five-pointed calyx and corolla. The flowers are borne in a spreading cluster, on stalks with a small bract in the middle. The fruits are capsules with 3 basal pores through which the seeds are shed.

Flowering time is from June to August, in meadows, grassy slopes, on hedge banks and in shady woods. It grows all over Europe, with the exception of Iceland and the most southerly regions.

OX-EYE DAISY
Chrysanthemum leucanthemum L.
Family: *Compositae*

This is a perennial herb, 20—70 cm. high, with a short, woody rhizome. Out of this grow flower stems, usually simple but sometimes slightly branched. The basal and lower stem leaves are roundish to spoon-shaped and long-stalked. On the upper part of the stem the leaves are stalkless, narrow-lanceolate and with toothed or lobed margins. All leaves are dark green.

At the ends of the stems appear large, daisy-like flower-heads (2.5—5 cm. across) with yellow, tubular disc florets surrounded by white, strap-shaped ray florets. The sepal-like bracts of the involucre have purple-brown margins and tips. The flowers bloom from June to September in meadows and grassy places on basic and neutral soils. It grows all over Europe, northwards to the Shetland Islands and north Scandinavia, eastwards to the Caucasus. The plant is coarse-textured and, although it may be common in meadows, is useless as fodder.

At one time the dried leaves were used for colds, in various essences, and as syrups. In pill form it was supposed to help in haemorrhages. These preparations were also used in black magic rituals.

DANDELION
Taraxacum officinale Weber
Family: *Compositae*

This common and familiar plant has a swollen taproot and a rosette of basal leaves. All parts of the plant contain a white latex. Leaf shape is variable, from those with cut and toothed margins to deeply lobed forms. All have a large, blunt, terminal lobe. The name Dandelion is a corruption of 'dent-du-lyon' (meaning the lion's tooth) and refers to the highly toothed leaves.

Delicate hollow stems 10—15 cm. high grow out of the middle of the rosette. At the ends of these stems, which are always solitary, are large inflorescences consisting of 100—200 florets. These are all ray florets, yellow and honey-scented. Before flowering the inflorescences are closed; they also close in bad weather and in the evening. Fruits are numerous. Each is a nutlet with a long stalked parachute-like hairy pappus which is clustered in the familiar fluffy white heads or 'clocks'.

Dandelions are extremely variable, over 100 forms being known. All are self-pollinated. The plant flowers all the year round but especially from April to August in meadows, lawns, waysides and waste places. It grows mainly in the northern and temperate zone of the globe.

It is a very old medicinal plant. Even today the milky root and the dried leaves are collected. The plant contains bitter substances including glycosides and tannins, as well as inulin (used in the preparation of biscuits for diabetics), and substances which affect kidney action. In some countries the plants are used as raw material for the pharmaceutical industry. The root is also used for the production of a coffee substitute.

In France, Italy and Germany the young leaves are used as saladstuff, and for this purpose the plant is cultivated by binding the leaves together and growing them in a dark place. This produces very delicate leaves. The flowerheads are used for wine-making. The latex contains caoutchouc — the raw material of rubber — but not sufficient for commercial use.

The genus *Taraxacum* presents many problems to the field botanist. If one collects a number of Dandelions a considerable variation can be seen between them in size and shape both of the leaves and also of the bracts which surround the florets. Nowadays as well as *Taraxacum officinale* three other species of Dandelion are recognised although hybrids between them may also occur. The Lesser Dandelion (*T. laevigatum* (Willd.) DC.) grows in dry pastures, also on heaths,

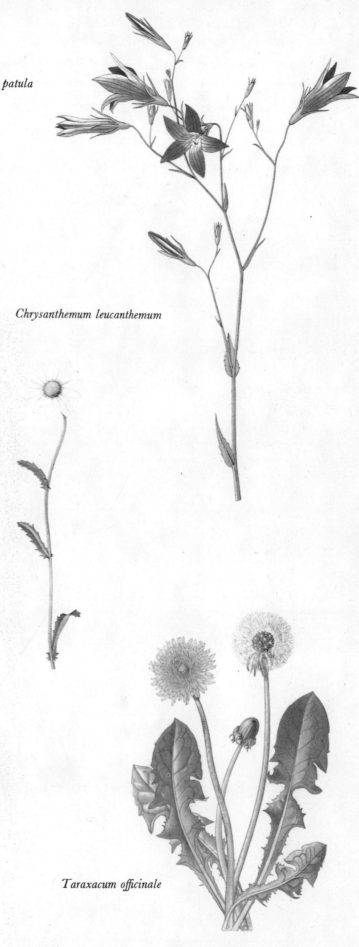

Campanula patula

Chrysanthemum leucanthemum

Taraxacum officinale

waste ground and even walls. It tends to be a rather small plant with narrow deeply cut leaves and pale yellow flowerheads. The surrounding bracts have tips which appear to be slit and fruits which are usually purplish-red. This is quite a common Dandelion, found throughout Europe, and probably well distributed in the lowland areas of Britain.

The other two species are found in wet places, where they may be quite common. The Narrow-leaved Marsh Dandelion (*T. palustre* (Lyons) DC.) has narrow leaves which may be undivided or only slightly toothed. The outer bracts cup themselves around the florets and are short and broad. The fruits are often olive-green in colour. The Broad-leaved Marsh Dandelion (*T. spectabile* Dahlst.) has broader leaves with a hairy upper surface and usually with a reddish midrib. The bracts which surround the flowerhead are loosely spreading or may be bent outwards.

Both species of Marsh Dandelion grow in marshes and fens and on the banks of streams but the Broad-leaved Marsh Dandelion also grows among wet rocks and in boggy grassland on hill and mountainsides.

AUTUMN HAWKBIT
Leontodon autumnalis L.
Family: *Compositae*

This is a perennial herb 10—60 cm. high. The leaves are in a basal rosette and are lance-shaped with a sinuous or pinnately lobed margin and a long, narrow stalk-like base. The stems are 1 to few, finely grooved and sparingly branched. They may bear small bracts beneath the flowerheads. Stems and leaves have forked hairs.

At the ends of the stems appear the flowerheads. These have bright yellow florets, the outer ones having

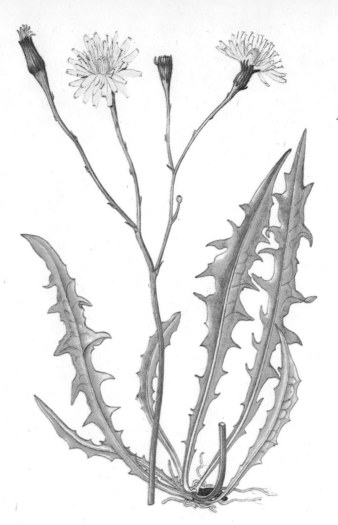

Leontodon autumnalis

reddish streaks beneath. The flowerheads are rather similar to those of the Dandelion. Flowering is from June to October in meadows, by waysides, in rubbish dumps and waste places, also on screes, and the plant may be found on mountainsides as well as on plains.
The plant grows throughout Europe, northwards to the Shetland Islands, Iceland and Greenland, but southwards seldom in the Mediterranean. It is also found in North and West Asia. The plant was introduced into North America.
The Hawkbits *(Leontodon* spp.*)* bear some resemblance to the Dandelion in having bright yellow solitary flowers arising from a rosette of elongate toothed leaves. However the surface of both leaves and flowerstems of the Hawkbits is markedly hairy. There are three British species and all are native, not introduced. Besides the Autumn Hawkbit, Britain has the Rough Hawkbit *(L. hispidus* L.*)* characterised by having forked hairs on the leaf surface and the Hairy Hawkbit *(L. taraxacoides* (Vill.) Meart).
All three are plants of dry places such as meadows and grassy slopes, waysides and screes and even fixed sand dunes. Unlike the Dandelion they are not usually weeds of gardens or farmland.

GOAT'S-BEARD, JACK-GO-TO-BED-AT-NOON
Tragopogon pratensis L.
Family: *Compositae*

This is an annual to perennial herb with a long brownish taproot and a basal leaf rosette. The leaves are linear to lanceolate, with a long point and a sheathing base. The stems are little-branched, 30-70 cm. high, with narrow stem leaves. The flowers resemble those of the Dandelion but differ in the long slender involucral bracts.
The plant flowers from May to July and grows in meadows and in grassy places generally. It is not usually common. It grows throughout the whole of

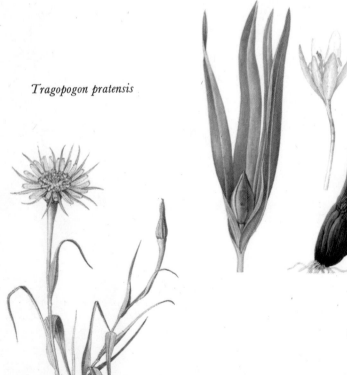

Tragopogon pratensis

Colchicum autumnale

Europe, except Iceland and Portugal, also in the Caucasus, Iran and Siberia. The plant characteristically closes its flowers at midday — hence its common name. Rather similar is:

Tragopogon dubium Scop.

This species is much less common. It is distinguished by its taller stems which are swollen beneath the flowerheads. It is a plant of dry woods.

AUTUMN CROCUS, MEADOW SAFFRON
Colchicum autumnale L.
Family: *Liliaceae*

This perennial plant is noteworthy because of its unusual life-cycle. The plant has a large corm, 3—5 cm. across, buried in the soil. A corm is a compact underground stem, unlike a bulb, which is an underground bulb. The corm is covered by a papery sheath which is the remains of last year's leaf sheath.

In spring a new bud grows on the upper side of the corm. Meanwhile 3 to 6 large, fleshy, bright green leaves grow above ground. These leaves are oblong to lanceolate in shape, 12—30 cm. long and 1.5—5 cm. wide, and their bases are buried in the earth and encircle the buried corm. The carbohydrates manufactured by these leaves will be stored in the new corm which will develop from the newly formed bud. By late summer i. e. August-September, the leaves have died down and the flowers are appearing. Because it is unusual to find bulbous flowers apparently without leaves, the old country name for this plant is 'Naked Ladies'. These flowers are a pale rosy-purple or white in colour and emerge from the ground, either singly or in small groups.

There are 6 perianth segments, which are fused into a slender tube 5—20 cm. long. The actual segments of the perianth are much shorter — 3—4.5 cm. — and they enclose 5 orange stamens and 3 styles, each bearing a strongly curved stigma. Despite the crocus-like appearance of the flower, with its cup-like perianth borne on the long slender perianth tube, Autumn Crocus belongs to a different family and may be distinguished by its 6 stamens, unlike the 3 stamens of the true crocus.

After pollination the young fruits stay deep in the soil until spring, then the short stem begins to grow, the lower part begins to thicken and a new corm grows next to the old one, which then dies. Meanwhile the new crop of leaves is beginning to emerge above ground, borne on a short stem which also bears the egg-shaped 3—5 cm. long, capsular fruits. At the same time, under the ground in the leaf-axil of the first leaf another bud is forming. The fruits contain brown-black seeds surrounded by a fleshy, jelly-like substance which sticks to the hooves of grazing animals. The animals, unknowingly therefore, disperse the seeds.

The flower may be found in woods and in damp meadows at the end of August to the end of September. It grows in South, Central and West Europe, (introduced in northern Europe), eastwards to the river Vistula, southwards to central Spain and Italy and to the northern part of the Balkans and also Greece. The original home of the plant was probably in the European part of the Mediterranean and from there it was taken to the more northern areas.

All parts of the plant are highly poisonous. *Colchicum* has been used as a herbal plant for several hundred years. The alkaloid colchicine which it contains is particularly concentrated in the seeds and corm, from which it is extracted. Three flowers are said to contain enough poison to kill a man. As a meadow plant in some countries, Autumn Crocus is harmful to stock, and animals tend to avoid it. If they should eat it, cattle will produce tainted milk. It is still a most useful drug plant as colchicine is used in the treatment of gout and rheumatism. The stamens were formerly collected for a yellow dye — saffron — and the Essex town Saffron Walden takes it name from the plant formerly grown there.

Nowadays, colchicine is valued as a compound which affects chromosome structure and the process of nuclear division in cells. Because of this it is possible to produce plant and animal mutations and thus it becomes possible to develop new varieties and even species. Research is also going on into the use of the plant substances in the treatment of malignant growths because of the known effects of colchicine on cell division.

The name *Colchicum* derives from Colchis on the Black Sea, the legendary home of the goddess and poisoner,

Medea, who spilt some drops whilst mixing the poison and there the flower began to grow.

MEADOW FESCUE
Festuca pratensis Huds.
Family: *Gramineae*

This perennial grass is tussock forming, dark green and 40—80 cm. high. It has narrow, rough-edged leaves; the laminae of the long thin leaves are smooth and hairless. The spikelets of 4—6 typical grass florets are grouped together into a much branched, rather slender inflorescence 8—15 cm. long, known as a panicle. This often has a glossy and sometimes purplish, appearance.

The plant flowers from June to July in virtually every meadow and in grassy places generally from the plains to the hills. It grows all over Europe and in temperate areas of Asia. It was introduced into America. It is one of the best grasses for fodder and hay.

QUAKING GRASS
Briza media L.
Family: *Gramineae*

This is a rather tufted perennial grass, which is easily recognised when in flower because of its distinctive inflorescence. This is an open spreading panicle borne on stems 20—50 cm. high, with pendulous trembling spikelets. These move in the slightest air current and thus give the plant its common name. The spikelets are triangular and purplish and are borne on slender stalks. The leaves are flat, only 2 mm. wide, and sharply pointed.

The plant flowers from May to July, in meadows and in grassy places, on a great variety of soils. It grows all over Europe and in the temperate zone of Asia, but is not found in the Arctic nor in some parts of southern Europe. It is of some value as a fodder plant.

MEADOW-GRASS
Poa pratensis L.
Family: *Gramineae*

This is a pale green tufted perennial grass, with creeping underground stems and smooth erect stems 10—14 cm. high, which end in spreading panicles 2—20 cm. long. The leaves are flat or rolled and generally smooth, variable in size and usually ending in an abrupt point. The spikelets contain 3—5 typical grass florets; the panicles are ovate or oblong in shape. The plant flowers from May to July in meadows, as well as on sand dunes, in open spaces in woodland and in grassy places from the plains to the hills. It grows in Europe, in North Asia and in the Caucasus, in Morocco and in Algeria, also in North America, Australia and New Zealand.

Meadow-grass is one of the best hay and fodder grasses, since it is extremely nutritious and grows well.

COCK'S-FOOT
Dactylis glomerata L.
Family: *Gramineae*

This coarse perennial bluish-green grass grows up to 1 m. high, and forms clumps of rough, rather thick leaves. These are flat and keeled, with a conspicuous pointed scale (ligule) where the leaf-blade joins the sheathing base. The flowerhead is a one-sided pyramidal cluster of purplish or green 2—5 flowered spikelets.

Cock's-foot is widespread in meadows and in rough grassland, and in a variety of grassy areas such as waste places and roadsides. It flowers from May to June and grows all over Europe, except in the Arctic region. It is found in the temperate zone of Asia, in North Africa and in Australia, New Zealand and America, but in these three countries it has been introduced.

A robust grass, this is one of the most valuable hay and fodder plants and a number of cultivated forms have been bred.

CRESTED DOG'S-TAIL
Cynosurus cristatus L.
Family: *Gramineae*

This is a perennial lawn or fodder grass 20—70 cm. high. It is tufted and wiry, with flat, smooth, thin leaves which have small ligules. The inflorescence resembles a dense oblong spike, 5—7 cm. long, con-

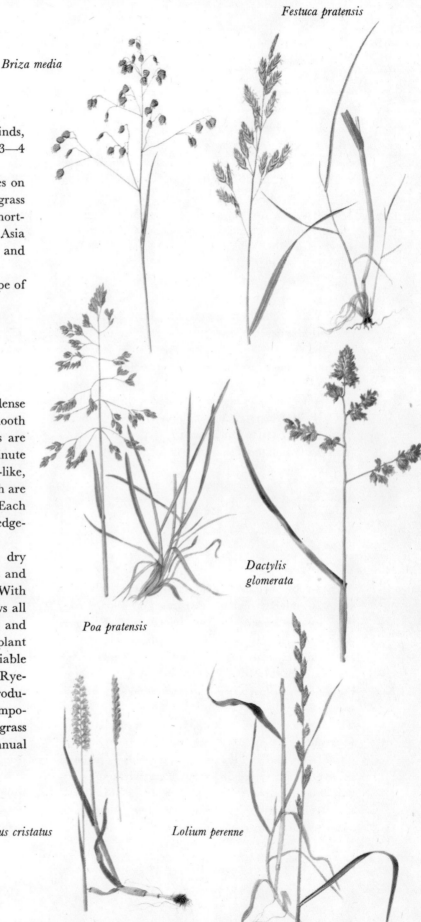

Festuca pratensis

Briza media

Dactylis glomerata

Poa pratensis

Cynosurus cristatus

Lolium perenne

sisting of numerous flattened spikelets of two kinds, sterile and fertile — the latter consisting of 3—4 florets.

The plant grows in meadows and in grassy places on a variety of acid and basic soils. It is a common grass and grows all over Europe (except in the most northern part), in northern Asia, the Caucasus and Asia Minor. This grass provides good green fodder and hay.

The common name of this plant refers to the shape of the spike.

RYE-GRASS
Lolium perenne L.
Family: *Gramineae*

This perennial dark green grass forms loose or dense tufts. The stems grow 25—50 cm. high and are smooth and slender, often bent at the base. The leaves are 2—3 mm. wide, smooth and glossy, with a minute ligule. The inflorescence is slender and spike-like, 8—15 cm. long, and has numerous spikelets which are borne alternately on opposite sides of the axis. Each spikelet is flat and yellow-green and attached, edgeways on, to the axis of the inflorescence.

This grass flowers from May to September in dry meadows, on grassy slopes, at the edges of paths and in other waste places from the plains to the hills. With the exception of the most northern parts, it grows all over Europe and in the temperate parts of Asia and North Africa. It was introduced as a fodder plant into North America and Australia. It is a very variable grass and has also hybridised with other grasses. Rye-grass is one of the earliest cultivated plants and produces fodder grasses of the finest quality, in both temporary and permanent pastures. Italian Rye-grass (*Lolium multiflorum* Lam.) is similar but is an annual grass, with more florets in the spikelets.

TUFTED HAIR-GRASS
Deschampsia caespitosa (L.) Beauv.
Family: *Gramineae*

This is a perennial grass forming thick clumps or tussocks and grows up to 2 m. high. It has numerous coarse, tough leaves and stiff smooth stems. The leaves are roughly ribbed above, smooth below, with ligules which are 6—8 mm. long.

The spreading, erect or pendant panicles (inflorescences) are 10—50 cm. long, pyramidal, with numerous rough-stalked spikelets. Each spikelet is 3—4 mm. long and consists of 2—3 awned florets which are violet, yellow or greenish in colour.

This grass grows in damp meadows, on moorland and in damp places in woodland, generally on badly drained clay soils. Flowering is from June to August and sometimes late into autumn. Tufted hair-grass appears almost everywhere in Europe, in West and North Asia, in the Himalayas, in Ethiopia, the Cameroons, Tasmania, Australia, New Zealand and North America. Although widely distributed it is not a particularly nutritious grass. It commemorates the French botanist Deschamps.

YORKSHIRE FOG
Holcus lanatus L.
Family: *Gramineae*

This is a familiar grass, forming tussocks of softly hairy leaves and stems. The plant is grey-green, with stems 20—60 cm. high and flat leaves 8—10 cm. long. The inflorescences are egg-shaped, rather dense, panicles which vary from 3 to 20 cm. in lenght, and are either erect or nodding, with hairy stalks. Each spikelet consists of 2—3 pinkish-white, pale green or purple florets, each with an inconspicuous hooked awn.

The flowering time is from May to August. It grows in meadows, on grassy slopes, in waste places and in forest clearings from the plains to the hills. It is found all over Europe, except in the most northern parts and also in temperate parts of Asia. It was introduced into Iceland and North America. The blades taste sweet but have no value as fodder.

SWEET VERNAL-GRASS
Anthoxanthum odoratum L.
Family: *Gramineae*

This is a perennial tufted grass which when crushed or wilted, emits the characteristic scent of hay. The plant has numerous short flat hairy leaves, and stems 20—50 cm. high. The panicle is compact, oblong and spike-like with three-flowered yellow-green spikelets. Flowering time is from April to July in dry meadows and other dry grassy places from the plains to the high mountains. It grows all over Europe although only on mountains in southern parts. It is also found in North Asia, Asia Minor and western North Africa. It was introduced in North America, Australia and Tasmania.

All parts of the plant contain a substance called coumarin, which gives the characteristic scent of new-mown hay. Coumarin tastes bitter and is the active principle of a poison used to kill rats (by causing internal bleeding) but is also used to control blood-clotting in patients with heart trouble or who suffer from blood-clots. The flowers are used for perfumes and essences.

This grass is very good fodder, but because of its strong odour can be used only in small amounts.

MEADOW FOXTAIL
Alopecurus pratensis L.
Family: *Gramineae*

This perennial grass has smooth stems which are up to 1 m. high and bent at the basal node. Its leaves are 3—10 mm. wide, flat, with a rough surface above and smooth below. They have torn ligules 4 mm. long. The flowerheads are long, cylindrical and spike-like and feel silky — suggesting the common name. The one-flowered spikelets are stalkless with inconspicuous awns and appear from April to June in damp meadows and grassy places in lowland and upland areas. It grows in most of Europe, except in the Mediterranean region, in northern Asia and in the Caucasus. It is planted as fodder and the seed used to be obtained from Finland. It is a very good fodder plant since it survives wintry and snowy conditions and grows well early in the year.

Deschampsia caespitosa

Holcus lanatus

Alopecurus pratensis

Anthoxanthum odoratum

Orchis morio

Phleum pratense

TIMOTHY GRASS
Phleum pratense L.
Family: *Gramineae*

Timothy Grass is a perennial yellowish-green grass, with smooth erect stems about 1 m. high, often tuberous at the base. The leaves are 4—8 mm. wide, with a very rough surface and 6 mm. long ligules. The inflorescences are long, cylindrical and spike-like, with spiny awns up to 2.5 mm. long. The spikelets are one-flowered with conspicuous violet anthers. Timothy grass grows in meadows, by roadsides and in waste places in both lowland and hill areas and is found in Europe, North Asia, Algeria and North America. It is often sown, with other grasses, for grazing; it also makes excellent hay. Improved strains are often cultivated.

GREEN-WINGED ORCHID
Orchis morio L.
Family: *Orchidaceae*

This is a perennial, like all orchids, with stems 10—40 cm. high, often violet and finely grooved. Below ground are 2 more or less globular tubers. The leaves are broadly lance-shaped and generally unspotted, 3—9 cm. long and .5—1.5 cm. wide. The lower leaves are spreading, the upper ones are upright and lie against the stem.

The inflorescence is a short rather open spike, 2.5—8 cm. long, of 7—12 flowers. The bracts are purplish, linear and as long as the ovary of the flowers. The purple, sometimes pink or white flowers have 2 conspicuously green-veined sepals (which are the 2 lateral outer perianth segments) and 3 inner perianth segments. All perianth segments, except the lower lip, form a hood by curving upwards. The flowers are scented and spurred. The fruits are capsules with many small seeds.

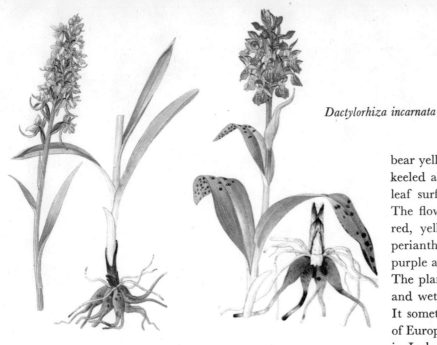

Dactylorhiza incarnata

Gymnadenia conopsea

Green-winged Orchid grows in meadows, especially on chalky soils, from the plains to the foothills and flowers from May to June. It may be locally abundant. It grows in Europe southwards from southern Sweden (including Britain), in the Caucasus, in Siberia and in Asia Minor.

The roots contain large amounts of easily digested starch which was formerly used as a food for children or in convalescence. The tubers are still collected in southern Europe and dried and sold under the name of Salep.

EARLY MARSH ORCHID
Dactylorhiza incarnata (L.) Soó
Family: *Orchidaceae*

This orchid grows 15—50 cm. high and has lobed root-tubers. The pale green stems are hollow and bear yellow-green leaves which are oblong-lanceolate, keeled and noticeably hooded at the tips. The upper leaf surface is, in some subspecies, darkly spotted. The flowers are in long spikes, and are pink, brick-red, yellow, purple or violet in colour. The outer perianth segments curve backwards and the lip is purple and narrow, because its sides are inrolled.

The plant flowers from May to July in fens, marshes and wet meadows from the plains to lower hillsides. It sometimes grows in dune-slacks. It grows in most of Europe, including southern Scandinavia — but not in Iceland — the Caucasus, Iran and Siberia. Early Marsh Orchid is a variable species with several sub-species.

FRAGRANT ORCHID
Gymnadenia conopsea (L.) R. Br.
Family: *Orchidaceae*

The Fragrant Orchid grows 15—40 cm. high and has flattened 3—6 lobed root-tubers. The stem is smooth, sometimes purplish above, with 2—3 brown leathery basal scales. The leaves are oblong-lanceolate, strongly keeled and usually unspotted.

The small flowers are reddish-lilac, sometimes white, with a strong scent reminiscent of cloves. The spur is bent downwards and is long and slender. The flowers form a long, dense spike. The plant flowers from May to July in meadows, fens and marshes, and in open woodland spaces in both lowland and upland areas. It prefers calcium-rich soil. Fragrant Orchid grows in Europe and in the temperate zones of North and West Asia.

154

PLANTS
OF
CULTIVATED
FIELDS

INTRODUCTION

Cultivated fields provide a special environment for the seeds which are carefully planted and tended by man. Fields are of great importance since they provide food, animal fodder, oils for food manufacturing processes, drugs and other pharmaceutical products, spices and flavourings and many other important raw materials.

The environment of these plants is carefully supervised. Fields remain fallow for certain periods during the year and are therefore exposed to wind, rain or frost which all break down the soil. At least once a year the field is limed or fertilised, ploughed, harrowed and afterwards rolled. These processes aerate the soil and improve its tilth (texture) by breaking down the larger clods and increasing its fertility.

When any kind of crop plant is raised in a field, mineral salts are taken from the soil by the plant and they have to be replaced by natural or artificial fertilisers. It is extremely important that a cycle is established whereby one field has a particular crop planted on it for a given period of time, and then another crop takes its place. This ensures that the soil is not unduly depleted. If leguminous crops are grown, these actually increase the nitrate content of the soil.

Crop plants are usually of ancient origin, and date back to the time when man changed from being a hunter or a nomadic shepherd, to becoming a primitive kind of farmer.

The crops planted today are the result of a gradual change which has taken place over thousands of years. Plants have been cross-fertilised and carefully cultivated. We do not know all the ancestors of all the crops we now grow, as many have died out and we now know only the cultivated variety. Maize (or corn) is one such example since it no longer exists in the wild state.

Many plants have come from other countries and even other continents; they might have been discovered by early explorers who brought home not only gold and treasure but also unknown plants, which could be used and cultivated for food or for other important purposes. Conversely settlers would take improved varieties with them to plant in other countries, which shows again the close connection between man and his crops.

It should be remembered that not only cultivated plants grow in fields; other plans, which can adversely affect our carefully nurtured crop plants, grow there too. Such plants are called weeds. Weeds grow well in fields because of the almost ideal growing conditions, but since they may harm the crops they are eradicated by the farmer.

For weeds to succeed in this habitat, seed-production must be completed within one season and the plants tend to be either annuals or herbaceous perennials. Various methods have evolved of either eliminating or at least reducing the size of the weed population. Older methods include burning, hoeing, or even hand-weeding, but nowadays a variety of chemical sprays are used, many of them being of the type known as selective weed-killers. These act, in the main, by being more readily absorbed by broadleaved plants, and are therefore particularly useful on cereal crops. These weed-killers are hormonal and induce excessive and highly distorted growth in the weeds, which quickly die off. By thus controlling them, the depletion of the soil is prevented.

Weeds have as long a history as crops and have always accompanied cultivated plants; some weeds do not appear anywhere else except in fields, and sometimes only in association with particular crops. By contrast, some plant species which were originally weeds have, in the course of time, developed into crop varieties. A good example of this is rye, which was originally a weed of wheat fields. However, although the range of specially bred crop plants is increasing, the number and variety of field weeds is now much diminished.

OPIUM POPPY
Papaver somniferum L.
Family: *Papaveraceae*

The Opium Poppy is a blue-grey annual herb 30—150 cm. high. All parts of the plant contain a milky latex which hardens to a brown mass on exposure to air. The leaves are large, 7—12 cm. long, oval-oblong, deeply lobed and toothed, the upper ones clasping the stem. The lower leaves are short-stalked. The conspicuous flowers are up to 18 cm. across, borne on smooth or stiffly-haired stalks and are pendant in the bud. The calyx is made of 2 sepals which soon fall off. The flower also has 4 large white, pink or purple petals — often with a dark basal blotch; these surround numerous bluish stamens and a globular ovary which has a flattened disc of 4—20 radiating stigmas. The fruits are capsules which contain numerous black or white seeds. These have a net-like surface and are rich in oil.

The plant flowers between June and August and has been cultivated almost everywhere. The plant has developed through cultivation and particularly from the subspecies *Papaver setigerum* (DC.) Corb. which grows in Mediterranean countries.

The Opium Poppy was known to the Sumerians 5,000 years ago and valued both for its oil and for its narcotic properties. It was also known to the ancient Egyptians and later to the Greeks, who saw it as a symbol of sleep and dreams.

The Opium Poppy is in many respects invaluable to man but it is also highly dangerous. The white milky juice, latex, contains over 200 different alkaloids of which the most important are morphine and codeine. Many of these substances, and especially morphine, are highly poisonous. These substances relieve cramp and have marked narcotic properties. They are pain-killing; they arouse pleasant feelings and hallucinations and can also induce sleep but, if taken in large doses, they can paralyse parts of the brain and this eventually leads to death. The derived drug, heroin, is highly addictive.

The medical properties of the plant cannot be rated too highly, since extracts free people from pain and can also heal certain ailments. However, the use of derivatives of Opium carries distinct risks because of the possibility of drug addiction. Opium is obtained by incising the still green capsules, and collecting the exuded brown dried latex. The alkaloids can also be extracted from dried stems and capsules. Yet Opium has become a curse in many ways, particularly in the Far East where smoking and chewing Opium is widespread. The Opium War between Britain and China highlighted the problem of addiction. Nowadays the chief centres of cultivation are in eastern Europe and also in East Asia.

The Poppy seeds provide a fine oil which is edible and is also used as a drying oil in paint-making. The dried seeds are used by bakers to sprinkle on bread or are used in cakes.

Papaver somniferum

RAPE, SWEDE
Brassica napus L.
Family: *Cruciferae*

This is an annual or biennial with a swollen taproot. The stems are usually branched and up to 1.5 m. high. The leaves are bluish-grey, cabbage-like but not fleshy; the lowest leaves are stalked and sparsely bristly, the upper leaves are narrower and half-clasp the stem.

The flowers have 4 sepals and 4 yellow petals. The fruits are long and pod-like, narrowing to a slender beak. The bluish-black seeds of cultivated varieties contain oil.

Rape or Swede flowers between May and August and is planted or seeded in autumn. These seeds overwinter, flower early and the seeds are ripe by June. The seeds are easily shed and so the harvest has to take place promptly.

Rape is cultivated for its high oil content and it grows well in temperate zones; where it originally came from is uncertain. Rape is not found growing in the wild, but the cultivated plant may revert to the wild state. An excellent vegetable oil is produced by this plant. It can be used for machine oil, edible fats and soap and was formerly used as an oil for lamps. The pressed residue makes an oil-seed cake used as cattle-feed. The variety known as the Swede, which has a yellow-fleshed swollen taproot, is also fed to cattle.

BEET
Beta vulgaris L.
Family: *Chenopodiaceae*

Beet is a smooth or slightly hairy annual, biennial or perennial plant |of differing form according to the variety. The small purplish or pale green flowers appear in June—September and are borne on stems 30—120 cm. high.

Beet has a stout root which may or may not become conspicuously swollen. The stems are more or less erect and branched and terminate in large much-branched inflorescences. Basal leaves are wedge or heart-shaped and stem leaves are usually lanceolate. This is a cultivated species which is grown in large quantities in fields. There are many subspecies cultivated, e. g. beetroot, which has an intense red dye and is an edible root vegetable. Sugar beet is a highly important variety. Its roots contain up to 18 percent sugar and this species has been a source of sugar since the 18th century and is cultivated all over Europe.

Beet is also used as fodder for livestock and varieties for this purpose produce large, rather fleshy leaves. The fleshy, red-tinged yellow or white stem has been used as a substitute for asparagus and the leaves are still used instead of Spinach. Beet was known to the ancient Egyptians, the Babylonians and the Greeks, and this was probably the first plant of its kind to be cultivated by them.

All subspecies are derived from *Beta vulgaris* ssp. *maritima* which grows wild along the coasts of the Atlantic Ocean in West and North West Europe, also in the Mediterranean countries and Asia Minor and eastwards to the coastal areas of India and China.

GARDEN PEA, FIELD PEA
Pisum sativum L.
Family: *Leguminosae*

The Pea is a blue-green climbing annual which grows up to 2 m. high. The leaves are pinnate, with 1—3 pairs of oval leaflets, and a pair of large leafy stipules and a terminal branched tendril. The stems are rather weak and climb by means of the tendrils. The flowers are long-stalked with whitish or purple wings which adhere to the paler keel. There are 1—3 flowers on each flower-stalk. The fruits are between 4 and 10 cm. long; the pods are flat at first but fill out as the Peas swell within. Modern varieties of Pea are very prolific and high-yielding.

The plant flowers between April and June and is largely grown in gardens, allotments and fields but sometimes becomes naturalised in cultivated ground and in bushy places. There are 2 subspecies, one with white to purple flowers and this is the cultivated form; the other has lilac flowers.

The Pea is an ancient plant originating from the East, though it is not known from what date it has actually been cultivated. However, it almost certainly existed in ancient parts of eastern India and was called 'harenzo' in Sanskrit. It is known that the Pea was cultivated in Europe during the Stone Age. The Vikings made bread from peas. This was discovered during excavations of Viking tombs. The Pea was cultivated as early as 5,000 B. C. in ancient Egypt. Originally only absolutely ripe peas were eaten. The Dutchman Jan Babel Adrian from the Hague was supposed to be the first person who brought green (not 'ripe') Peas to the market. These were thought to be a delicacy even during the 17th century and were only served to rich men and to royalty.

Pisum sativum

Beta vulgaris

Brassica napus

The seeds contain sugar and starch, as in all legumes, and are also rich in vitamin B and C. They are a valuable foodstuff and are often preserved by drying, canning and freezing.

Today the Pea is cultivated in areas with a temperate climate, from some parts of the tropics to north temperate regions. On mountainsides it may be grown as much as up to 2,000 metres above sea level. In some areas it is grown and ploughed in as green manure.

RED CLOVER
Trifolium pratense L.
Family: *Leguminosae*

This is a softly hairy perennial herb with erect or spreading stems up to 60 cm. long. The stipulate leaves are trifoliate, with 3 oval or elliptical leaflets which are often marked with a white crescent towards the base. The petioles are long, up to 20 cm.

The flowers are light red or pink-purple (sometimes white) in a dense cluster of between 30—40 small flowers. The nectar is situated deep down in the flower and fertilisation can only be brought about by insects with long tongues (butterflies and particularly bumble bees). Bumble bees had to be imported into Australia in order to ensure the fertilisation of Red Clover there. The plant flowers between May and September and grows in meadows and fields, also waysides, on fertile moist well-drained soils. It is cultivated as a forage plant, being rich in proteins and minerals. The fruits are one-seeded pods.

Red Clover is known over almost all of Europe, and in western parts of Asia acros to Lake Baikal and also to Kashmir. In North and South America, as well as in New Zealand, Red Clover has been introduced.

Red Clover was cultivated by the ancient Medes in 700 B. C. in the highlands of Iran. During the Middle Ages it was the monks who grew it both as fodder and also as a medicinal plant. It is widely grown as a fodder plant, especially in short-term pastures ('leys'), because it grows so fast that a profitable crop can be cut three times a year. Like all leguminous plants, Red Clover increases the nitrate concentration in the soil.

LUCERNE, ALFALFA
Medicago sativa L. (ssp. *sativa*)
Family: *Leguminosae*

This is a deep-rooted perennial growing 30—90 cm. high. It has trifoliate stipulate leaves with 1.5 cm. long leaflets. The flowerheads contain 5—40 small pea-like flowers. The flowers are varying shades of purple, but some varieties have yellow, green or even black flowers.

The fruit is a spirally twisted pad with 10—20 seeds. The plant flowers between June and September. Lucerne comes from Central Asia and has been cultivated for a very long time, although it has also become a field escape. It is known all over Europe, from Asia to China, Tibet and India as well as in North Africa but grows in any temperate region. The seeds were supposed to have been carried by the armies of Alexander the Great, in about 470 B. C. and then brought from western parts of Asia to Greece.

Only since the beginning of the 19th century has this plant been widely cultivated in Europe, but it has since become invaluable as an easily grown and nutritious fodder plant.

CULTIVATED FLAX
Linum usitatissimum L.
Family: *Linaceae*

Flax is an annual herb that grows up to 1 m. high with erect, leafy, generally single stems. The leaves of Cultivated Flax are linear, 2—4 cm. long and they have 2 marked veins. They are spirally arranged along the stem.

The flowers are bright blue, with darker veins. The petals are 1.5 cm. long, 2—3 times as long as the sepals which are also blue. The flowers close and sometimes bend downwards towards evening, or just before it rains. The fruits are ovoid or rounded capsules, 1 cm. across containing 10 seeds and opening into 10 valves.

Flax flowers between June and August and is grown everywhere in the world for its textiles and for its oil. This particular species is known only in the cultivated state and does not appear in the wild.

It is of unknown origin.

Flax is very probably one of the oldest known plants producing a textile, and was used to make linen in China and India. It was probably from there that it reached ancient Egypt and other parts of the world. Pictures from the XIIth Dynasty of ancient Egypt show how linen was made in those days. Mummies were not only covered in cotton — but also in sheets of linen.

Flax was also cultivated during the early Stone Age in Europe. A field of flax in bloom has always been a striking sight. The fibres were formerly used to make sails, nets and ropes, as well as cloth, but these are now often made of synthetics.

Flax is today mainly cultivated to produce textiles, the exception being in the tropics. One subspecies has been cultivated in temperate regions because it gives a very good fibre, whereas another subspecies is grown in the warmer regions and produces superb oil. It has recently become possible to cultivate a plant that produces both oil and fibre.

Linen-producing flax was, for a very long time, all-important as far as textiles were concerned, but it fell out of favour when cotton came into fashion. Later however, linen became more fashionable and it therefore became increasingly cultivated again. The most important flax growing countries today are Russia, Belgium, Holland and Ireland, but production is falling because of the enormous increase in the range of man-made fibres.

The other major product is linseed oil which contains mucilage (a gummy secretion), albumen and approximately 40 percent oil, which is used in making soap, linoleum, drying oils, varnish and printers' ink. Properly refined linseed oil is edible and the crushed seeds make an important food for cattle. If the oil is mixed with calcium-rich water it makes an emulsion formerly used to treat burns. The seeds were also used as a household remedy to relieve constipation and infections of the urinary tract, and to make cough mixtures and poultices.

All parts of the plant, particularly the seeds, contain a substance which, if eaten to excess by farm animals or pets, can cause poisoning, but the decline in production of flax makes this now a very rare occurrence.

POTATO

Solanum tuberosum L.
Family: *Solanaceae*

This familiar plant has erect stems 30—80 cm. high, and underground stems which produce swollen tubers i. e. potatoes. The plant is actually an herbaceous perennial but, as a cultivated plant, is treated as an annual.

The leaves are large, 20—35 cm. long, and pinnate, with 3—5 pairs of oval or heart-shaped segments. Both leaves and stems are hairy. The flowers are white or pale violet and 2.5—4 cm. across. The 5 anthers form a projecting cone and open by apical pores. The fruits, when allowed to form, are globular, green berries, 2—4 cm. across, and, like the flowers, borne in long-stalked clusters.

The potato plant flowers between June and August

Trifolium pratense

Linum usitatissimum

Medicago sativa

and is cultivated, particularly in Europe, in large fields. Many subspecies have been created through cross-fertilisation and cultivation. The plant is very robust and grows at heights of up to 1,700 metres above sea level.

Originally the potato was brought over from South America where it grew in fields between Mexico and Chile. The Spanish commander Gonzales de Quesada was probably the first European who, together with his soldiers, tasted potatoes in an Indian village (Sorokotain, today's Columbia) in 1536 or 1537. The Spaniards called them 'truffles'.

However, it is not quite clear who exactly brought the potato to Europe. Columbus did not bring back

Solanum tuberosum

potatoes from his expeditions, but brought back the sweet potato, *Ipomea batatas*. John Hopkins probably brought the potato back in 1565, as did Sir Walter Raleigh in the same year, followed by Sir Francis Drake in 1578, but for a while the plant was merely regarded as a curiosity.

One of the most likely accounts states that King Philip II brought back the first potatoes from Cuzco, a town in Peru, in 1565. He sent some to the Pope as a medicine. The royal botanist of the Emperor Maximillian II, Charles d'Ecluse (Carolus Clussius), was given some of these potatoes and in turn gave some to his friend, Sir Francis Drake, who took them to England. It is therefore quite possible that most of the potatoes grown in Europe up to the middle of the 19th century actually derived from those few. Charles d'Ecluse published his findings and a description of the potato in 1601 in his work *Rariorum plantarum historia;* he called the plant *Papas peruanorum*.

At first the plant was cultivated as a rare and exotic plant; much later the actual potato was eaten, when it became a delicacy. Only in 1616 did potatoes reach the tables of the French king. At the beginning of the 17th century the potato was brought from Italy to Germany still named 'tartufo' i. e. 'truffle', as it had been called in Spain during the time of Columbus. It was only because of the French pharmacist, Antoine Parmentier, that the potato was eventually cultivated in France; essentially this was done to guard against famine.

The potato reached Ireland and became a popular vegetable but, in 1845, the potato plants of Ireland were attacked by a fungus (Potato Blight) which caused famine and eventually the emigration of hundreds of thousands of people to North America. One hundred and fifty years after it was first discovered in South America, in fact in 1719, the plant reached North America where it was called the 'Irish Potato'.

The cultivation of the potato in Europe spread particularly during the Thirty Years' War and potatoes formed the most important food for both civilians and soldiers. Before this Friedrich Wilhelm, Elector of Brandenburg in Germany, advertised and advised the cultivation of potatoes; he was backed up by the priests. However, people claimed that the plant was poisonous and fought against its cultivation. King Frederick II of Prussia too, ordered that potatoes should be planted and cultivated; but it was the famine which broke out after the Seven Years' War, which furthered the cultivation of potatoes on a much larger scale.

Soldiers had to guard potato fields against thieves and also had to try and establish a monopoly for certain people, by preventing others from growing the plant. However, since the fields were guarded during daylight only, the potatoes spread fairly quickly over a wide area, in fact right across France. Potatoes contain a great deal of starch and some protein and are very nourishing; and yet this plant is poisonous. All parts of the potato contain the alkaloid solanine and other poisonous substances, most of which appear in the young leaves and flowers, but in the berries as well. The green tops of potato plants are dangerous to livestock. The potato tuber itself contains little poison whereas the young shoots are very poisonous to man. Should the tubers, after being dug up, be kept in the light, the skins turn green and the outer cells develop solanine.

Potatoes have reduced the effects of many famines. Vitamin C is present in sufficient quantity to prevent scurvy, should no other source be available. Potatoes are also used as a raw material for the production of alcohol by industrial fermentation.

Potatoes are mostly cultivated in Europe and less so in America, where maize is more commonly grown for food. In America potatoes form the basis for the manufacture of synthetic rubber. In Ireland they are used in making whiskey.

MAIZE
Zea mays L.
Family: *Gramineae*

Maize is a robust annual up to 5 m. high and is now increasingly grown in Britain. The stems are stout and bear many large leaves 5—12 cm. wide, lance-shaped, with smooth blades.

The flowers are unisexual. The female flowers form a long rounded spike, in the axil of the basal leaves, and this is covered by leafy bracts. The stigmas are highly conspicuous, 12—20 cm. long and are

protruding. The male flowers are in much-branched panicles at the ends of the stems. The fruits are shining, angular or rounded when ripe, and yellow, white or purple in colour.

Maize too, is a very old plant which was first cultivated in America, very probably in Mexico or Guatemala. Nobody has ever discovered wild Maize, and all Maize goes back to the same American sources. The plant is unable to establish itself independently of man, and appears to require the standard methods of cultivation to ensure its survival.

In parts of Mexico and also in Peruvian burial chambers, remains of Maize have been found which must have been cultivated 2,500 years B. C. Indian tribes like the Mayas and Aztecs thought that Maize was a gift from the gods; they were convinced that man originally came from the flower of Maize.

In 1543 Columbus brought Maize to Europe for the first time, and the plant was almost an exhibition

Zea mays

piece and only cultivated as such. But this soon changed and Maize was cultivated in France and Italy, spreading further across to other Mediterranean countries and the Near East. Other European countries were introduced to Maize which had by then reached Turkey. The Portuguese took Maize to Africa, India, China and Java. Today Maize is planted in many, many countries.

Maize can be used for a great many purposes and is one of the most important of the crop plants. Maize contains up to 65 percent starch and a great deal of sugar. It is used to make flour for bread and cakes, biscuits, breakfast cereals and other similar foods. However, if Maize is the sole source of food for any length of time, a non-contagious disease called pellagra may develop. This is characterised by skin changes, severe nervous disfunction, and diarrhoea. This disease is due to a deficient diet and a lack of the complex vitamin — vitamin B.

The flour made from Maize is the basis of many a national dish — in Italy it is 'Polenta', in Rumania it is 'Mamaliga', and it is 'Türkenzwiebel' in Switzerland. The corn can be eaten raw, boiled, or fried as popcorn. Syrup can also be made from various kinds of Maize and some are used for distillation; wine, beer and a liqueur are made from it. Maize beer was a drink that was also known to the more primitive peoples of America. Corn oil and industrial oil can also be obtained from the plant; the oil can also be used in the manufacture of synthetic rubbers. The corn oil is used for salad oil, for cooking and in the manufacture of margarine. A glue is made from the corn starch.

All parts of the plant are valuable fodder for livestock; the dried plant can be used in the paper industry and the pulp is used in the manufacture of linoleum, celluloid and insulating materials. Packing paper can be made from the fibrous parts of the plant and it can also be used as a fertiliser. Thus, in warmer climates, Maize is one of the most useful cereals grown.

BREAD WHEAT
Triticum aestivum L.
Family: *Gramineae*

Wheat is a familiar cereal grass which grows 70—160 cm. high. The stems are hollow, bear, flat and rather rough leaves. By cultivation the plant is encouraged to tiller. Tillering is the production of a number of shoots from the base of the young plant by using a roller. Each stem bears a dense, four-angled spike of stalkless spikelets. The florets have rounded bracts with inconspicuous awns.

Wheat (known as Corn in Europe) may have originated in the Middle East but is also said to have come from Armenia. Many different varieties are cultivated and wild forms are still known. It is grown in temperate climates all over the world as far north as Scandinavia in Europe. The plains of North America produce most of the world's Wheat supply and it is also grown on the Russian steppes.

Wheat contains about 64 percent starch, sugar and, just beneath the surface of the grain, granules of protein. Wheat used to be roasted and was only later made into flour. Starch, glue and malt can be extracted from Wheat and it is also used for industrial distillations. The straw is used as fodder or bedding for livestock and also for making thatched roofs, mats, baskets, straw hats and wrapping paper. Wheat is the most important cereal grown today and forms nearly 50 percent of the European grain output.

RYE
Secale cereale L.
Family: *Gramineae*

This is a less familiar cereal plant 1—2 m. high. Both stem and leaves are blue-green; the leaves are 3—8 mm. wide, rough and with a short grooved ligule. The inflorescence is dense, slender and spike-like, 15—20 cm. long. It may be erect or slightly pendant. The spikelets are numerous and stalkless with florets whose outer bracts are keeled and narrow to a long awn-like tip. The inner bracts are also keeled and each bears an awn up to 3 cm. long. The fruit is ovoid, grey-green or yellowish-brown.

Rye flowers between May and July and is an important cereal crop in Central and eastern Europe. It is cultivated all over the world and grows in mountainous regions at up to 2,000 metres above sea level. About 20 wild species are known today and it is assumed that Rye originated from the species *Secale segetale.* This species was actually a weed in the Wheat and Barley fields in mountainous regions of the Caucasus and Asia Minor. It was probably able to survive and thrive in more severe climatic conditions which would have been detrimental to the growth of Wheat and Barley. It thus developed through natural selection into a cultivated species which can grow much further north.

Another hypothesis suggests that Rye came from Asia Minor where it developed through cross-fertilisation between two older species.

In comparison with wheat, Rye is a comparatively 'young' crop plant. Discoveries of prehistoric grain of this kind were made in Europe dating back to the Bronze Age (about 2,500—900 B. C.). Most of the other cultivated plants were known to the Babylonians and ancient Egyptians, but Rye was not.

The Greeks and Romans first saw Rye during their early campaigns against the Germanic people. The Slavs are often thought to have helped to spread Rye, even though Rye was cultivated in Europe before the invasions of the Slavs. The Romans did not appreciate Rye, they thought the corn ears too small and the bread made from it too black and coarse.

Though the flour made from Rye is darker, it is also said to be more nutritious than Wheat flour. Malt is made from it and Rye is also used for alcoholic fermentation. Young Rye is an excellent food for livestock, and the straw is used as bedding and for thatching.

TWO-ROWED BARLEY
Hordeum distichon L.
Family: *Gramineae*

This is a perennial cereal plant which grows up to 130 cm. high. The inflorescence is four-sided and spike-like with 2 longitudinal rows of spikelets, arranged in clusters of 3. All the bracts of the florets have awns of up to 15 cm. long, giving a characteristic 'bearded' appearance to the grain.

Two-rowed Barley is cultivated today in the more temperate zones all across the world, and may grow up to 2,000 metres above sea level. Special varieties are cultivated in cooler regions; in China one variety grows at up to 4,000 metres above sea level and in

the Himalayas at up to 5,000 metres above sea level. Today several kinds of barley are cultivated, but it is thought that all these species originated from *Hordeum spontaneum* which grows in North Africa, in parts of the Far East and Central Asia. They also originate from the Six-rowed Barley *(Hordeum vulgare)*

Secale cereale

Triticum aestivum

Avena sativa

which may also have originated in eastern Asia, possibly in China or Tibet.

Barley has been cultivated in Europe since about 2,800 B. C. In Asia it was cultivated 7,000 years ago and was not only known to the Egyptians, Assyrians, Sumerians and Babylonians but was also used as a raw material for making beer 4,000—5,000 years ago. Documents found in ancient Egypt show that an Egyptian queen was allowed 4 jugs of beer a day and the royal household consumed altogether 130 jugs of beer every day.

Barley was originally roasted or roughly ground, and only later was flour made from Barley. However, it must have been of poor quality since the Roman legionnaires were punished by having to eat bread made from Barley flour if their work did not come up to standard, or if disciplinary action had to be taken against them.

Barley contains approximately 60 percent starch and sugar, as well as some protein. In Tibet, Barley is used chiefly for making bread. In northern and Central Europe, malting Barleys are grown for the production of malt for beer, and in North Africa and South West Asia it is used as fodder for livestock.

OAT
Avena sativa L.
Family: *Gramineae*

Oat is a familiar cereal about 150 cm. high with a compound branched inflorescence up to 30 cm. long. This has large long-stalked drooping spikelets, each of 2—4 florets. The outer bracts are 2—2.5 cm. long, and the inner bract of the lowest floret of each spikelet has a long, twisted and jointed awn. When ripe, the oats are a silvery cream colour.

Oats flower between May and July and are cultivated as food for livestock and also for human consumption. Oats grow in the more hilly areas of temperate zones. It is a tough, undemanding plant and can grow at up to 1,600 metres above sea level.

There are about 8 species of Oat growing in Europe

Hordeum distichon

today, all of them with the characteristic much branched, open inflorescence. They are all widespread either as weeds of cultivated land or in waste places. The species are usually distinguished by minor characteristics of the awns and also of the bracts surrounding the florets.

Oats probably originated in eastern European countries or in Central Asia. Common Wild Oat (*A. fatua*) may have given rise to *A. sativa* but is now regarded as a weed. It is an important food for livestock, particularly for horses and poultry. It is supposed to give horses a shining coat. In poor mountainous regions, Oats are ground into flour for human consumption.

Oat has been cultivated since classical times, but may originally have been a cornfield weed. Up to the 16th century beer was brewed from Oats, and even today a special beer is brewed in Belgium using Oats. Oats contain many valuable substances including albumen, starch, sugar and dextrin as well as vitamins B and K and is thus an extremely nutritious cereal. They are still grown extensively in Central and northern Europe. As the plant tolerates cool, moist conditions it can therefore be cultivated as far north as 60 degrees, being able to thrive where other cereals are unable to grow. A gruel made from Oats is strengthening during convalescence, for it is bland and easily digested by people suffering from stomach complaints; gruel is also given to babies.

Oat flakes are made into porridge, which was formerly a basic item of diet, particularly in Scotland, and it is still an important breakfast cereal.

SUMMER PHEASANT'S EYE
Adonis aestivalis L.
Family: *Ranunculaceae*

This is an annual weed 30—50 cm. high with erect sparingly branched stems. The leaves are usually thrice-pinnate, with linear, pointed segments. The basal leaves have short stalks, the upper ones have none. All leaves appear very feathery.

The flowers are 2—3 cm. across and have 5—8 bright red petals each with a black basal blotch. Some varieties have light or bright yellow flowers. The sepals are characteristically hairy. The flowers

have many dark purple stamens and numerous carpels. The fruits are borne in elongated heads and are numerous, one-seeded, wrinkled nutlets, each with a long beak.

The plant flowers between June and August. It grows in cornfields in the warmer parts of Europe where it is a weed, but it prefers limestone ground. It originally came from the Near East and spread from there right across Europe but in the cooler regions, including Britain, it is rare or absent.

Yellow Adonis (*Adonis vernalis* L.) which belongs to the same family and grows on warm, sunny slopes contains the same substances as *Adonis aestivalis* L. These plants are poisonous to livestock but are useful to man because they form the source of a valuable heart tonic. Both of these species are grown in gardens in Britain but are usually treated as annuals. *Adonis flammea* Jacq. is a species with bright red flowers and hairy sepals which are pressed close to the petals. The carpels have a rounded projection just below the style.

CORN POPPY, FIELD POPPY
Papaver rhoeas L.
Family: *Papaveraceae*

Corn Poppy is an annual, rarely biennial, plant 20—40 cm. high. The stem has bristly hairs and is sparingly branched. The leaves are once or twice pinnate with coarsely toothed segments. The basal leaves are stalked, and the upper leaves are stalkless and three-lobed. All parts of the plant contain latex.

The flowers are scarlet, 7—10 cm. across, with 4 rounded petals, sometimes with a dark basal blotch. The flowers droop when in bud. The calyx is green, rough and falls off early. The petals surround numerous black stamens and the characteristic flat-topped globular ovary. The fruits are rounded and contain numerous seeds.

The plant flowers between May and August and is a common and familiar plant. It grows in cornfields, by waysides or on waste land; it is particularly abundant on recently disturbed land.

It is possible that this plant developed from a biennial species, native to Asia Minor, which grew in Turkey and in parts of Siberia. The Corn Poppy is known all over Europe, in Mediterranean countries, in North Africa, from Iran to the Orient and in western parts of Siberia up to the Altai region. It was introduced in North America, Australia, and New Zealand.

The poppy was thought to be a plant symbolizing grief and the ancient Egyptians used it in burial ceremonies. Well preserved dried poppies were found next to Princess Nsichons, daughter of the Pharaoh Tonthont-Huti (1,100—1,000 B. C.); these flowers were part of the gifts and utensils then thought necessary for life after death.

The flowers were later used as medicine; brews made from the petals loosened coughs. Today, the petals are used in some areas to colour wine, syrup, and other beverages or sometimes medicines. The flowers contain a red dye often used for ink. In Britain, the poppy is a symbol of World War I, as it grew in such abundance in the shell-torn fields of Flanders. Artificial poppies are still worn on Remembrance Day.

WILD RADISH, WHITE CHARLOCK
Raphanus raphanistrum L.
Family: *Cruciferae*

This is an annual herb which grows 15—150 cm. high. It has a slender white taproot and erect stems which have spreading bristles, especially at the base. The leaves are stalked; the lower ones are pinnately lobed with 1—4 pairs of smaller lateral lobes and a large terminal lobe. The upper leaves are usually entire and toothed.

The flowers are usually white, but they may be yellow or lilac, often with violet veins. They have 4 sepals closely pressed against the petals. In this, and in the nature of the fruit, Wild Radish (or White Charlock) differs from the troublesome weed Charlock *(Sinapis arvensis* L.*)* which is otherwise similar but has spreading sepals.

The fruits resemble a string of beads as they are constricted into a number of barrel-shaped, one-seeded joints which eventually separate. Each fruit terminates in a seedless beak which is up to 5 times as long as the top joint.

The plant flowers between May and September and

grows almost anywhere. It is a common and unwelcome weed in fields, on coastal rocks and sands, on bare and waste ground, particularly on low ground but also in the hills. It prefers sandy non-calcareous ground. It is difficult to eradicate the weed since its seeds remain viable in the soil for a very long time.

Wild Radish comes from southern parts of Europe but it has spread across Europe, very quickly reaching Asia Minor, North Africa and practically all countries which cultivate any type of wheat or corn. It is known also in eastern parts of North America, Uruguay, Argentina, Japan, South Africa and Australia.

The seed contains a yellow oil which has a sharp, burning flavour. It was formerly used as a household remedy against rheumatism but was used externally only, since the plant is poisonous. It can be dangerous to livestock if eaten in large quantities.

CHARLOCK
Sinapis arvensis L.
Family: *Cruciferae*

Formerly known as *Brassica arvensis*, this annual weed has a slender taproot and erect simple or branched stems which are 30—80 cm. high. These bear stiff hairs at least at the base, but they are sometimes smooth.

The lower leaves are pinnate with small lateral lobes and a coarsely toothed terminal lobe. The stem leaves are usually simple and lance-shaped. All leaves bear rough hairs.

Charlock flowers between May and September producing four-petalled bright yellow flowers. The fruits are pods each with a straight beak one-half as long as the pod. Each pod contains 6—12 dark red-brown seeds which become slimy in water. Each plant can produce about 25,000 seeds and since these can live in the soil for up to 25 years, it can be troublesome.

Charlock grows in fields, in cultivated ground, in vineyards and along waysides. It prefers limy soils. It probably originated in Mediterranean countries and spread with the cultivation of Wheat and Corn. It is an unwelcome weed and has spread right across Europe, to Siberia, to south western Asia and into North Africa. It was introduced into North and South

America, the West Indies, Uruguay and New Zealand. Wild Radish and Charlock both threaten crops since they carry an eelworm which attacks the roots of the crop plants. Potatoes and other crops attacked by eelworm become sickly and eventually die off. Thus the crop yield is dramatically reduced.

Charlock is therefore a dangerous and troublesome weed and is also poisonous to livestock which may eat it. The plant is more troublesome in spring-sown crops. It can be controlled by spraying with selective weedkillers, acids or copper salts.

FIELD PENNYCRESS
Thlaspi arvense L.
Family: *Cruciferae*

This is a light green annual herb which sometimes overwinters; it grows up to 60 cm. in height and has erect angular stems. If these are broken they exude an unpleasant odour reminiscent of garlic. The lower leaves are stalked, lanceolate, not in a rosette; the upper leaves clasp the stems. The small white flowers have petals twice as long as the sepals and are borne in an elongate flowerhead. The winged fruit is a large flat pod which looks like a coin with a wide rim; the pod is 12—22 mm. across and has a deep apical notch with a persistent style.

It flowers between May and August and grows in fields and in cultivated ground generally, as well as in waste places. It can be a very troublesome weed. It has spread all over Europe, (including Scandinavia), western parts of Asia, Siberia and Japan. It has been introduced in North America. It is doubtfully native in Britain, where it is widespread. Although it is visited by flies and small bees it is, in fact, automatically self-pollinated. Surprisingly, although it can be a pest, it is not particularly common.

SHEPHERD'S PURSE
Capsella bursa-pastoris (L.) Medic.
Family: *Cruciferae*

Shepherd's Purse is a common annual or biennial

herb up to 40 cm. high, with smooth or hairy stems. The leaves are pinnately lobed, the lower ones forming a basal rosette. The stem leaves are smaller, much less lobed and clasp the stem with basal triangular lobes. The flowers are small and white, in an elongate but rather flat-topped flowerhead. The fruits are triangular to heart-shaped; their characteristic shape gives the plant its common name.

Adonis aestivalis

Thlaspi arvense

Sinapis arvensis

Raphanus raphanistrum

Papaver rhoeas

The plant flowers virtually all the year round and grows on cultivated and waste land, also by waysides from sea level into the hills. Originally the plant probably came from the Mediterranean and spread with the cultivation of wheat and corn. It occurs all over the world, with one exception, Polynesia. Otherwise it can be found as far north as Iceland and other northern areas; it can grow at up to 3,000 metres above sea level in the Alps.

Shepherd's Purse is sometimes attacked by a kind of mildew (*Albugo candidans* or *Cystopus candidans*) which deforms it. Affected parts of the plant become thick and distorted and develop white powdery pustules.

This herb contains many substances which were formerly used medically. For instance, it was used as a remedy for internal bleeding and has also been used in medicines treating gynaecological conditions.

WILD PANSY, HEARTSEASE
Viola tricolor L.
Family: *Violaceae*

This is an annual or perennial herb up to 50 cm. high. The leaves are stalked, almost heart-shaped or lance-shaped; the stipules are deeply lobed with a large, entire middle lobe.

The flowers are multi-coloured, yellow, white or violet; the lower petal usually shows yellow patches and dark veins and is spurred. The flowers are 1.5—2.5 cm. across. The fruit is a round capsule with numerous seeds.

This is a very variable plant with a number of sub-species which differ somewhat in their habitat and also in their geographical distribution.

Wild Pansy flowers from March to September and grows as a weed of fields and cultivated land, on waste ground and grassland, often near the sea. It is a robust plant and can flower several times during a year, each time producing a fresh crop of seeds. The plant is known over almost the whole of Europe, excluding Portugal, and eastwards to Siberia, Asia Minor and into parts of India. It was introduced in North America. Wild Pansy is a plant with medicinal properties and was recognised as such even in the 16th century. It used to be cultivated, and it is thought that it must

have escaped and flourished almost everywhere because of its adaptability and thus it became a weed in the wild state.

The plant is still used in herbal medicine and contains amongst other substances, volatile oils. When simmered in water, the plant was used to make a tea which was given for whooping-cough, lung infections, rheumatism and for heart trouble. Alcoholic extracts of the plant were also used. The plant is chiefly pollinated by long-tongued bees.

CORN COCKLE
Agrostemma githago L.
Family: *Caryophyllaceae*

The Corn Cockle is an annual herb up to 100 cm. high, with sparingly branched stems. These and the leaves are covered in white, silky, closely pressed hairs. The leaves are 5—12.5 cm. long, linear or lance-shaped, and are borne in opposite pairs on the stem.

The flowers are solitary, long-stalked and measure 3—5 cm. across. The sepals form a tube with 5 spreading teeth which are much longer than the petals. The flower has dull violet or magenta petals. The fruits are ovoid capsules with numerous poisonous seeds. The plant flowers between June and September and is a rare weed (becoming rarer still) growing amongst wheat and other cereals, clover and other cultivated plants.

It probably originated in South West Asia from where it spread, with the cultivation of cereals, all over the world. Its ancestor might have been the Asiatic species *Agrostemma gracilis* Boiss. which became a weed and later evolved as the Corn Cockle.

The plant is known all over Europe — from the Mediterranean to Scandinavia — also in Asia Minor, Central Asia and Siberia and eastwards to the Far East. With the cultivation of cereals it spread to Algeria, South Africa, Australia, New Zealand and North America. This spreading was possible because of the inadequate measures taken to clean the corn. The seeds of the Corn Cockle are difficult to separate from the grain, but modern techniques of cleaning the crop have hindered the spread of the Corn Cockle and have led to a reduction, if not a complete disappearance, of the weed in several areas. The seeds, in particular the black ones, contain starch, volatile oils and glycosides. One of these appears to be easily absorbed during the process of digestion so that, if the grain is contaminated by Corn Cockle seeds, this can lead to poisoning. Flour produced from wheat which had not been sufficiently cleaned tasted bitter and was also dangerous.

The seeds were used as a household remedy, particularly as a cure against worms. Animals ignore the plant quite instinctively.

BLACK BINDWEED
Polygonum convolvulus L.
Family: *Polygonaceae*

This is an annual with angular climbing or spreading stems of up to 120 cm. long. The leaves are lance-shaped with spreading lobes at the base which are heart-shaped or arrow-like. The flowers are small, pale pink or greenish-white, with short stalks and a perianth of 5 rough-backed segments; the 3 outer ones are keeled.

The plant flowers between June and October and grows in cultivated fields, on waste ground and in gardens all over Europe, except for the Arctic areas. It also grows in the temperate regions of Asia and North Africa. The seeds of Black Bindweed have been found in prehistoric sites.

EARTH-NUT PEA, TUBEROUS PEA
Lathyrus tuberosus L.
Family: *Leguminosae*

This is a smooth sprawling perennial herb which has roots bearing small tubers. These are floury and may be dug up by animals such as pigs, which particularly like them. The creeping or climbing angular stems can be up to 120 cm. high. The stipulate leaves are stalked, with a pair of elliptical leaflets 1.5—3 cm. long and a simple or branched terminal tendril. The perfumed flowers are crimson with dark wings and

are borne in groups of 2—5 in long-stalked inflorescences. The fruits are smooth cylindrical pods 2.5 cm. long.

The plant flowers between June and August and grows as a weed in cultivated fields, along waysides and in meadows; it prefers limestone ground and warmer regions.

This plant originated in western Asia and from there it spread over much of Europe. It grows in several

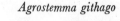

Agrostemma githago

Capsella bursa-pastoris

Polygonum convolvulus

Viola tricolor

parts of western Asia and in the Caucasus. It was introduced into Algeria as well as in North America. It is rare in the Mediterranean and northern Europe. The plant was introduced in Britain although it has been naturalised in Essex since 1800. Earth-nut Pea is always rare.

COMMON STORKSBILL
Erodium cicutarium L. L' Her.
Family: *Geraniaceae*

This variable annual or sometimes biennial herb grows up to 50 cm. high with generally sticky-haired stems. The basal leaves form a long-stalked rosette. Both they and the stem leaves are very variable but are usually once or twice pinnate, with several pairs of deeply cut or toothed leaflets. The flowers are pink-violet (sometimes white), 2 with basal black blotches — 14 mm. across, and often slightly irregular. The fruits of Common Storksbill are dark brown, with a long twisted beak.

The plant flowers between March and September and is a common weed. It grows in cultivated fields, dry grassland and waste places, mainly on sandy soils and often near the sea. It is found throughout Europe (except Iceland), probably having spread from south west Europe and into temperate Asia and North Africa. It has been introduced in the Far East, Australia and New Zealand, also in North and South America.

An extract of this plant was formerly used to stop bleeding. Like all species of *Erodium*, the common name of 'Storksbill' derives from the shape of the fruit.

SUN SPURGE
Euphorbia helioscopia L.
Family: *Euphorbiaceae*

Sun Spurge is a smooth annual herb up to 50 cm. high. The stems are single and generally unbranched, with leaves 1.5—3 cm. long, which are bluntly oval. The stem ends in a five-rayed umbel surrounded by broad yellowish bracts. As in all Spurges, the Sun Spurge flower has no sepals or petals. A solitary female flower is surrounded by several one-anthered

male flowers and each flower has 4—5 oval green glands.

The plant flowers between April and November, and throughout the winter if mild, and grows in fields and other cultivated areas including gardens. It is a very common weed in Europe southwards to the Mediterranean, as well as in Central Asia. It has been introduced in Africa, North America, New Zealand and Australia.

SCARLET PIMPERNEL, POOR MAN'S WEATHER-GLASS
Anagallis arvensis L.
Family: *Primulaceae*

Scarlet Pimpernel is a sprawling annual, with stems which are four-sided and which grow 6—30 cm. long. The leaves are oval to lance-shaped, 15—28 mm. long, without stalks and dotted beneath with black glands. The leaves are borne on branched stems which are also glandular.

The flowers are scarlet (rarely pink or blue), with 5 blunt petals with hairy margins and are up to 14 mm. across. They have 5 stamens. The fruits are rounded capsules which open by a small round lid.

The plant flowers between May and October. It grows in cultivated areas including fields and gardens, by roadsides and also on sand dunes. It grows in practically every part of the world except in the tropics. The flowers open only in sunshine and thus it has received its common name of 'Poor Man's Weather-glass'.

The seeds are slightly poisonous. Scarlet Pimpernel has medicinal properties and was formerly used effectively against snake bites.

There are two subspecies of Scarlet Pimpernel in Britain; ssp. *arvensis* which has flowers usually red or pink in colour and which is the common and familiar type, and ssp. *foemina* which has slightly smaller blue flowers. Both are native to Britain but ssp. *arvensis* is widely distributed (being rare only in the extreme north of the country), whereas ssp. *foemina* is always rare and is confined to fields in the south and west of Britain.

The Bog Pimpernel [*Anagallis tenella* (L.) L.] is a perennial with pink, funnel-shaped flowers borne on spraw-

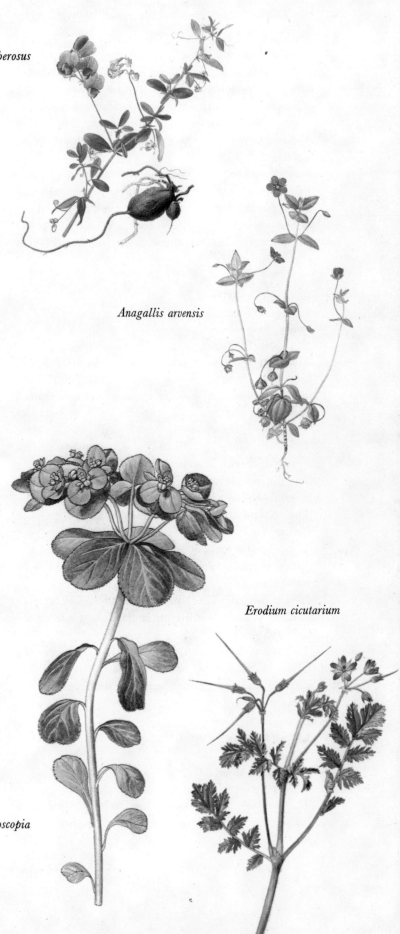

Lathyrus tuberosus

ling stems which root at the nodes. As its name suggests this is a plant of bogs or wet grassy places, and although it may be found throughout most of Britain, it is usually a fairly rare plant.

Altogether there are about 20 species of *Anagallis;* all are small slender herbs with simple leaves and small solitary flowers. The globular capsules with their transverse dehiscence exposing numerous seeds are especially characteristic of the genus, all other British members of the family Primulaceae having capsules which open by apical teeth e. g. Water Violet *(Hottonia palustris)* or which split into valves e. g. *Primula* spp.

FIELD BINDWEED
Convolvulus arvensis L.
Family: *Convolvulaceae*

This is a scrambling perennial, with a long underground rhizome which is stout, often spirally twisted, and which may grow deep in the soil. The leaves are arrow-shaped, 2—5 cm. long, which twist in an anti-clockwise direction.

The flowers are 3 cm. across. They are white or pink, veined red; they either grow singly or in groups of 2—3. The corolla is five-angled and funnel-shaped. The flower smells faintly of vanilla and opens up between 7 and 8 in the morning and closes again around noon, the corolla soon shrivelling.

The fruits are pointed capsules containing usually 4 black seeds. The capsules are about 3 mm. in diameter and hairless. Although seeds are produced they are said to germinate well only in warmer areas. The plant spreads highly successfully by broken pieces of rhizome.

The plant flowers between May and October and grows on cultivated land, in waste places including roadsides and railway banks, and in short turf—often near the sea.

Anagallis arvensis

Erodium cicutarium

Euphorbia helioscopia

It probably originated in the Mediterranean countries or East Asia, but today Field Bindweed is known all over the world except in tropical regions.

The roots contain a rubber-like latex as well as a glycoside which relieves constipation. The leaves and roots used to be made into a tea which was taken for this complaint.

Field Bindweed is a very unwelcome weed in cultivated fields and gardens, since it twists around plant stems pulling them down and so choking the plant. It also becomes affected by a virus which can spread to potatoes, tomatoes, tobacco and other cultivated plants.

CORN GROMWELL
Lithospermum arvense L.
Family: *Boraginaceae*

This rough-haired erect annual grows 10—60 cm. high. The lower leaves are bluntly oval and have usually shrivelled by the time Corn Gromwell flowers.

The upper leaves are lance-shaped and stalkless. They are borne on simple or sparingly branched stems which end in flowerheads.

The flowers are white, yellowish or blue with a violet corolla tube which is a little longer than the calyx. The fruits are brown, wrinkled and triangular nutlets.

The plant flowers between April and September and is a fairly common weed in cultivated fields and along waysides.

It is known all over Europe, in northern and western parts of Asia to North West India. It was introduced in North America.

The root contains a red dye which was formerly used on the Continent to help make ham look more appetising and is now used in the manufacture of lipsticks.

LESSER HONEYWORT
Cerinthe minor L.
Family: *Boraginaceae*

This is a biennial or perennial, up to 50 cm. high, and is the only genus in the family which is bluish-green

and hairless. The stems are grooved, erect and somewhat branched at the upper ends. The upper leaves clasp the stem, the lower ones narrow into a stalk. They are usually covered in white spots and small warts. The flowers are nodding, yellowish and often purple-blotched. The corolla is 1—1.5 cm. across, a little longer than the calyx. The fruits are smooth, erect, globular nutlets.

The plant flowers between May and August and grows in cultivated fields, in meadows, woods, by waysides and in rocky places in mountainous areas. It is known in South East and Central Europe, Asia Minor and the Caucasus.

Lesser Honeywort is very sought after by bees. The poet Virgil described it as the 'bread of the bees' and its common name is undoubtedly apt. It is a plant of warmer limestone regions. It is not found in Britain.

FIELD MADDER
Sherardia arvensis L.
Family: *Rubiaceae*

This is an annual herb with spreading hairy stems 5—40 cm. high. The leaves are lance-shaped with bristled margins, and are borne in whorls of 5—6 at the upper ends of the stems. The flowers are small and pale lilac (rarely white) in terminal heads of 4—8 flowers. The corolla is 4—5 mm. across, funnel-shaped and with a long slender corolla tube. The fruits are crowned by the dried up calyx.

The plant flowers between May and September and is a weed of cultivated ground and waste places, often on limestone soil. It originated in Mediterranean countries but is today known all over the world in temperate climates. It is a common plant in Britain.

Valerianella dentata (L.) Poll.
Family: *Valerianaceae*

This annual grows up to 30 cm. high with erect, slender and much-branched stems. The lower leaves are spoon-shaped, the upper ones are more linear. The leaves may be toothed. The bracts below the stalked flowerheads are lance-shaped and leaflike. The flowers are small, bluish-white and with a calyx of 5 small teeth, one of which is much longer than the others.

178

The corolla is five-lobed with 3 projecting stamens. The flowers are borne in rather open clusters. The fruits are toothed and narrowly ovoid.

The plant flowers between June and September and is a locally common weed. It grows in cultivated fields, especially cornfields. It is known all over Europe, including Britain, but particularly in Central and southern Europe, in the Caucasus, in North Africa, the Azores and the Canary Islands, as well as in West Asia and the Far East.

COMMON OR SMOOTH SOW-THISTLE
Sonchus oleraceus L.
Family: *Compositae*

This is an annual or biennial herb 20—150 cm. high, with erect, hollow 5-angled branched latex-containing stems. The leaves are very variable, bluish-green, the basal leaves are stalked and usually

oval; the lower stem leaves are pinnately lobed with a wide terminal lobe and spreading basal lobes. The upper stem leaves are smaller but with a more widely winged stalk. The flowers are yellow with violet or brown stripes on the outside; the flowerheads are umbel-like clusters 2—3.5 cm. across, with yellow-haired stalks and bracts. The fruits are ribbed nutlets, each with a pappus of 2 rows of hairs, grouped into a dandelion-type 'clock'.

The flowers are produced in May to September and the plant is regarded as a weed. It grows in cultivated

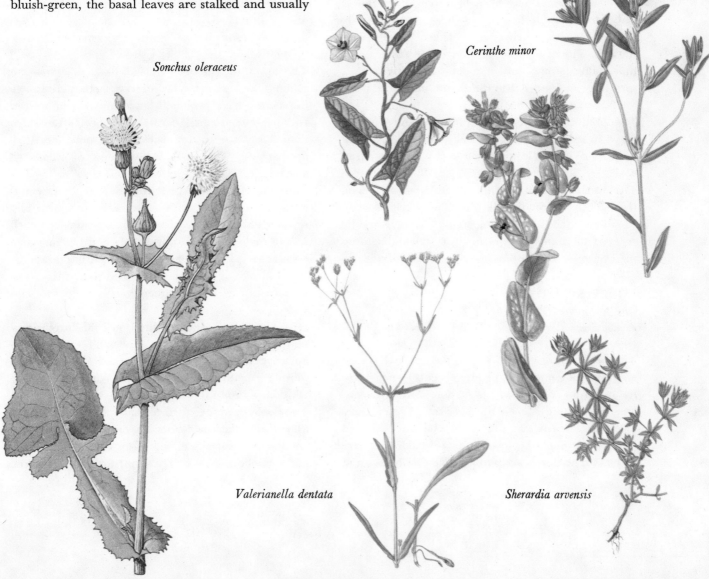

Convolvulus arvensis

Lithospermum arvense

Cerinthe minor

Sonchus oleraceus

Valerianella dentata

Sherardia arvensis

fields and in gardens, also in waste places and on bare ground. It is found almost everywhere in Europe, in western and northern parts of Asia, Arabia, North Africa and in the Canary Islands. It was introduced into eastern parts of Asia, South Africa, Australia and North and South America.

During the Middle Ages the plant was used as a salad. The milky juice was supposed to heal liver complaints and to relieve gout. Today the plant is regarded solely as a common but not especially troublesome weed. Abroad, the plant is valued as a foodstuff for rabbits, goats and pigs.

CORNFLOWER, BLUEBOTTLE
Centaurea cyanus L.
Family: *Compositae*

This is an annual or biennial cottony herb, 20—90 cm. high, with erect much-branched stems. The lower leaves are stalked, 10—20 cm. long, and pinnately lobed. The upper leaves are smaller, narrow and stalkless. The flowerheads have violet or white, sometimes pink, florets; the outer florets are bright blue, spreading and larger than the central ones. The fruits are nutlets, each with a pappus of rough hairs.

The plant flowers between June and August and grows in cornfields and other cultivated areas, as well as in waste places. It originated in the Mediterranean countries — Sicily and the southern Balkans — and also in south western parts of Asia, and it spread mainly through the cultivation of wheat and other cereals. Modern methods of cleaning seed-grain have greatly reduced the numbers of plants in cornfields, both on the Continent and in Britain, where it is now rare.

CREEPING THISTLE
Cirsium arvense (L.) Scop.
Family: *Compositae*

This perennial thistle grows up to 150 cm. high. It has a number of white creeping lateral roots which throw up numerous erect flowering and non-flowering stems. The leaves are lance-shaped or elliptical, deeply lobed with thorny teeth; the lower ones are narrowed into a short stalk, the upper ones are stalkless. All are cottony. The florets are pink, purple or whitish, and

are borne in flowerheads with purple tinged involucral bracts which have thorny tips. The fruits are smooth and brown with a long brown pappus.

The plant flowers between July and October, and grows as an unwelcome weed in cultivated fields. It is also found by waysides and on stony or waste ground. It is known almost all over Europe, in the north up to Iceland and northern Scandinavia, also in Siberia, China and Japan. It was introduced in North America. This is a very variable species which spreads quickly, chiefly by broken pieces of root which regenerate the plant, but also by the wind-blown fruits.

WILD CHAMOMILE
Matricaria recutita L.
Family: *Compositae*

This is an annual herb with a pleasant aromatic scent. The smooth erect stems are 15—60 cm. high and are usually branched. The leaves are stalkless and 2—3 times cut into narrow, linear segmenrs with have bristle tips.

The flowerheads are long-stalked, 1—2 cm. across and solitary, with numerous white ray florets and yellow disc florets. The involucral bracts are yellowish-green with papery margins. After flowering begins, the strap-shaped ray florets curl backwards; sometimes they are lacking. The fruits are without oil-glands or a pappus.

The plant flowers between June and September and grows in cultivated fields or waste ground, generally on sandy or loamy soils. Wild Chamomile is well known for its medicinal properties and has in places been collected to such an extent that it has disappeared. Since it is an important medicinal plant it is often cultivated, but frequently reverts to the wild state.

Wild Chamomile grows in most parts of Europe, and also in Asia Minor, the Caucasus, and eastwards to northern India and eastern parts of China; it was introduced into North America and Australia together with wheat and other cereals.

The flowerheads are used to make tea and ointments as well as other medicines. It contains an aromatic volatile oil which is excellent for treating infestions and for relieving pain. The plant makes a fine tonic and stimulant. Another substance in the flower relieves cramps.

Chamomile tea is used to induce sweating and to relieve and control digestive upsets. It is used as a gargle to relieve infections of the gum and jaw and is also used to wash and cleanse open wounds. Ointments made from the plant are used in the healing of wounds and are also applied to the skin after radioactive treatment. It is also said that Chamomile furthers the growth of hair and is used to lighten hair colour.

CORN CHAMOMILE
Anthemis arvensis L.
Family: *Compositae*

Corn Chamomile is an annual herb, with many-branched stems growing to about 50 cm. high. It has a scent somewhat similar to that of Wild Chamomile. The leaves are pinnately divided 1—3 times into segments which are short, oblong and woolly beneath. The flowerheads (2—3 cm. across) are solitary and terminal on long stalks. They have yellow disc florets and strap-shaped white ray florets. The receptacle is conical and covered in pointed scales. The fruits are ribbed and the pappus is reduced or absent.

The plant flowers between June and September, growing on cultivated and waste land, especially on calcareous soils. It grows in most parts of Europe, in Siberia and across to the western parts of the Himalayas and also in North Africa. It was introduced into North and South America, Australia and New Zealand. Unlike Wild Chamomile it is of little, if any, medicinal value. The aromatic scent makes the plant attractive to both bees and flies, which are frequent visitors.

COLTSFOOT
Tussilago farfara L.
Family: *Compositae*

Coltsfoot is a perennial up to 30 cm. high when fruiting. It has white, scaly creeping rhizomes which

terminate in leaf rosettes and which penetrate the soil up to a depth of 1.5 metres. During early spring purple-scaled stems appear bearing solitary yellow flowerheads. The outer i. e. ray florets are long and strap-shaped and are arranged in several rows. These florets are female. The disc florets are few in number

Centaurea cyanus

Cirsium arvense

Matricaria recutita

Anthemis arvensis

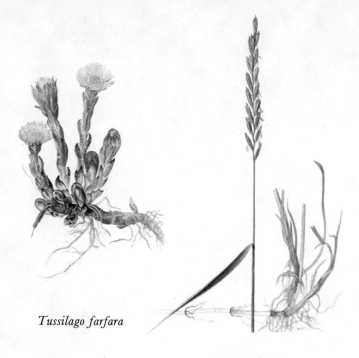

Tussilago farfara

Agropyron repens

and are male. The flowerheads close and droop at night, becoming erect again by day. They also droop after flowering, but as the fruit ripens the stalk elongates and the head becomes erect. The fruits are pale achenes with a long white pappus and grow in a dandelion-like 'clock'.

The leaves appear only after flowering. They are long-stalked and round to polygonal in shape; they are shallowly 5—12 lobed with black-toothed margins. The leaves are 10—20 cm. accross, with white felt-like hairs underneath. The plants appear in great numbers, on clay soils, in cultivated fields and waste places, on banks and clay cliffs (both inland and by the sea), also on dunes, screes and shingle.

Coltsfoot is known throughout most of Europe, in northern and western parts of Asia as well as in mountainous regions of North Africa. It was introduced in North America.

The flowers and leaves have medicinal properties and are collected to make drugs or medicines. They con-

tain tannins, volatile oils and other medicinal compounds. Coltsfoot is used as a remedy against chest complaints, especially coughs, and is used as an anti-neuralgic substance. The leaves are also used to treat conditions or infections of the joints, as well as rheumatism. The leaves, when smoked like tobacco, are used to relieve conditions such as coughs and asthma; the Latin name derives from *tussis*, a cough.

COUCH-GRASS, TWITCH
Agropyron repens (L.) Beauv.
Family: *Graminae*

This is a perennial, dull bluish-green grass, with stems up to 120 cm. high. It has abundant yellowish creeping rhizomes. From these grow the erect stems, which often form large patches. The underground stems readily give rise to new plants, making Couch-grass a most pernicious weed in fields and gardens. This is a very variable species particularly in regard to the leaves, which are about 1 cm, wide and sparsely hairy above. The spike-like inflorescence has numerous flattened, 1—2 cm. long, overlapping spikelets and grows 5—30 cm. long.

The grass flowers between June and September and grows in cultivated fields, on waste ground, along waysides and in rough grassland. It is known all over Europe, also in Siberia, North Africa and North America.

The rhizomes contain several compounds which are used medicinally and are made into a tea. This tea is taken to cure constipation and was formerly taken by diabetics to relieve their condition. In some countries the roots are still collected and exported as an important raw material for the drugs industry.

During the First World War a syrup was made from the sugary roots and they were also roasted and used as a coffee substitute. Beer and spirits were made from them in Norway.

PLANTS
OF
WASTE
PLACES

INTRODUCTION

Certain species of plants are able to colonise ground which has either been destroyed or totally changed by man and which is an uncultivated 'no man's land'. Such areas incude land used for open-cast mining, tips and rubbish dumps, paths and roadsides, railway cuttings and disused railway tracks, ruins or old walls, quarries, and gravel, chalk and clay pits, also the desolate wastes surrounding industrial areas. The plants which grow in such places are often termed weeds. The waste areas have loose or compacted soil which may be lacking in soil nutrients but which may be rich in nitrogen. Weeds growing on nitrogen-rich soils may become quite luxuriant and their leaves will shadow the soil and reduce evaporation. On the death of the plants humus begins to be laid down. These plants usually live undisturbed by animals or man and can therefore grow without restraint.

Smaller plants grow successfully along roadsides, on paths, at the base of walls and fences as well as in holes in roads or pavements. Such weeds are often cosmopolitan and many of them have been carried unknowingly by man into different countries. Some of these plants have been known for a very long time but others have been introduced more recently, due to the increase in road and rail communications. Many such 'casuals' or 'aliens' have come in ships or lorries and even in aeroplanes, and this explains why such plants were often first found near harbours, railways stations and airports. From there they have been able to spread rapidly on uncultivated and waste ground.

The majority of these weeds are hardy and adaptable and either form numerous seeds or spread rapidly through vegetative means.

Where weeds have become acclimatised and have grown in a country for some time, even though not indigenous, they become an accepted part of the local flora and may even become common.

GREATER CELANDINE
Chelidonium majus L.
Family: *Papaveraceae*

This is a perennial herb with almost smooth, brittle branched stems up to 90 cm. high. All parts of the plant have a system of vessels which contain a bright orange bitter-tasting latex. The greyish leaves are pinnate or deeply pinnately lobed, with 5—7 ovate to oblong leaflets, the terminal one often three-lobed. The leaf-stalk is short and winged.

The flowers have long stalks and are bright yellow, with 4 petals, 2.5 cm. across, and with 2 yellowish sepals. There are numerous stamens with filaments narrowed at the base.

The fruits are slender pod-like capsules up to 5 cm. long. The seeds are numerous, kidney-shaped and with a white fleshy protuberance known as an *aril*. The aril is attractive to ants which collect the seeds and then distribute them. The seeds are very rich in oil.

The plant flowers between May and October. It grows on waste ground, and often in derelict or neglected areas near towns. Greater Celandine is also found besides roads and walls, in rubbish dumps, in shady hedges as well as on banks by rivers and lakes. In mountainous areas the plant grows only near towns and villages.

It is known all over Europe, from the Mediterranean countries northwards to Scandinavia. It is not found in Iceland. The plant also grows in the temperate to sub-arctic zones of Asia. It has been introduced in North America.

This is a very old, formerly cultivated, medicinal plant which was called a 'miracle plant' in the Middle Ages. The alchemists thought that the orange sap contained the four basic elements; air, earth, water and fire and was used by them in their search for the legendary alchemist's stone.

As a household remedy this plant has been used to remove corns, warts and verrucas, and to bleach away freckles. From it were made medicines for a variety of complaints.

Greater Celandine is a poisonous plant containing many substances, including alkaloids. It is sometimes used as a purgative. When extracted, the latex turns

Chelidonium majus

brown and has been used as a pain-killing or tranquillising drug.

The substances contained in the latex are also thought to affect the heartbeat and to dilate the arteries, thus affecting the blood pressure. The plant is still used as a raw material in the manufacture of medicines and is used in drugs to control asthma, coughs, and stomach and gall-bladder ailments. In Russia research is going on into these substances to investigate whether they have any effect on malignant diseases.

HOARY PEPPERWORT, HOARY CRESS
Cardaria draba (L.) Desv.
Family: *Cruciferae*

This perennial is up to 90 cm. high and the green parts are not necessarily hairy, despite its name. The ovate basal leaves have a sinuous margin and shrivel early.

The upper leaves usually clasp the stems and are slightly toothed and lobed. The flowers are small, pleasantly scented and white. They have 4 petals which are twice as long as the sepals, and are borne in dense flat-topped clusters. The fruits are heart-shaped to kidney-shaped with the style forming a kind of beak. The seeds were a pepper substitute.

The plant flowers between April and July and is often found in clumps on waste ground, beside roads and also in cultivated fields.

189

Cardaria draba

Chenopodium bonus-henricus

It originated in the steppes of Central Asia and spread quickly, particularly in warmer regions of eastern, Central and southern Europe. It is also known in western parts of Siberia and has been introduced into many countries all over the world, where it has acclimatised quickly.

GOOD KING HENRY
Chenopodium bonus-henricus L.
Family: *Chenopodiaceae*

This is a perennial slightly mealy plant 5—80 cm. high with erect yellowish-green stems. The leaves, also yellowish-green, are up to 10 cm. long, triangular and somewhat lobed at the base.
The flowers are small and are held in a 4 to 6-lobed perianth in which the ripe fruit capsules are enclosed. The flowers are in elongate clusters in the tapering inflorescence which, unlike those of related species, is nearly leafless.
This plant flowers between May and August and grows on waste ground, in farm-yards, pastures and by roadsides in lowland and hilly areas. It prefers to grow near towns and villages also in nitrogen-rich soils. Good King Henry grows everywhere in Europe as far north as Norway and Finland, in West Africa and also in North America.
The plant was at one time used as a household remedy and the young leaves as a substitute for spinach.

FAT HEN
Chenopodium album L.

This is a very tall weed up to 1.5 m. high and covered with white woolly hairs. It is known all over the world as a plant of waste ground. Its greenish flowers resemble those of *C. bonus-henricus*. It was formerly important for food.

Atriplex nitens

Urtica dioica

Atriplex nitens Schkuhr
Family: *Chenopodiaceae*

This is a hardy plant up to 2.5 m. high, with branched
stems bearing leaves which are shiny green above and
covered in greyish hairs beneath. The leaves are
triangular and lobed, and the flowers are small, greenish
and unisexual, in long pendant clusters in a spike-
like inflorescence. The fruits are enclosed by 2 encirc-
ling bracteoles. The plant usually forms colonies on
waste ground and rubbish dumps and spreads quickly.
It prefers flatter regions. In Britain it is found only
occasionally and sporadically.

It grows in north eastern Europe, and as far south as
southern Italy; also in the Far East, in Central Asia
and in Siberia. It was introduced into many countries
including Denmark, Belgium and Sweden.

STINGING NETTLE
Urtica dioica L.
Family: *Urticaceae*

This familiar perennial grows up to 150 cm. high,
with creeping much-branched yellowish roots from
which new erect stems appear in spring. All parts
have stinging hairs.

The paired leaves are stalked, ovate, with a toothed
margin and pointed tips. The long hollow hairs have
a thick cell wall and a sharp siliceous point. These
points prick the skin, break off and the contents of the
hairs enter the small wound like an injection. The
hairs do not contain, as is often claimed, formic acid,
but a variety of irritant substances which cause a burning pain and inflammation of the skin.

The Nettle has either male or female plants. The male
flowers appear in the leaf axils, at the top of the plant;
the female flowers are in long pendant tassels, about
10 cm. long, and borne along the greater part of the
stem. The small flowers, with their green perianths,
are also covered with the stinging hairs.

The plant flowers between June and October and
forms colonies. It grows in mountainous as well as
lowland areas. Though this is a typical waste-ground
weed it also grows in woods, fens, damp meadows,
hedgerows and waysides. It is often found growing on
litter or rubble and prefers nitrogen-rich soil.

It grows anywhere in the world except in tropical
regions.

Although this plant is basically regarded as a weed
and one that is difficult to eradicate, it is also useful in
some ways. It contains several organic acids, including
acetic and formic acids, and is also very rich in chlorophyll. For this reason it has been collected, the
chlorophyll being a dye.

The stinging hairs contain histamines and acetyl-
choline, and other substances affecting muscle action
and tissue response. The stinging and irritation of the
skin which occurs when touching a Nettle, is caused
by the histamines and acetyl-choline. Nettles are rich
in vitamins C and A; probably also vitamins E, K and
B, as well as calcium, iron, manganese and phosphorus.
All parts of the plant are collected for herbal use.

Chenopodium album

An infusion made from the leaves was formerly used in cases of kidney trouble and diabetes, to relieve gall bladder and liver ailments, as well as to ease rheumatism and infections of the respiratory system. It was therefore highly valued.

The young Nettle has been used to feed poultry and may, even today, be used by man — boiled like spinach. The plant can also be made into a soup or salad and, being rich in iron, is a nutritious food for sufferers from anaemia. During the Middle Ages Nettles were commonly used as a vegetable, as spinach was then unknown, and this use was revived in World War II. The Nettle is a plant which has thick fibres towards the outside of the stems and these fibres were used, during the Middle Ages, in the manufacture of fine textiles. Although this raw material was superseded by cotton, it was rediscovered during the First and Second World Wars and used as a substitute for cotton. A form of beer has also been made from the leaves.

In addition to the many uses already mentioned, the Stinging Nettle is also valued by gardeners since it can be rotted down to make a high-quality compost, and it is often harvested for this purpose. Country folk have long held that Nettles and Docks grow together and indeed, this is often so. Dock leaves are applied for Nettle stings and are effective because they contain an anti-histamine.

SMALL NETTLE
Urtica urens L.

This annual is between 10 and 60 cm. high and densely covered with stinging hairs. The erect stems are soft. The leaves are oval-elliptical and toothed. The lower leaves have stalks which are longer than the leaf blades. The flowers are small, light green and borne in erect clusters which are 1—2 cm. wide. Both male and female flowers are found on the same plant.

The plant flowers between June and September and grows on waste ground, besides roads, and in fields and gardens. It prefers light soils. It is known all over the world except in circumpolar regions and in South Africa. In mountainous areas it is found at up to 2,000 metres above sea level.

This Nettle is a small annual plant very similar to the larger species *U. dioica* — but differing in having male and female flowers on the same plant. It is of little use to man.

SILVERWEED
Potentilla anserina L.
Family: *Rosaceae*

This perennial has a thick branched rhizome, with a rosette of leaves and creeping stems growing above ground and up to 70 cm. long. From these stems develop roots, leaves and solitary flowers. The rosette leaves are 7—15 cm. long, pinnate, with 7—25 toothed leaflets which are oval and silvery (at least on the lower side) because they bear silky white hairs. The silvery leaves give the plant its common name.

The flowers are golden-yellow, about 2 cm. across, with 5 sepals and 5 petals and usually 20 stamens. The fruit is a group of nutlets. Silverweed flowers between May and August and grows in waste places, on fixed sand-dunes, by roadsides and in damp meadows. It grows abundantly on well grazed grassland, and its specific name *anserina* (from the Latin *anser* — a goose) was applied because such grass was formerly often grazed by geese which were kept on village greens. The soil would be well manured and rich in nitrogen and the plant would thrive on it. Silverweed also flourishes in damp places such as ditches.

The plant is known virtually all over the world, from Greenland and northern Russia to North and Central Asia, the Himalayas, Japan, Australia, New Zealand and North America.

The plant and the sweet rhizome were collected for their medicinal properties, and also for food. They could be eaten raw or cooked, or made into flour. Extracts from the plant were used for a variety of complaints; they were used to bathe wounds, sores and ulcers, since it was considered that such extracts had healing properties. These extracts were also taken internally for stomach upsets.

COMMON MELILOT
Melilotus officinalis (L.) Pall.
Family: *Rosaceae*

This is an annual or biennial up to 2.5 cm. high with

192

erect branching stems. The leaves are stalked, stipulate and trifoliate, with leaflets 1.5—3 cm. long and elliptical to oval in shape, with toothed margins.

The small yellow, pea-like flowers smell of coumarin and are borne in elongate inflorescences with 30—70 loosely spaced flowers. The lateral wings and the standard are of equal length; both are longer than the keel. The fruits are wrinkled pods, brownish-black and contain usually one seed. The plant flowers between June and September and grows besides roads and along railway lines, on waste ground, and also on cultivated land — especially if the soil is clay or saline.

Common Melilot was introduced into Britain, and probably other parts of Europe, as a weed of cultivation. It is absent from the extreme south of Europe but grows as far east as China.

Common Melilot was known in ancient times when it was used as a medicinal plant. The plant is still collected today since it contains coumarin and other medicinal compounds. Coumarin is invaluable in the long-term treatment of blood-clotting, blood pressure and heart trouble. Extracts of the plant were formerly used to cleanse wounds, and the leaves were boiled and applied as a poultice to festering wounds and sores. The leaves were also used to repel clothes' moths and other insects.

In some areas the plant was made into snuff because of its aromatic perfume, and young leaves were used for salad. It has also been added to certain cheeses. During War II an attempt was made to use the plant to make textiles. This proved useless and also extremely costly.

The plant is also sought after by bees and is cultivated in some areas as a fodder crop.

WHITE MELILOT
Melilotus alba Medic.

This is a similar species, but it has smaller, white flowers and grows in fields and waste places.

DWARF MALLOW
Malva neglecta Wallr.
Family: *Malvaceae*

This is a hairy annual (sometimes perennial) plant with erect or sprawling stems. The leaves are long-stalked, rounded to kidney-shaped with 5—7 toothed palmate lobes.

The flowers have pinkish or whitish petals with lilac veins. They are usually solitary, arising on long stalks from the leaf axils. The 5 notched petals are nearly

Melilotus officinalis

Urtica urens

Potentilla anserina

twice as long as the sepals; the numerous stamens are in bunches.

The fruit stalks bend down when the fruit is ripe. The disc-shaped, flattened fruits ('cheeses') break up when ripe into single seeded half-moon shaped segments.

Dwarf Mallow flowers between May and September and is also found in mountainous regions. It grows beside roads, fences, walls and on waste ground. It is known almost all over the world; in Europe, and parts of Asia (including Tibet and India), also in North Africa. It was introduced into North America, Chile and Australia.

The plant has sometimes been used as a vegetable. In Britain, several other species — differing chiefly in details of the fruit — are often confused with *Malva neglecta*.

WHITE DEAD-NETTLE
Lamium album L.
Family: *Labiatae*

This perennial plant is 20—80 cm. high, with a creeping rhizome and erect unbranched stems which are covered in downy hairs and reddish-tinged, turning to violet at the base. The leaves are stalked, oval, heart-shaped at the base and toothed. The upper leaves have shorter stalks and form bracts near the top of the stem.

The flowers are white or cream with a long, hooded and bi-lobed corolla and a bell-shaped five-pointed calyx. They are borne in whorls in the upper leaf axils. Of the 4 stamens, 2 are longer than the others. The fruits are 4 three-angled nutlets.

The plant flowers between March and November, growing in colonies on hedgebanks, by roadsides, in gardens and allotments and in uncultivated ground near towns and villages. It is known over most of Europe (except in the south), also in the Himalayas and Japan. It was introduced in North America.

This was formerly a valuable medicinal plant. Only the flowers (without the calyx) were collected, but because the collecting of the flowers was so time-consuming, the drug made from them became prohibitive. The plant was in the past recognised by doctors, as well as being used as a household remedy.

The flowers contain mucilages and tannins, a soap-like compound, and also at least one other medicinal substance not yet fully identified. The medicine from White Dead-nettle was used for kidney complaints and also a variety of infections. An extract of the plant was used to bathe wounds.

Dead-nettle leaves are similar in shape to those of the Stinging Nettle (but lack the stinging hairs), and like them have been used as a substitute for spinach.

BLACK HOREHOUND
Ballota nigra L.
Family: *Labiatae*

This softly hairy perennial grows up to 1 m. high and has erect branching stems with leaves 2—5 cm. long. These are rounded, heart-shaped at the base, coarsely toothed and wrinkled.

The flowers are pink, purplish or white and are borne in clusters in the axils of leafy bracts. The calyx is funnel-shaped with 5 pointed teeth. The corolla is characteristically two-lipped, with hairs outside and a ring of hairs within.

It flowers between June and September and grows on waste ground near towns and villages by waysides and on hedgebanks, as well as in woods and shady places. In Europe it is found southwards from England, southern Scandinavia and Central Russia to Spain, Italy and Greece. It also grows in the Azores, in Morocco, Palestine and Iran. It is never common enough to be a troublesome weed. It was introduced into North America where it spread rapidly.

The plant has an unpleasant odour. It has in the past been used to make a lotion for hair and skin, to relieve convulsions in babies, and as a treatment for dog bites.

HENBANE
Hyoscyamus niger L.
Family: *Solanaceae*

This is an annual or biennial herb 30—80 cm. high. It is a coarse, hairy, sticky plant with a strong unpleasant odour. The stems are stout, woody at the base, with many leaves which are 15—20 cm. long, oval with rounded teeth.

The flowers are pale yellow, patterned with purple

194

veins. They are 2—3 cm. across, borne in leafy clusters, and have a five-toothed tubular calyx and a slightly irregular five-lobed bell-shaped corolla, which is purple-blotched at the base inside. The five stamens have purple anthers.

The fruits are rounded capsules opening by a circular lid and containing numerous brownish-black seeds. When the fruits are ripe, they are 1.5—2 cm. across and are surrounded by the papery calyx.

It flowers between June and August and grows on waste ground — bare or disturbed, by waysides, in farmyards and in sandy places, especially near the sea. It is never common but is found almost throughout the whole of Europe, also in West Asia and in North Africa. It has been introduced in East Asia, North America and Australia.

Henbane is very poisonous since all parts of the plant, particularly the seeds, contain the alkaloids hyoscyamine, and scopolamine. The seeds also contain oil. Deadly Nightshade *(Atropa belladonna)* and Henbane contain a range of rather similar alkaloids. These have a variety of effects, including a tranquillising and sedative action and also dilation of the pupil of the eye. Atropine from Deadly Nightshade has a specially marked effect.

Henbane has been known since ancient times, both as a poisonous and as a medicinal plant. It was known in ancient Egypt, Assyria, Babylon, India, Greece and Rome. Ancient Egyptian paintings depict people inhaling either the smoke or the steam which comes from a potion made from the seeds, and which was used as a pain killer to relieve tooth ache.

Henbane played a large part in the Middle Ages in witchcraft and alchemy. It was also used as a household remedy. It was largely cultivated in gardens. According to old recipes, ointment made from the plant was used by witches who would annoint themselves in order to take part in the witches' sabbath. The explanation for this usage is that the poisonous substances absorbed through the skin caused the witches to enter into a sleep-like, hallucinatory state in which they thought they experienced riding on a broom stick to their sabbath.

Henbane was once used as a love potion or aphrodisiac. However, because it is poisonous, it was also sometimes used to eliminate rivals or enemies. During the Middle Ages the plant was used to anaesthetise patients during operations. Unprincipled brewers even added Henbane to beer to make it more intoxicating.

Malva neglecta

Hyoscyamus niger

Ballota nigra

Lamium album

Today the plant and seeds are used as raw material for drugs which are made into tranquillisers or sedatives. Henbane can also be used to stop coughing fits and, as an ointment, it is used to relieve rheumatism and ear aches.

Taken internally it is used to relieve nervous disorders and stomach ulcers. Henbane should never be taken as a house-hold remedy or without medical supervision since the effects can be deadly. Since it is so valuable a source of important drugs, the plant is actually cultivated in some countries.

THORN-APPLE
Datura stramonium L.
Family: *Solanaceae*

This is a smooth or hairy annual up to 2 m. high. The leaves are 5—20 cm. long, stalked, oval to elliptical in shape, with a pointed tip and a broadly toothed margin. They are bright fresh green in colour and emit an unpleasant odour.

The flowers are trumpet-shaped and up to 8 cm. long, with a white or purple corolla and a pale-green, tubular five-angled calyx. There are five stamens. The flowers are tightly folded in bud and close in wet weather; they are usually terminal on the branches and few in number. The flowers open in the evening, emitting an unpleasant odour, and are pollinated by moths. The fruits are up to 5 cm. long and are very spiny, egg-shaped capsules which open by four valves, exposing a number of dark brown kidney-shaped seeds.

The plant flowers between July and October and grows on waste and also cultivated ground and in fact may sometimes be an escape from cultivation. It is never common.

Almost certainly it originated in America, presumably in Florida, Minnesota, Texas and Mexico. From there it spread to other parts of America and was probably brought to Europe in 1577 or even earlier — in 1542 — by the physician to the court of Philip II of Spain, Francesco Hernández.

Today it is found throughout most of the temperate and subtropical parts of the world. It is absent from Iceland, Ireland and Russia. During the 17th and 18th centuries, Thorn-apple was cultivated both as a medicinal and as an ornamental plant.

The leaves and seeds of the plant are used for the manufacture of drugs, since they contain much the same poisonous alkaloids as Deadly Nightshade and Henbane — hyoscyamine, atropine and scopolamine — and have the same effects on the nervous system and also on the iris of the eye. For these reasons the plant is cultivated since it is so essential a raw material in the pharmaceutical industry.

A cultivated species of Thorn-apple which is sometimes double and variously coloured is known as *Datura metel*, which is believed to have originated in South America and which contains a greater percentage of alkaloids.

BLACK NIGHTSHADE
Solanum nigrum L.
Family: *Solanaceae*

This hairy annual grows up to 70 cm. high. The erect or prostrate angular stems bear leaves which are 2.5—7 cm. long. oval, broadly toothed or lobed, and narrowing on to the leaf-stalk. The flowers are white, 5 cm. across, and borne in groups of 5—10 forming loose clusters. The five stamens of Black Nightshade form a cone.

The fruits are ovoid berries, 6—10 mm. across, which are at first green but turn black and shiny when ripe. The numerous seeds are small and ovoid. It flowers between July and October and grows on waste and cultivated ground, including gardens. It is essentially a weed of cultivation. It is found throughout most of the world except in circumpolar regions.

Black Nightshade is a poisonous plant but is not usually lethal even when the berries have been eaten by children, although it produces unpleasant reactions. It contains the alkaloid solanine (which is also found in green potatoes) as well as varying amounts of some of the compounds found in Henbane and Deadly Nightshade.

In some countries the plant is used in the pharmaceutical industry. The leaves were formerly used as a household remedy to make compresses for burns and boils.

196

Solanum nigrum

GREAT PLANTAIN
Plantago major L.
Family: *Plantaginaceae*

This is a familiar and common plant with flat rosettes of oval leaves 10—15 cm. long, conspicuously marked with parallel veins and narrowing into a long stalk. From the middle of each rosette grow several leafless stems, 10—60 cm. high and bearing a long terminal spike of small whitish flowers with parts in fours. The conspicuous anthers are at first lilac, later yellowish brown. The fruits are small rounded capsules which open by a lid and contain 8—16 small seeds. The plant flowers between May and September and grows in rather open habitats including garden lawns, roadsides, farmyards, meadows and cultivated ground. Great Plantain originated in Europe and Central and northern Asia and has been introduced into countries all over the world.

Great Plantain contains tannins and several medicinal compounds, as does Ribwort Plantain. Because of this the plant was formerly used as a herbal remedy — principally using the sap and leaves. The seeds, both of this and other species, swell on contact with water because of the gelatinous nature of the seed coat. They can be used as food for cage birds.

Plantago major

GOOSEGRASS, CLEAVERS
Galium aparine L.
Family: *Rubiaceae*

This annual grows up to 120 cm. long with scrambling spreading and branched four-angular stems and downward-pointing prickles which give it a rough texture. These stems easily break off and — because of the prickles — become attached to clothing and animal fur. The leaves are linear, 1—5 cm. long, with hooked prickles along the margins. They are arranged in whorls along the stems, 6—8 leaves in

Datura stramonium

each whorl. There is a conspicuous main vein; the upper surface may be smooth or bristly.

The flowers are greenish white and are borne in 2—5 flowered, stalked clusters in the leaf axils. The fruits are hooked, bristly capsules which stick to clothing or animal fur and are spread in this way. This explains the species name *aparine*, which comes from the Greek, and means 'to cling'. It flowers between June and October and grows on waste ground, beside roads, in woods, fens and on limestone screes. It is also found on cultivated land and on shingle near the sea.

It is known almost all over Europe, in West, North and Central Asia, including the Himalayas. It has been introduced into most other temperate parts of the world.

The plant contains medicinally active compounds, and extracts from the stems and leaves were once used to bathe and cleanse wounds.

WILD TEASEL
Dipsacus fullonum L. (ssp. *fullonum*)
Family: *Dipsacaceae*

This biennial plant grows up to 2 m. high with erect, spiny or prickly, angled stems that branch above. The basal leaves form a rosette in the first year. The leaves are large (up to 25 cm. long), oblong to elliptical in shape, with an entire margin, and bearing scattered swollen-based prickles. Early in the second season these basal leaves die away. The stem leaves are lance-shaped and borne in opposite pairs which fuse at the base to form a kind of cup, in which water often collects.

The small rose-violet or white flowers are in large cylindrical or ovoid flowerheads. The involucral bracts below the flowerheads are spiny tipped and of unequal lengths, some being longer than the flowerheads. The flowers have a corolla with a long tube (9—11 mm.). The fruit is a nutlet without a pappus. The plant flowers between July and August, preferring low-lying areas and growing on waste ground, rubbish dumps, in rough pastures and in cultivated fields, beside roads and also alongside streams. It is known over almost all of Europe, in the Caucasus and in Asia Minor, in Iran and in North Africa.

The roots were used in the past for kidney disorders. This is the wild form of Teasel; Fuller's Teasel *(D. fullonum* ssp. *sativus)* was formerly cultivated and the dried heads used for combing cloth.

MUSK THISTLE
Carduus nutans L.
Family: *Compositae (Asteraceae)*

This is a biennial (sometimes annual) plant which grows up to 1 m. high. It has sparsely branched spiny-winged stems which carry large nodding flowerheads.

The stem leaves are lance-shaped, deeply pinnately lobed with spiny-tipped segments. The basal leaves are elliptical. All leaves have wavy, spiny margins and sparse hairs. The veins are woolly below. The flowers are reddish-purple and are borne in pendant flowerheads. The flower-stems are without spines or leaves for some distance below the flowerheads. Outer flower bracts are pointed and covered in white cottony hairs; the innermost bracts are papery and erect. All bracts have a spiny tip. The fruits have a long downy-haired pappus.

Musk Thistle flowers between May and September and grows on waste ground, in meadows and cultivated fields, and along roadsides, almost always on limy soils. It is rather variable and is found in Europe from Ireland and Scotland to Denmark and southern parts of Norway, eastwards to Siberia, the Altai mountains, the Caucasus, Asia Minor and southwards to North Africa. It was introduced into North America. It is an aromatic plant that smells of honey and is also slightly musky (hence the common name). It is attractive to a variety of bees, hover-flies and butterflies. The hairy fruits, with their very long pappus, are wind dispersed.

WELTED THISTLE
Carduus acanthoides L.

This biennial plant grows up to 2 m. high and has branched, cottony, winged stems. The wings are lobed and spiny. All leaves are dull green, with weakly spiny margins and cottony hairs beneath. The leaves are lance-shaped, lobed and toothed, and continue down

Galium aparine

the stems as wings. The basal leaves are elliptical. The flowerheads are 1—2 cm. across, spherical, and usually in dense clusters of 3—5 heads. Each flowerhead has an involcure of narrow bracts. Flowers are red-purple or white, and two-lipped.

The plant is often found with *Galium aparine*, *Urtica dioica* and *Poa trivialis*, and flowers from June to September on waste ground, in hedgerows, by the sides of streams, and in damp verges and generally grassy places.

It is widespread in Europe spreading north to Ireland, Scotland, Denmark and Sweden; southwards to Spain, Italy, the Balkans, southern parts of Russia and the Caucasus. It has been widely introduced in other parts of the world.

MUGWORT
Artemisia vulgaris L.
Family: *Compositae*

This perennial grows 60—120 cm. high and has a branched nodular rhizome. It has a faint aromatic scent. It has a rather tufted habit, with a number of erect downy stems which are grooved and angled, and often tinged red.

The basal leaves are short-stalked, lobed and covered in white hairs on the underside. They are pinnately-lobed with toothed segments. The stem leaves are similarly hairy beneath and with translucent main veins. They are stalkless and clasp the stem. The flowers are yellowish to reddish-brown, in heads 2—3 mm. across, which are arranged in sparsely leafy, dense panicles.

The plant flowers between July and September and grows on waste ground, in hedgerows and waysides and in similar rather open habitats. It is a familiar and abundant weed and commonly grows near towns and villages. It is known in most of temperate Europe

Carduus acanthoides

Carduus nutans

Dipsacus fullonum ssp. *fullonum*

and Asia, as well as in North America, where it grows from Mexico to Alaska.

Mugwort is an old medicinal and 'magical' plant and was used to relieve many illnesses, including colds, fever and rheumatism. Some of its uses were based on superstition as, for example, giving preparations from the root in cases of hysteria. The plant was much valued by some primitive groups and used in tribal ceremonies. The Goths were reputed to have used Mugwort in this way, as also did the Californian Indians.

Today the plant is collected for its volatile oils, inulin and quinine-like substances. Herbal teas are made from it, as well as medicines to relieve digestive ailments and stomach cramps. These are also used as a tonic and stimulant. Extracts are sometimes used in brewing.

A related species — Wormwood *(A. absinthium)* — is used to flavour the liqueur known as absinthe and is also used in brewing in place of hops. Another species which is widely grown and used for flavouring and in salads is Tarragon *(A. dracunculus)*. In fact the production of aromatic oils occurs in most species of *Artemisia*.

CHICORY, WILD SUCCORY
Cichorium intybus L.
Family: *Compositae*

This handsome perennial grows up to 120 cm. high and has a short upright rhizome from which grow usually hairy, grooved, branched stems. A basal rosette of stalked, deeply pinnately-lobed leaves appears in the first year and the spreading or upright stems develop in the second year. The upper stem leaves are somewhat toothed, lance-shaped and clasp the stem. The flowerheads are numerous and are 2.5—4 cm. across. They consist entirely of ray florets. These are large, strap-shaped and bright blue (rarely pink or white). The flowerheads open in the early morning and close shortly after mid-day.

The fruits are angled and flat-topped, with a pappus of 1—2 rows of short scales. The plant flowers from June to September and grows by roadsides, on waste ground and in fields. It may be quite common, especially when growing in chalky soils. It is found throughout Europe (with the exception of Iceland), as well as in western Asia and North Africa. It was once extensively cultivated and spread rapidly in a wild form. It was introduced into most other parts of both hemispheres. The cultivated Endive *(C. endiva* ssp. *endiva)* is grown for salad, both blanched and in the green form i. e. Endive.

Chicory roots are roasted and ground to produce commercial Chicory which is added to some blends of coffee, particularly on the Continent. It reduces the cost and strengthens the flavour. Doctor Prosper Alpini, who was also a botanist, was supposed to be the first person to roast the roots to make coffee, in 1600 in. Padua. Dutch farmers cultivated the root for this purpose in 1690, and it became well-known as a coffee substitute in the middle of the 18th century. The first commercial producer of Chicory was the royal gardener Timo von Amstadt from Erfurt. Chicory reached Paris in 1770 and the first Chicory-producing factories were created in the 19th century. During the Napoleonic blockade the cultivation of Chicory was encouraged, since no coffee reached Europe. Chicory is still cultivated in France, Germany, Poland, Hungary, Austria, Holland and Russia. In some parts the boiled roots are eaten as a vegetable. The seed is sometimes added to grass mixtures, particularly on shallow, chalky soils. The resultant plants are beneficial in two ways; the long tap-roots break up the subsoil and the leaves are relished by cattle. The roots were also valued for medicinal purposes; they were crushed and made into a tea, which was taken for stomach upsets and kidney complaints.

TANSY
Chrysanthemum vulgare (L.) Bernh.
Family: *Compositae*

Also known as *Tanacetum vulgare* L. this perennial grows 30—100 cm. high. It is highly aromatic, with a creeping rhizome and many stiffly erect angular stems. The pinnate leaves are 15—24 cm. long, deeply pinnately lobed and divided. They are dark green and the underside is dotted with glands.

The small flowers are yellow and borne in flowerheads which are about 1 cm. across and grouped in dense, flat-topped inflorescences. Ray florets are absent. The fruits are five-ribbed and surmounted by a cup-like pappus.

The plant flowers between July and September and tolerates a variety of habitats. It grows in waste places, by waysides, in hedgerows and in grassy places, also on screes. It is found throughout Europe, although it is said to have been introduced in Ireland and Iceland. It also grows in the Caucasus and in some parts of western Asia.

This is a plant which contains both a yellowish-green, aromatic, bitter-tasting, volatile oil and also a poisonous compound which, in large amounts, causes vomiting, breathlessness, damage to the kidneys and the central nervous system. Despite these drawbacks the plant was used during the Middle Ages as a sedative, and also as a remedy for worms and for rheumatism.

The plant has been widely cultivated for medicinal and culinary use, as it was formerly a valued pot-herb. A related species is the Dalmatian Pyrethrum *(C. cinerariifolium)*, which is widely grown — in many parts of the world — for the production of the insecticide pyrethrum, which is obtained from the dried flowerheads.

During the Middle Ages Tansy was used for making mulled wine, as well as being added to beer instead of hops. Sometimes it was added to meat dishes and the young buds were often used as a substitute for capers. A green dye was produced from the plant.

PINEAPPLE WEED, RAYLESS MAYWEED
Matricaria matricariodes (Less.) Porter
Family: *Compositae*

This annual grows 5—40 cm. high with smooth, erect, much-branched leafy stems. It is strongly aromatic. The pinnate leaves are stalkless, and dissected 2 or 3 times into linear segments. The yellow-green tubular disc florets are crowded together on a hollow cone-shaped axis, and the whole flowerhead is 5—8 mm. across. The fruits have 4 inconspicuous ribs and a pappus which is represented by a shallow rim.

Artemisia vulgaris

Chrysanthemum vulgare

Cichorium intybus

The plant flowers between June and September and is a common plant of waste places, especially where well-trodden. Thus it is found on paths and tracks and also in much-used gateways. The plant probably originated from North East Asia and has since spread throughout Europe, North America, Chile and New Zealand and has become established in most temperate zones.

The Pineapple Weed contains volatile oils which are akin to those of Chamomile *(Chamaemelum nobile)* but which are not of commercial importance. The common name — Pineapple Weed — probably derives from the flowerhead shape rather than from its scent.

PRICKLY LETTUCE
Lactuca serriola L.
Family: *Compositae*

This is a biennial or overwintering herb 30—150 cm. high. It has stiffly erect leafy stems, which are whitish or reddish, and prickly below. All parts of the plant contain a milky latex. The related species *(Lactuca sativa)* is the garden lettuce.

The lower leaves are stalked, oblong and usually deeply lobed. The upper leaves are lance-shaped and clasp the stems. All leaves are stiff and bluish-green, and have stiffly-haired margins and white main veins which are prickly below.

The plant prefers sunny areas and its upper leaves grow with their blades held vertically and in the north-to-south plane. This helps to protect the leaf-blades from excessive sunlight. The plant is therefore termed a 'compass plant'.

The inflorescence is much-branched and is an elongate pyramid in shape. The flowerheads are 11—13 mm. across and closely spaced along the upper ends of the inflorescence axes. The flowers are all ray florets i. e. strap-shaped, and are pale yellow, sometimes tinged mauve. The fruits are small, ribbed and greenish-grey, with a white pappus.

The plant flowers between July and September and grows on sunny often rocky slopes, on uncultivated or waste ground, beside walls, by waysides and even on fixed sand dunes. It is known in Central Europe and the Mediterranean countries, in northern parts of Asia to the Himalayan mountains and the Altai,

in Siberia as well as in North Africa. It was introduced into North America.

The plant is probably native to Britain but is confined to southern England and Wales. In Central Europe it may be found on the steppes, growing with *Artemisia campestris* and *Stipa pennata*.

The mature plant is said to be poisonous but the young plants may be boiled as a vegetable — tasting somewhat like asparagus — or the young leaves used in salads. The fruits contain a considerable amount of oil, although this is of no commercial use.

CANADIAN FLEABANE
Erigeron canadensis (L.) Cronq.
Family: *Compositae*

Formerly known as *Erigeron canadensis*, this annual herb has erect, hairy, very leafy stems and grows 8—100 cm. high. The leaves are lance-shaped and soon wither. The stem leaves are 1—4 cm. long and linear.

The flowers are small and are borne in small heads, 3—5 cm. across, which are numerous and arranged in long spike-like inflorescences. The ray florets are white to lavender, female, and as short as the yellow disc florets, which are bisexual. The downy fruits have a yellowish pappus 1.5 cm. long.

The plant originated in North America and flowers between July and September. It has been introduced into almost every country in the world. It grows on waste ground, by waysides, on walls and in cultivated fields, especially on sandy soils. It is said to have reached Europe during the 17th century.

This is a medicinal plant and Oil of Erigeron is obtained from it. This oil increases the number of white blood cells. Herbal teas were formerly made from the plant and were used for kidney complaints and intestinal disorders. The plant is not common in Britain.

LESSER BURDOCK
Arctium minus Bernh.
Family: *Compositae*

This is a biennial plant of variable habit up to 1 m. high. A basal leaf rosette is formed in the first year

Lactuca serriola

from which grow much-branched, woolly-haired, grooved stems.

These leaves are broadly oval to heart-shaped, with hollow stalks. They are somewhat toothed and covered in grey, felt-like hairs on the underside. They grow up to 30 cm. long, with the smaller leaves higher up the stems. They function as bracts towards the upper part of the stem.

The flowerheads are between 1.5 and 3 cm. across with reddish-purple flowers. These flowerheads are short-stalked, egg-shaped and borne in spike-like clusters.

The flowers are all disc florets, tubular, and surrounded by involucral bracts with stiff, spreading, hooked tips. These, if they become entangled in clothing or animal fur, distribute the fruits. The fruits have a pappus but are not distributed separately. The plant flowers between July and September and grows on waste ground, along roadsides and on hedgebanks, at the edges of woods and in clearings and also in scrub. It grows in most of Europe, up to 65° north in Scandinavia, also in the Caucasus and in North Africa. It is totally absent from southern Europe, and in the Balkans is confined to hilly regions. It has become naturalised in North America.

This was formerly a medicinal plant. Its roots contain volatile oils, up to 40 % of the carbohydrate inulin, and a range of medicinally active compounds. The fruits contain up to 30 % oil as a food reserve.

The plant is rarely collected nowadays but a related species — Great Burdock *(Arctium lappa)* — is still used. The Great Burdock is collected for its leaves and roots, which are made up into preparations for the skin and hair and which are also applied to sores and festering wounds. It is a larger plant altogether than the Lesser Burdock; the leaves are broader — with solid stalks — and the flowerheads are globular rather than egg-shaped.

Arctium minus

Matricaria matricariodes

203

WOOLLY BURDOCK
Arctium tomentosum Mill.

This plant is similar to those already described on the previous page. The involucres of the flowerheads are white and cottony, and the bracts have no hooks. The flowerheads are in globular clusters. The plant is a Continental species and does not grow naturally in Britain.

GREAT BURDOCK
Arctium lappa L.

Some details of this plant have already been given under the Lesser Burdock entry. In Britain it is the commonest species of *Arctium* and is quite a familiar waste ground and wayside plant.

GALLANT SOLDIER
Galinsoga parviflora Cav.
Family: *Compositae*

This is an annual herb growing 10—75 cm. high. The stems are much-branched, with opposite leaves which are oval and pointed. The flowerheads are small (3—5 mm. in diameter) and borne in few-flowered clusters. Each flowerhead has 4—8 white female ray florets and a few yellow disc florets. The fruits of the disc florets are oval-shaped, black and covered with short white bristles. The fruits of the ray florets are flattened and bristly above. Both have a pappus of scales.
The plant flowers between May and October. The plant originated in South America, where it was regarded as an unwelcome weed, and from there it spread across the whole world. It entered Europe during the 18th century and is thought to have escaped from a botanical garden in Paris. From there it rapidly invaded waste ground, gardens and cultivated fields. In London, in World War II, it became temporarily abundant on bomb-sites.

SHAGGY SOLDIER
Galinsoga ciliata (Raf.) Blake

This species originated in Central America. It is dark green and covered in white hairs and often hybridises with *Galinsoga parviflora* which at first glance it closely resembles.

PALE GLOBE THISTLE
Echinops sphaerocephalus L.
Family: *Compositae*

This is a thistle-like herb 5—2 m. high. The leaves are stalked, lance-shaped and deeply pinnately-lobed. They have strongly spiny-toothed margins and also end in a strong spine. All leaves are covered in white, felt-like hairs below and are densely glandular above. The pale blue or whitish flowers are in rounded flowerheads which are long-stalked and 4—6 cm. across. The florets are tubular-shaped and have blue-grey anthers. The flowerheads are really compound, consisting of a number of one-flowered flowerheads. Flowering is from June to September. The plant grows on waste ground, in quarries and in other dry stony places. In Britain it is a common garden plant, which sometimes escapes.
It prefers a warm climate and has spread from the Mediterranean right across Europe and is known in France, Belgium, Denmark and Germany, as well as in Central and southern parts of Russia, Siberia and the Caucasus.

ANNUAL MEADOW-GRASS
Poa annua L.
Family: *Gramineae*

This is an annual (sometimes a short-lived perennial) tufted, spreading or erect grass, 5—30 cm. high. The spreading stems sometimes root at the nodes. The leaves are smooth and flat, often with transverse wrinkles. They are slightly keeled and pointed. The spikelets are 3—5 cm. long, of 3—5 florets, and borne in a spreading or compact, much-branched pyramidal inflorescence.
This grass is a weed which flowers almost all the year round. It grows beside roads, in gardens, on waste ground, in fields and grassland, in damp places or dry, in lowland and mountainous areas. It is found throughout almost the whole world, but in tropical regions it is restricted to the mountains.

Galinsoga parviflora

Echinops sphaerocephalus

Poa annua

Bromus sterilis

BARREN BROME
Bromus sterilis (L.) Nevski
Family: *Gramineae*

Also known as *Anisantha sterilis* L. this is an extremely common annual grass. It has erect or semi-prostrate stems 30—100 cm. high and soft, flat, downy leaves. The lowest leaves soon wither. The stems bear drooping inflorescences 10—15 cm. long which are simple or slightly branched. The spikelets are flattened, 2—2.5 cm. long, with awns about 2 cm long, and are borne on long stalks which are rough to the touch. The florets have bracts 1.5—2 cm. long.

The genus *Bromus* has been considerably revised and so the number of species is in some dispute. Probably there are 65—90 species growing in temperate regions, of which about 16—20 species are British.

Bromus sterilis is native to Britain and grows in waste places and along waysides, but is also a very common garden weed. It grows in much of Europe, especially in western Europe; as well as in the Mediterranean region as far east as Iran. It also grows in North America, where it was introduced.

The genus *Bromus* formerly included grasses now grouped as species of *Zerna*, *Anisantha* and *Ceratochloa*. The differences between them include such features as an annual or perennial habit, the shape of the spikelets and small differences in the length of the awns and the size and shape of the bracts associated with the florets. Like the Barren Brome, many of the species are grasses of waste places. Some species, again like the Barren Brome, are native but others are introduced and scattered in distribution throughout the greater part of Britain. For example the Drooping Brome (*Anisantha tectorum* (L.) Nerski) grows in a variety of sandy places. It is however a native of Central and western Europe, and of Mediterranean countries as far east as Iran, and also in western parts of Siberia.

Hordeum murinum

WALL BARLEY
Hordeum murinum L.
Family: *Gramineae*

This is a rather yellowish annual which grows 20—60 cm. high. The spreading stems bear flat hairy leaves and the uppermost leaf almost reaches the spikelets.

The inflorescence is a compressed spike 4—10 cm. long, and is made up of a number of spikelets clustered together in threes. The central spikelet is bisexual, with bracts which are lance-shaped and hairy and which bear long awns — the awn of the innermost bract is 2—5 cm. long. The lateral spikes are sterile or have 2 male florets. The awns stick to animal fur, or to clothing, and the fruits are dispersed in this way. The grass flowers between May and August and grows in waste places (especially near the sea), along roadsides and on dry ground generally.

It is known in Central and southern Europe, northwards up to southern parts of Sweden, in North Africa, western parts of Asia and in North America.

WOODLAND
PLANTS

INTRODUCTION

In many parts of the world the natural vegetation would be woodland if the plants were allowed to grow without interference by man. Sub-arctic and high mountain regions, deserts, coastal areas and dry grasslands are the only habitats where trees are not found.

The actual species of trees present are controlled by various factors including geographical location, climatic conditions (especially temperature and rainfall), altitude and the composition of the soil.

In tropical zones (which are damp and hot) jungles are found and in monsoon areas tropical rain forests grow. Beside muddy, swampy and flooded rivers grow mangroves (evergreen trees with characteristic aerating and also supporting roots). Subtropical jungles are found in zones which have a drier climate, together with temperatures which swing between extremes in summer and winter.

In the northern temperate zones we find different types of forest and woodland typical of various regions. For example, pine woods occur in the most northerly regions towards the plains of the tundra. Other evergreen coniferous trees grow mainly in Europe but also in North America, sometimes in pure stands but often together with numerous deciduous trees. Siberia in particular, has vast areas covered by a number of species of both coniferous and deciduous trees and also shrubs.

In more central areas of the northern temperate zone deciduous woods are typical. For example oak and beech woods are common in Europe whilst other varieties of trees are found in America, China and Japan. In areas which have long hot summers the tree cover gives way to evergreen shrubs as in the maquis of Mediterranean countries but in damper regions of the Mediterranean grow species of oak, olive and laurel. In the western hemisphere grow firs, spruce and hemlock; the famous redwood coniferous trees also grow in America.

The composition of woods is noticeably influenced by altitude. In the northern temperate zone — particularly in Europe — deciduous trees such as ash and alder, willows and poplars grow in low-lying areas, whereas oak and beech grow in more hilly parts and spruce, pines and other conifers grow in mountainous areas.

At some distance below any mountain summit is a tree-line above which trees do not grow. Their place is taken by shrubs and the more resistant herbaceous plants and, nearer the summit, lichens.

Man has greatly influenced the composition of woods since he cultivates only those trees which are of most use to him. Because of this, instead of mixed natural woodland, man grows plantations of a limited number or even of a single species.

A special feature of most natural woodland is the layering formed by various species according to light, rainfall and soil composition. Thus we can distinguish the tree layer, the shrub layer and the ground layer, and the more natural the woodland, the easier it is to see these layers. The greatest range of species is found in the ground layer with lichens, fungi and mosses, as well as flowering plants. Each type of woodland has a particular composition of plants growing within it. Deciduous woods have an especially rich variety of species, the majority of these plants preferring damp, shady conditions. Coniferous woods have far fewer species chiefly because of the reduced amount of light and also because of the acid and virtually undecomposed leaf litter. In deciduous and mixed woods, plants are adapted to flower and ripen their seed early in spring, before the trees are fully in leaf. This applies chiefly to those plants which require light and sunshine. Others which prefer shady and damp places will flower and set seed much later.

Woods obviously provide a shaded environment and competition seems to be characteristic of all plants that grow there. They compete for space, light, water and soil nutrients. These nutrients are constantly replenished by the deposits of dead leaves and plants. Below ground, root systems compete for space with each other. The roots of many plants, especially those of trees, form beneficial symbiotic associations (mycorrhiza) with fungal hyphae, and this aids absorption of nutrients.

In places where woods have been destroyed by man or by natural forces, the variety of plant life changes considerably, since the shrubs and herbs become exposed to sun and wind, and water is less easily retained in the soil. Those plants that need damp shady conditions therefore tend to disappear, being replaced by other more resistant species; eventually a very different vegetation appears, which remains until the area is reafforested.

Except in late summer and autumn, the majority of woodland fungi are not obvious since their hyphae (absorbing filaments) grow buried in the humus layer. Their fruit-bodies are conspicuous but usually short-lived. An exception is shown by the woody 'plates', sometimes reaching 30 cm. or more across, which are developed by 'bracket fungi'. A selection of woodland fungi follows.

CORAL FUNGUS
Ramaria formosa Fr.
Family: *Clavariaceae*

This fungus has a branching white stalk (stipe) with rosy or orange coloured branches with lemon-yellow tips. It is fleshy and grows 10—25 cm. high and up to 15 cm. across.
It appears between July and November in clumps, and grows in humus in deciduous woods in northern temperate zones. This is not an edible mushroom. It is poisonous and the flesh tastes bitter if cooked.

Ramaria botrytis Fr.

This species is very fleshy and is at first white, but the stipe later becomes yellowish-brown. It is much-branched with numerous red to purplish tips. The flesh is brittle but juicy and has a rather fruity smell. The flavour is mild but may become bitter as the fungus grows older.
Ramaria botrytis grows 5—10 (sometimes 15) cm. high and up to 20 cm. broad and appears in August to November. It grows in acid humus in deciduous woods in all parts of the northern temperate zone, and also sometimes in North America.
It is edible but it is advisable to remove the bitter-tasting ends.

YELLOW CORAL FUNGUS
Ramaria flava Sch.
Family: *Boletaceae*

Also known as *Clavaria flava*, this species has a thick whitish stipe and many sulphur-yellow branches.

YELLOW RING BOLETUS
Boletus elegans Snell.
Family: *Boletaceae*

This fungus has a golden-yellow to orange or yellow-brown cap. The cap is 5—15 cm. across, flat or domed, and slimy. As in all species of Boletus there are no gills on the underside of the cap. Instead there are pores leading into tubes.
When young both stalk and cap are covered in a yellow membrane — the volva — which tears loose with growth and remains as a dried ring (annulus) round the stalk. The pores on the underside of the cap are yellowish or greyish-yellow. The lemon-yellow flesh turns pinkish-lilac when the fungus is cut. It has a pleasant smell and taste.
The stalk of this fungus is up to 12 cm. high and is usually brownish at the base. *Boletus elegans* grows only under or near larch trees (i. e. as far as the tree roots spread) because of a mycorrhizal association between the two plants. It grows in Europe and in North America, appearing between March and November. This is an edible fungus with a good flavour, but before cooking, the skin of the cap should be removed.

Ramaria formosa

Ramaria botrytis

Boletus elegans

Ramaria flava

BROWN-RING BOLETUS
Boletus luteus L.

The cap of this species is also slimy and is chocolate or yellowish-brown with a tinge of purple. It grows 5—10 cm. across. When young the cap and stalk are covered in a white membrane which later tears loose and forms a ring round the stalk. The pores on the underside of the cap are golden yellow at first, but later become brownish. The stipe is white below, and yellowish with dark spots above the ring.
The flesh is white when young, later becoming pale yellow. It is pleasantly scented and of excellent flavour. *Boletus luteus* takes its common name from the ring on the stipe which changes from white to purplish-brown with age.
This fungus grows in coniferous woods usually in grass. It is found in lowland and upland regions and is known all over the northern temperate zone. This is an edible fungus with an almost fruity flavour. The skin and pores of Brown-ring Boletus should be removed before cooking.

RED-FOOT BOLETUS
Boletus chrysenteron Dill. ex Fr.

This species has a domed cap 4—10 cm. wide which is dark brown or olive and, in young specimens, is smooth. Later it develops fine cracks and then has a reddish tint.
The skin is always dry and dull — never slimy — and is not easily removed. The pores are at first yellow, later turning olive, and becoming greenish when bruised.
It has a rather slender stalk which is yellowish-brown and may be tinged with red above. The young flesh is whitish or yellowish except just below the skin of the cap, where it is a dull red; it changes to reddish-buff with age, but turns pale blue when cut or bruised. It grows mostly in deciduous woods between August and November and is known in most parts of the northern temperate zone.
This is an edible species but of indifferent flavour. A very similar species is *Boletus rubellus* which differs only from *Boletus chrysenteron* in having a red or reddish-purple cap.

CHESTNUT BOLETUS
Boletus badius Dill. ex Fr.

This species has a fleshy chestnut-brown or reddish-brown cap 5—15 cm. across. Both cap and stalk are downy when young but later become smooth and shiny. During damp weather the cap turns slimy.
The pores are first whitish, later turning yellow or yellowish-green but, when bruised, they become bluish-green. The stalk is at first rather thin and never becomes swollen. It is pale brown — lighter in colour than the cap — and with slight vertical ridges. The flesh is whitish and hard, later becoming yellowish and soft as it matures, and turning blue if bruised.
It grows between August and November in all types of wood but chiefly in coniferous woods. It is a species known all over the northern temperate zone.
B. badius is edible and has a very pleasant flavour.

Boletus aurantiacus (Bull.) Roques

This species has a rather striking brownish-orange or red cap, 8—15 cm. across, and with a dry, downy skin. The cap is at first hemispherical but later becomes convex and rather thin at the edges. The pores on the underside are whitish and minute in size.
The stalk is sturdy, becoming more slender later, and covered in conspicuous light to dark brown scales. The flesh of both cap and stalk turns slate-blue or brownish-black when bruised or cut. Although the flesh turns almost black when prepared, it is favourably regarded since the flavour is good and the flesh is rarely maggot-infested.
This handsome fungus grows in August to November in deciduous woods and in particular under birch and aspen. It grows virtually all over the northern temperate zone but not in Britain.

Boletus scaber (Bull. ex Fr.) S. F. Gray

This species has a smooth (sometimes slightly wrinkled) dome shaped cap, 6—20 cm. across, which is brownish-grey or dark brown. The cap is firm and downy when young, becoming soft and slightly sticky as it matures. The pores on the underside of the cap are whitish or greyish-brown. The long stalk

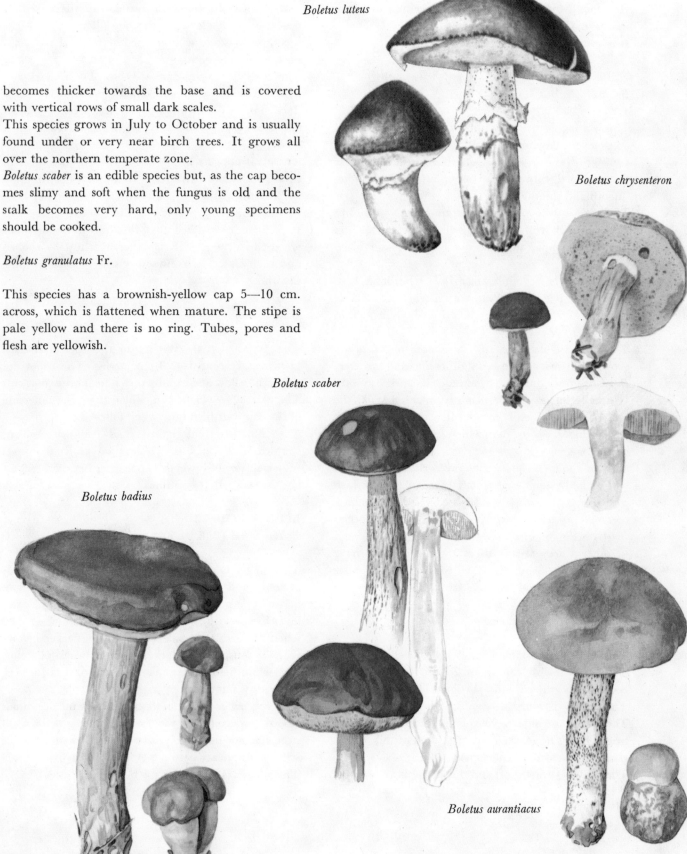

Boletus luteus

becomes thicker towards the base and is covered with vertical rows of small dark scales.

This species grows in July to October and is usually found under or very near birch trees. It grows all over the northern temperate zone.

Boletus scaber is an edible species but, as the cap becomes slimy and soft when the fungus is old and the stalk becomes very hard, only young specimens should be cooked.

Boletus granulatus Fr.

This species has a brownish-yellow cap 5—10 cm. across, which is flattened when mature. The stipe is pale yellow and there is no ring. Tubes, pores and flesh are yellowish.

Boletus chrysenteron

Boletus scaber

Boletus badius

Boletus aurantiacus

It is found from August to November and grows in woods under conifer trees.

It is edible and has a good flavour.

CÈPE
Boletus edulis Bull. ex Fr.

This is a highly regarded species of *Boletus* since it has an excellent flavour. The firm but fleshy cap is 5—25 cm. across and light or dark brown in colour. It is dome-shaped, slimy when young, but later becoming smooth and shining.

The pores of the young fungus are at first white but later turn yellowish-green. The flesh is white, slightly tinged with pink, and does not change colour when broken.

The stalk is short and thick. It is whitish at first, later becoming pale brown, with a white network of slightly raised veins. The whole fruit-body is rich in vitamin D.

The species is variable, with a number of subspecies growing in association with different kinds of tree. *B. edulis* grows during late summer in Spruce woods. It usually has a white or slightly coloured stalk, the upper part of which is covered in a network of veins. In deciduous woods, particularly underneath or near oak trees grows *Boletus edulis* ssp. *reticulatus* — obviously in a more or less specific mycorrhizal association with oak. In coniferous woods (particularly beneath pine trees), grows *Boletus edulis* ssp. *pinicola*, sometimes regarded as a separate species. Another subspecies *Boletus edulis* ssp. *aureus* grows in southern Europe and in other warm areas. All of these subspecies have a rich nutty flavour, whether cooked fresh or after drying.

Boletus luridus Schaeft. ex Fr.

This rather uncommon species has a fleshy light olive to yellowish cap about 20 cm. across. This is occasionally tinged red, particularly at the edges. The fungus is at first downy, later becoming smooth. The pores are olive yellow, later turning orange or bright red. The marked red coloration of this species gives it the specific name *luridus*.

The stalk is at first short and thick, and later becomes club-shaped. In colour it varies from dark red at the base to yellow at the top. This species has a conspicuous and wide-meshed network of red veins on the surface.

The flesh is mainly apricot-yellow but is dark red at the base of the tubes. When cut it quickly turns dark blue — sometimes with red patches. *Boletus luridus* has a pleasant odour, and a good flavour when cooked.

The plant appears between August and November in deciduous woods in warmer areas. It is not common in Britain although it is known all over the northern temperate zone.

It is sometimes stated that this fungus is poisonous when eaten raw. Since, however, it is usually cooked and then eaten, its poisonous properties are in some doubt.

Boletus erythropus (Fr. ex Fr.) Pers.

The dry, fleshy, downy cap of this species is dark brown and grows 5—20 cm. across. The tubes are greenish-yellow and rapidly turn blue if bruised or cut. The pores are blood-red, colouring the underside of the cap, but turn blue when touched.

The stalk is club-shaped and yellowish-brown, stippled with red dots. This species grows in woods (especially conifer woods) appearing between August and November. It is edible.

BITTER BOLETUS
Boletus felleus (Bull. ex Fr.) Karst.

This fungus is also known as *Tylopilus felleus* and has a fleshy and slightly velvety brown cap 5—12 cm. across. The pores are at first white turning pink later and have pinkish-fawn spores. The stalk is club-shaped when mature. It is pale olive-brown (darker below) with a conspicuous dark brown network of veins. The white flesh turns pink when cut and tastes very bitter; it is odourless.

This species grows in both coniferous and deciduous woods (especially in the former) and is known all over the northern temperate zone. Like most other species it appears between August and November.

This fungus is not poisonous but is very bitter.

216

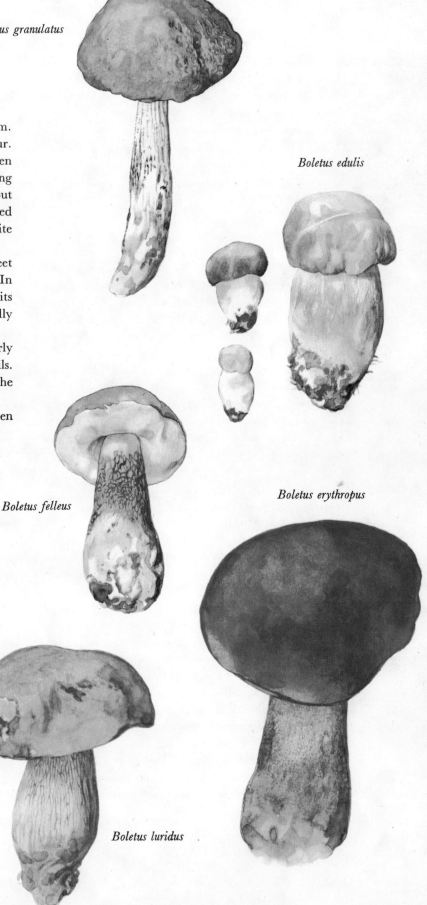

Boletus granulatus

Boletus edulis

Boletus satanas Lenz

This fungus has a very fleshy cap, about 15 cm. across, which is dry and light greyish-green in colour. The tubes are yellowish-green (turning blue when cut) and the pores are purplish-red, also turning blue when cut. The stalk is swollen and reddish, but becomes paler at the top and base. A network of red veins covers the top of the stalk. The flesh is white but turns pale blue when cut.

Young specimens smell pleasant and taste sweet but older ones have a very unpleasant odour. In Britain it is not a common species and, despite its specific name *satanus*, is not one of the more deadly fungi, although it is poisonous.

It grows in warm deciduous woods particularly amongst oak and beech trees on calcareous soils. It appears in July to September and is thus one of the earlier species.

This is a fungus which is more poisonous when eaten

Boletus erythropus

Boletus felleus

Boletus satanas

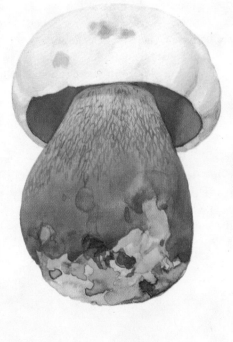

Boletus luridus

raw and it can cause continuous vomiting and diarr-hoea. The poisonous substances in it have not been completely identified and, although it is known that some of the poison disappears when the fungus is cooked, it is not advisable to collect it despite its attractive appearance.

Boletus is a large-and easily recognisable genus with a cap-and-stalk form combined with pores instead of gills.

CHANTERELLE
Cantharellus cibarius Fr.
Family: *Cantharellaceae*

The Chanterelle is one of the most highly regarded edible fungi and is rich in vitamins A and D. It is funnel-shaped and golden-yellow in colour, the stipe being about 5 cm. long and the cap 3—10 cm. across, with a markedly wavy margin. The lower surface is folded and resembles gills.

The Chanterelle grows from July to October in both coniferous and deciduous woods, usually in large clusters. It is known all over the northern temperate zone for its pale yellow flesh, which smells faintly of apricots, and which tastes slightly peppery when cooked.

SAFFRON MILK-CAP
Lactarius deliciosus (L. ex Fr.) S. F. Fray
Family: *Agaricaceae*

This fungus has a cap 4—10 cm. across, orange or yellowish-pink in colour, with concentric darker (mainly greenish) zones.

Young fungi have flat caps, but those more mature have caps with a depressed centre and an incurved margin. Chacteristic of the genus is the 'milk' which is exuded when the flesh is broken or cut. It is at first yellow and tasteless but quickly turns deep orange and develops an acrid flavour. The gills and stipe have the same colour as the cap and all become greenish when bruised. The whitish flesh is soft and, when cooked, is tender to eat.

Despite the name *deliciosus* this species of *Lactarius*, although edible, has a somewhat unpleasant flavour. It is said to be improved by first washing well in water.

It grows from August to October in damp soil in woods and is known all over the northern temperate zone.

Lactarius volemus Fr.

This species has a cap 7—11 cm. across, depressed in the centre, and bright tawny-orange in colour. The gills are cream coloured. The fungus exudes an abundance of white 'milk' when broken or cut and which becomes grey when exposed to the air. The stalk is the same colour as the cap, except for a lighter zone just below the cap.

The flesh is pale yellow and somewhat tough. When the fungus is young the flesh tastes sweet, but it smells and tastes fishy when old. It is edible but is an acquired taste. It grows in mixed woods appearing in August to October.

Russula virescens
Family: *Agaricaceae*

This fungus has a dry, very firm verdigris-green cap 7—15 cm. across. The cap has a warty skin which becomes brittle and cracked, exposing the white flesh. The cap is at first rounded but soon becomes flattened and paler in colour, with brownish-green or yellowish-brown spots. The stalk is short and thick, tapering towards the base, with spongy white flesh within.

The gills are white, narrow and crowded. The white flesh of the cap is firm and mild in flavour. The fungus is edible and has a pleasant taste when cooked. It appears between August and October.

Russula virescens grows in light deciduous woods, especially beech, and is quite a common European fungus.

Russula vesca Fr.

This species has a slightly hollow cap 4—10 cm. across and varying in colour between brownish-red and pinkish-buff. The stalk is white but slightly rust-coloured at the base. When the fungus is cut or broken it colours yellowish-brown.

The gills are narrow, crowded and white — often

Cantharellus cibarius

with rust-brown spots. The margin of the cap is often withdrawn, exposing the flesh above the gills. The firm white, slightly aromatic flesh has a nutty flavour. It is sometimes marked by rust-brown spots.

This is an excellent edible fungus appearing in deciduous woods, especially oak, from August to October.

Russula cyanoxantha Schaeft. ex Schw.

This species of *Russula* has a rather flattened cap 5—12 cm. across which is violet to green in colour, often becoming paler as it matures. There are usually faint radial veins and the cap becomes rather slimy when wet. The margin is slightly inrolled. The flesh is firm, white and odourless.

The gills are soft and white, very thin and elastic and rather greasy to the touch. The stalk is thick and white, flushed purple, and becomes hollow with age.

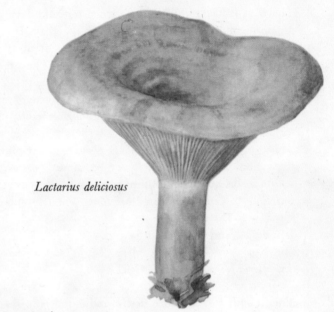

Lactarius deliciosus

Russula virescens

Russula vesca

Lactarius volemus

Russula cyanoxantha appears between July and November. It grows in deciduous woods all over the temperate zone and may be found particularly in beech woods.

This is an edible fungus which can be used to prepare many dishes and is of excellent flavour.

YELLOW-KNIGHT FUNGUS
Tricholoma flavovirens Pers. ex Fr.
Family: *Agaricaceae*

This fungus has a somewhat flattened but undulating greenish-yellow cap about 5—10 cm. across. It is rather irregular in outline and is often split at the margin. The surface is smooth and silky. The gills are sulphur-yellow; the smooth stalk is stout and pale yellow, but is sometimes tinged brown. The whitish or pale yellow flesh is firm with a characteristic slightly mealy odour.

This fungus usually grows in large clusters under pine trees, and prefers sandy soils. It has a rather short season in Britain appearing in August and September but on the Continent can be found — even under snow — in December.

It is edible and has a good flavour.

Tricholoma portentosum (Fr.) Quél.

This fungus has a rather fleshy undulating cap 6—12 cm. across, which is at first rounded but later is flat. The cap, when mature, is grey with greenish, brownish or violet tints and fine black radiating veins. The centre (which may be depressed) is almost black.

The gills are at first white but later become pale yellow. The stalk is stout and can be up to 15 cm. long. It is white or grey (sometimes tinged with sulphur-yellow) and shiny. The flesh of *Tricholoma portenosum* is firm and white (sometimes grey) and virtually without taste or odour.

This fungus grows in pine woods, preferring sandy soils, and is known all over the northern temperate zone. It appears in large numbers in autumn and can sometimes still be found after the first frosts in November. It is an edible fungus but with no specially marked flavour.

220

HONEY FUNGUS, HONEY AGARIC
Armillaria mellea (Fr.) Kummer
Family: *Agaricaceae*

This fungus is usually found in large tufts. The cap is honey-coloured or brown, between 4 and 15 cm. across, and covered in hairy dark brown scales which are denser towards the centre of the cap.

Young fungi have a membrane connecting the cap with the stalk and covering the gills completely i. e. the *velum*. In mature specimens of the Honey Agaric this forms a ring around the stalk. The stalk is often bulbous below, yellowish or whitish and, towards the base, it is frequently mottled with a yellow, olive or black down.

Towards the top, the stalk has the ring which has already been mentioned. This ring is whitish with yellow flecks. The arched gills are first whitish, becoming pale brownish — yellow, and often with dark spots later. Older specimens have gills which are covered in a whitish powder — these are the cream spores.

The flesh is whitish with a faint slightly unpleasant odour, and a bitter taste if eaten fresh. This species usually forms large colonies and is a highly destructive parasite growing on the trunks and roots of trees, and on tree stumps.

The Honey Agaric grows on both deciduous and coniferous trees and is known all over the northern temperate zone as well as in Australia. It appears between July and December.

The Honey Agaric attacks the inside of tree trunks and causes extensive damage. It forms dark root-like cords at the base of the trunk, which grow through the wood and often below the bark of both living and also dead trees. These so-called rhizomorphs can grow to several metres in length. They absorb and store nourishment for the growing fungus and also serve to increase its spread. This is in addition to its spread by spores. Both mycelium and rhizomorphs are phosphorescent and wood which has been attacked will glow in the dark.

This is an edible fungus but is not popular since its flavour is rather indifferent. Mostly the young plants are eaten. Cooking will eliminate the unpleasant taste of the fresh fungus.

FLY AGARIC
Amanita muscaria (L. ex Fr.) Hook.
Family: *Agaricaceae*

The Fly Agaric is a handsome fungus, at first egg-shaped, then developing a broad cap 6—20 cm. across. This is scarlet or orange-red with white warts or patches — the remnants of a membrane which entirely covers the young fungus and known as the *volva*. Older specimens lack these patches as they are easily rubbed or washed off.

The gills are white (sometimes yellowish) and are crowded. The stalk is white with a bulbous base which has several concentric warty rings. These too are the remains of the enveloping membrane. Just below the cap, around the stalk, is a pendant white or yellowish ring which, when young, covered the gills. The flesh is white (yellow just below the skin), almost odourless and is said to have a pleasant flavour, although it is poisonous and should not be eaten.

The Fly Agaric grows under pine and birch trees, usually on poor soils, and is found all over Europe, the northern parts of Asia, North America and Australia. The shape and the conspicuously red cap became a symbol of toadstools in woods and it was thus used in many stories as well as becoming a toadstool symbol in many paintings. This identification of the Fly Agaric with all toadstools, led to its being associated with all deadly poisonous toadstools, and also with death and magic. In fact, although it is poisonous,

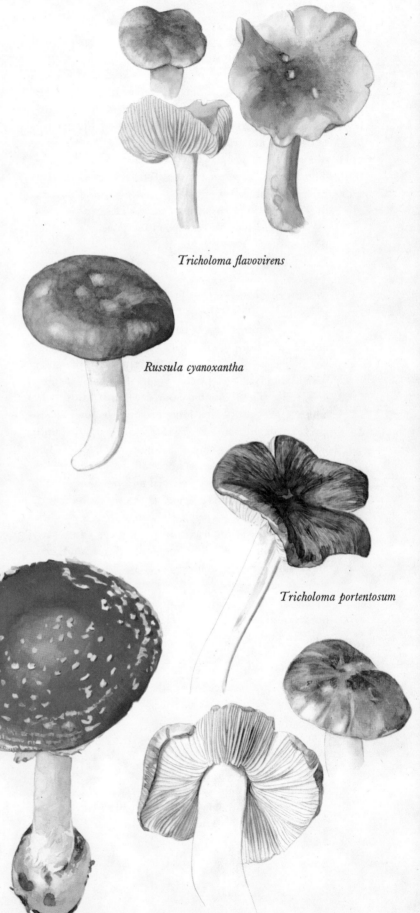

Tricholoma flavovirens

Russula cyanoxantha

Tricholoma portentosum

Armillaria mellea

Amanita muscaria

it contains only the poisonous alkaloid muscarine (and only 0.002 %) and so is rarely fatal.

In some areas the fungus is collected and its less poisonous stalk eaten. The poisonous substances of the fungus affect the nervous system and lead to an intoxication similar to that of alcohol. Some country people make an intoxicating drink from Fly Agaric juice mixed with that of several other plants.

The fungus, as its name suggests, has been used to kill flies. The cap was placed on a plate and covered in sugar in order to attract flies which then not only ate the sugar, but also absorbed the juice and so were poisoned.

THE BLUSHER
Amanita rubescens (Pers. ex Fr.) S. F. Gray

The cap of this fungus is between 6 and 12 cm. across and is reddish-brown with small dirty white or red-tinged patches. These are the remains of the volva which totally envelops the young fungus. The gills are at first pure white but later develop reddish spots. The white stalk (which later becomes hollow) thickens towards the base into a white or reddish-hued bulb which is covered by several rows of warty scales. The ring at the upper part of the stalk is usually tinged red, rarely white, and is grooved and pendant.

All parts of the fungus, including the white flesh, turn red when bruised — hence the common name — the Blusher. It tastes unpleasantly sweet when eaten raw, and may cause an irritation in the throat and may also result in indigestion.

Amanita rubescens grows in large clumps in both coniferous and deciduous woods and is known all over the northern temperate zone. It appears between July and November.

This fungus is edible when cooked, but caution is advisable when collecting this species, since it is very similar to other related and extremely poisonous species.

FALSE DEATH CAP
Amanita citrina (Schaeff. ex Fr.) S. F. Gray

The cap of this fungus is 5 to 9 cm. across, greenish-yellow to bright yellow, sometimes pale white (when it is the variety *alba*). The cap becomes sticky when damp and is covered in fairly large irregular white patches which are the remains of the original enveloping volva.

The gills are white and crowded. The stalk is thin with a soft round bulb at the base which is surrounded by a collar-like membrane — the basal remains of the volva. The upper part of the stalk has a thin pale yellow, rather flared ring. The white flesh of False Death Cap smells of raw potatoes and tastes unpleasant.

The fungus appears from July to November usually in deciduous woods, less often in coniferous woods. It prefers calcareous soils and is particularly associated with oak and beech trees. It grows all over the northern temperate zone.

This is a common species of *Amanita* and was formerly known as *A. mappa*. It was thought to be poisonous but this is not so, although it smells and tastes disagreeable.

FALSE BLUSHER, PANTHER
Amanita pantherina (DC. ex Fr.) Kromeh.

The cap of this fungus is between 5 and 8 cm. across, greyish-brown with an olive tinge. The centre of the cap is usually very dark and the margin has narrow ridges. The white remains of the volva cover the cap in warts which are easily rubbed off. The white gills are crowded.

The slim stalk is white, smooth and silky and forms a basal bulb. Above this are 2 concentric rings which are the basal remnants of the volva. The upper part of the stalk has a smooth drooping ring. Both the stipe and the flesh are white, and neither changes colour when bruised. The raw flesh has no marked taste or odour.

This poisonous fungus grows between August and October, mostly in deciduous woods (rarely in coniferous woods) and usually in association with beech trees. It grows all over the northern temperate zone including Asia and North America.

Amanita pantherina is extremely poisonous and has been known to cause deaths, possibly because it may be confused with the harmless *A. rubescens* and eaten by mistake.

222

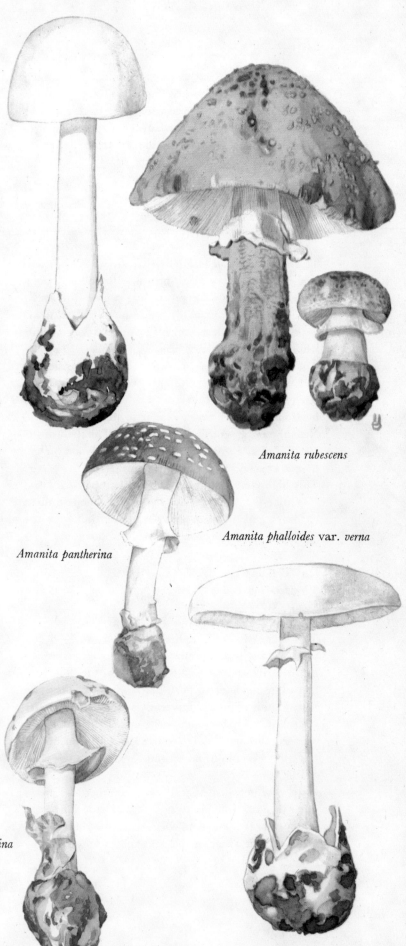

Amanita phalloides

DEATH CAP
Amanita phalloides (Vaill. ex Fr.) Secr.

This dramatically named fungus has a flat, rather fleshy, yellowish or brownish-green cap between 5 and 15 cm. across. The cap is slightly slimy and faintly streaked with dark fibrils. Although it develops within a volva, it lacks the warty remnants found in several other species. The gills are white and crowded.

The stalk is soft at the base and forms a large bulb which is usually beneath the ground and is covered by a white irregularly lobed thin membrane — the remains of the volva. The stalk is at first white, later becoming green or pale grey, and is dotted with irregularly shaped scales. Towards the top of the stalk is a white or yellowish frilled ring — the remains of a velum (the membrane covering the gills). The flesh is white but beneath the skin of the cap it is often yellowish-green. It emits a faint but nauseating odour when mature.

This fungus is deadly and well deserves the name of Death Cap. It appears between July and October in deciduous woods, especially of beech or oak. It is found in the northern temperate zone and in northern parts of Asia. It is often confused with other fungi which are edible and this can lead to fatal accidents. *Amanita phalloides* and the all-white Destroying Angel *A. virosa* are together responsible for nearly all fungal deaths. The Death Cap contains the poison (amanitine) which affects the heart, liver and kidneys.

Another poisonous substance (phalloidine) present in the fungus destroys the red blood cells. People who have been poisoned by this fungus die a painful death. They lose consciousness only at the end, and death usually follows ingestion of the fungus 6 to 10 days later. The sixth day is usually critical and if the patient lives through this he may survive. Antidotes are effective only if administered very shortly after

Amanita rubescens

Amanita pantherina

Amanita phalloides var. *verna*

Amanita citrina

eating the fungus, but as the symptoms of poisoning do not appear for 12 hours, their usefulness is limited. The Death Cap has a pure white variety *A. phalloides* var. *verna* (sometimes regarded as a separate species *A. verna*) which grows in similar areas and is just as poisonous.

PARASOL MUSHROOM
Lepiota procera (Scop. ex Fr.) Quél.
Family: *Agaricaceae*

This fungus has an umbrella-shaped cap 10—20 cm. across. The cap is greyish-brown with coarse shaggy brown scales. Only the protruding centre (the *umbo*) of the cap remains brown and smooth. The white flesh looks somewhat like cotton wool and retains its white colour even when bruised.
The gills are white and crowded. The stalk is slender and up to 40 cm. high. It has a conspicuous bulbous base, is hollow and breaks off easily. It is brown with horizontal rings of scales similar to those on the cap. Near the upper end is a double ring. The flesh of the cap is dry and soft, unlike that of the stalk which is tough. It smells and tastes pleasant.
This highly edible fungus appears between July and November at the edges of deciduous woods and in clearings and grassy places. It is found all over the northern temperate zone but is never common.

EARTH BALL
Scleroderma aurantium L. ex Pers.
Family: *Sclerodermataceae*

This fungus is nearly spherical and grows 4—8 cm. across. It is virtually stalkless, with a tough yellowish-brown scaly and cracked wall. Within, the flesh is at first white and later purplish-black, when the spores are ripe. Whitish threads traverse the spore mass. After the spores ripen the fungus dries up and the spores are released through the cracked wall. The ripe fungus has a rather curious odour said by some to resemble that of ink.
It appears between August and December and grows often in peaty soils, in woodland and especially near birch trees. It is found all over the northern temperate zone and is a common and well-known fungus.

In Britain this is not usually considered an edible fungus but on the Continent the young Earth Balls are collected at the white-flesh stage. They are said to be poisonous if eaten in large quantities.

COMMON PUFF-BALL
Lycoperdon perlatum Pers.
Family: *Lycoperdaceae*

The greyish or brownish pear-shaped fruit-body of this fungus grows up to 8 cm. high and is densely covered in small white prickles or warts. Within are the white, later olive-brown, spore-forming tissues.
Once the spores are ripe, the fruit-body dries out and the wall becomes thin and almost papery. The ripe spores are released through a raised pore which develops at the top of the fruit-body and puffs of spores are given off whenever the Puff-ball is touched.
The Common Puff-ball grows between July and December and can often be seen even after the first frost. It grows, usually in groups, in woodlands generally and is common throughout the northern temperate zone.
In coniferous woods a variety called *nigrescens*, which has blackish-brown spines, may be found.

STINKHORN
Phallus impudicus L. ex Pers.
Family: *Phallaceae*

The young fruit-body of this fungus is quite different in shape from the ripe Stinkhorn. The immature fruit-body is like a white goose egg and grows in humus deposits or in rich soil in woods. Within the leathery skin is a greenish jelly-like layer which contains the spores and surrounds a white spindle-shaped stalk. At this stage the Stinkhorn smells pleasant. The skin of the immature fungus breaks during its development and the white hollow stalk appears, covered at the tip by the jelly-like spore layer. This sticky mass has an offensive and nasty stench. Flies and insects are attracted to it and live off the sticky spore mass, leaving only a white stalk behind, and carrying away the spores.
This interesting fungus grows during warm periods from May to the autumn in woods (preferring deci-

224

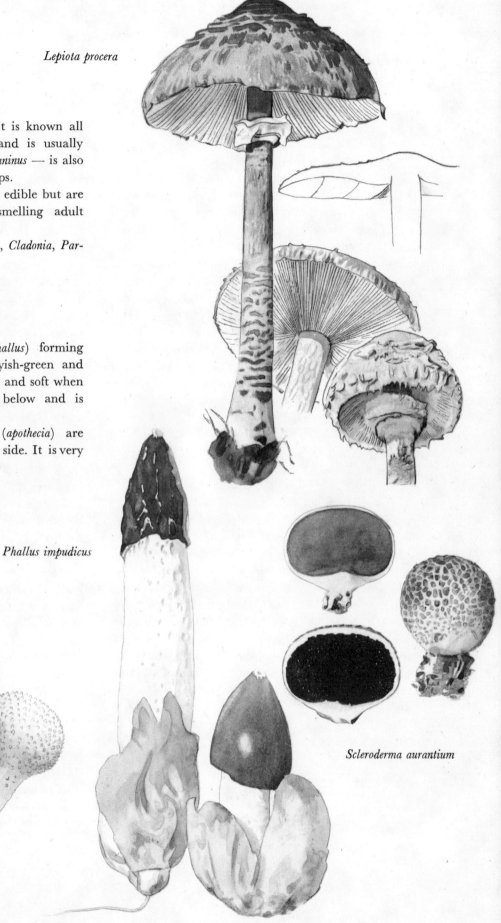

Lepiota procera

duous woods), but also in gardens. It is known all over the northern temperate zone and is usually common. A smaller type — *Mutinus caninus* — is also common and grows around tree stumps.

The young stages (i. e. the 'eggs') are edible but are not popular because of the evil-smelling adult stage.

The following four genera — *Peltigera*, *Cladonia*, *Parmelia* and *Cetraria* — are lichens.

Peltigera canina (L.) Willd.
Family: *Peltigeraceae*

This lichen has a flattened body (*thallus*) forming patches 5—10 cm. across. It is greyish-green and papery when dry, and brownish-green and soft when moist. It bears root-like structures below and is whitish with light-coloured veins.

Rounded reddish-brown fruit-bodies (*apothecia*) are borne towards the margins of the upper side. It is very

Phallus impudicus

Lycoperdon perlatum

Scleroderma aurantium

common on heaths, dunes, walls or grassy ground.

REINDEER MOSS
Cladonia rangiferina (L.) Web.
Family: *Cladoniaceae*

This 'moss' usually forms large patches about 8 cm. high. It commonly grows on moorland and in pine woods and resembles a small greyish spreading 'shrub', with brown fruit-bodies borne on whitish-grey stalks. *C. fimbriata* (another species) has conspicuous stalked greyish fruitbodies and is common on soil, rocks and tree stumps in woodlands. *C. coccifera* is rather similar but has bright red fruit-bodies. *C. digitata* bears numerous fruit-bodies on much-branched stalks *(podetia)*. The upright almost 'twiggy' habit of *Cladonia* is more advanced than that of the flat body of *Peltigera* but the internal structure of all lichens is basically similar. Lichens are formed of a symbiotic association between a fungus and a simple alga. The fungal threads form the main body with algal cells either scatterd or in a single layer in the lichen body.

Parmelia physodes Ach.
Family: *Parmeliaceae*

This species, like all other species of *Parmelia*, grows on trees as well as on rocks and walls, forming flat grey rosettes 5—10 cm. across. The thallus is lobed — almost fan-shaped. The under surface is black with root-like hairs; the fruit-bodies are dark brown.
The genus *Cetraria* is in the same family as *Parmelia* but is more tufted in growth. Iceland Moss *(Cetraria islandica)* grows in the Scottish Highlands, in Central Europe and in Scandinavia on heather moors and in woods. It is reddish-brown, about 2—7 cm. high with black spines along the margin. It is one of the few edible lichens and was also a herbal remedy for coughs and indigestion.
The following mosses form a selection of species which may be found in woodlands.

Dicranum scoparium (L.) Hedw.
Family: *Dicranaceae*

The stems of this moss are up to 10 cm. high and bear numerous finely toothed leaves. The capsule which contains the spores is curved and cylindrical and borne on a reddish-yellow stalk *(seta)* which is 3—4 cm. long. This species tolerates a wide range of conditions, growing in open woods and at the base of tree trunks, and is particularly abundant on heathland. Other varieties grow on mountain ledges, on chalk hills and in marshes.

The following species *Leucobryum glaucum* is in the same family as *Dicranum*.

Leucobryum glaucum (Hedw.) Schp.

This distinctive moss forms greyish-green (almost white) cushions up to 1 m. across on moors and in forests. The leaves are lance-shaped and of variable lengths up to 10 mm. long. The leaf-base is wide, the tip is pointed and the leaf margins inrolled. Each leaf has a wide 'nerve' — like a simple midrib. Capsules are rare, the moss reproducing vegetatively. The dense cushion absorbs water and the moss can live through long dry periods. It may be found under beech, oak or pine trees.
Of all the mosses found in Britain, *Leucobryum glaucum* is so very different from all other British mosses that it is sure to be recognised immediately. Its large rounded cushions have closely crowded leaves which are pale green when wet but become almost white when dry, and hence the generic name *(leuco* meaning white and *bryum,* a moss). The cushions are very easily detached. It is the only species of *Leucobryum* to grow in Britain and, although it is well known as a woodland moss, may also be found in bogs on acid soil.

Mnium punctatum Hedw.
Family: *Mniaceae*

This is a distinctive and robust moss with stems 2—8 cm. high which are covered in reddish-brown hairs. The leaves are small and oval, increasing in size upwards so that the leaf-bases form a kind of funnel. The leaves are light green when young, but darker green or red when old. The plants are either male or female, the capsules being borne on orange stalks

Peltigera canina

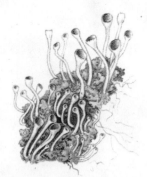

Cladonia fimbriata

Cladonia digitata

Cladonia rangiferina

Parmelia physodes

Cetraria islandica

Dicranum scoparium

Leucobryum glaucum

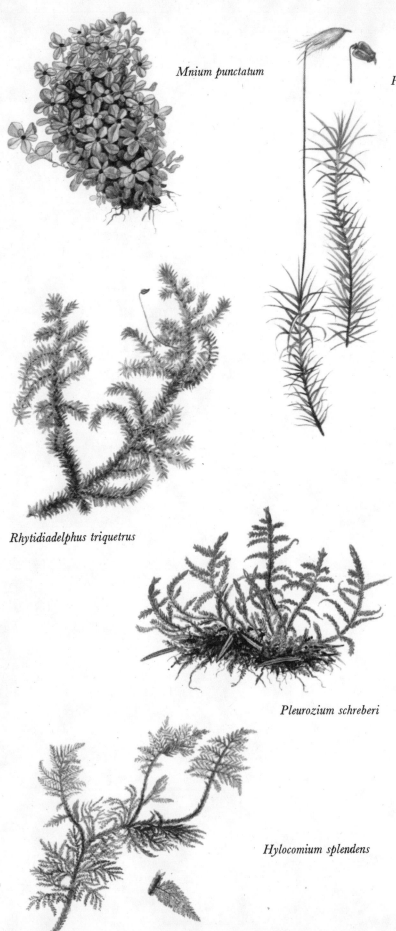

Mnium punctatum

Polytrichum commune

Rhytidiadelphus triquetrus

Pleurozium schreberi

Hylocomium splendens

2—4 cm. long. It grows on damp humus-rich soils in woods and moors, and also on wet stony ground beside streams.

The genus *Mnium* includes several species of moss found in shaded woodland areas. Among them are *Mnium hornum* Hedw., (2—3 cm. high), and *M. undulatum* Hedw. with erect stems up to 7 cm. high. The leaves of the latter species are large and pale green and, as they dry, become twisted — hence the specific name *undulatum*.

HAIR MOSS
Polytrichum commune L.
Family: *Polytrichaceae*

This is one of the largest and best known mosses. It grows up to 20 cm. high with glossy toothed leaves. The four-sided capsules are borne on stalks 6—12 cm. long and each is covered with a hairy cap *(calyptra)*. *P. commune* is abundant on wet, acid moors but is also found on acid soils in open woods.

The following genera are all in the family Hypnaceae:

Pleurozium schreberi (Brid.) Mitt.

This is a moss of variable size but often reaching 10 cm. in height. It has robust pinnately branched stems and light green leaves which are 2—2.5 mm. long. Characteristically the stems are red but are hidden by the closely overlapping leaves. In Britain capsules are rare.

It grows on acid soils on heaths and in open upland forests of birch, oak and pine.

Hylocomium splendens (Hedw.) B., S. and G.

This handsome moss has rather flattened bipinnate shoots, the red stems being densely clothed with small oval rather glossy leaves. The appearance is of a miniature fern. The long-beaked capsules are rarely formed. It is almost always found in association with flowering plants amongst grass and heather, but also forming large carpets in upland and lowland coniferous and deciduous woods.

Rhytidiadelphus triquetrus (Hedw.) Warnst.

The bushy habit and large size of this moss, which forms deep cushions in woodland clearings and on shady roadside banks, make it very conspicuous. It is markedly pale green in colour, with strong erect stems up to 18 cm. high. The leaves are large and glossy, about 6 mm. long, and triangular in shape, hence the specific name *triquetrus*. The leaf tip is long and twisted and there is a double nerve. Capsules are rare. It is usually found on steep shady slopes on chalk downs, but also on chalky clay soils in woodlands, on dunes and on grazed moorland.

The following two plants are termed Clubmosses but should not be confused with true mosses from which they differ in a number of ways. Essentially there are two distinct plants in the clubmoss life-history (life-cycle). The main plant is perennial, leafy and with spores produced in small yellowish sporangia. These develop singly in the axils of leaves termed *sporophylls*. Both *Lycopodium* and *Huperzia* (formerly also known as *Lycopodium)* are in the family Lycopodiaceae.

COMMON OR STAG'S-HORN-CLUBMOSS
Lycopodium clavatum L.

This species has creeping much-branched stems up to 1 m. long. Both stems and branches are tough, wiry and yellowish-green. All are densely covered with small leaves and also produce at intervals thick white branched roots. The leaves are about 5 mm. long, ever green, and linear with a long white point. The sporangia are borne in stalked dense cylindrical cones *(strobili)* about 3 cm. long, which are terminal and usually paired on stems sparsely covered in smaller leaves. The sporophylls are yellowish and papery. The spores when shed develop into colourless gametophytes (the second plant in the life-history).

It grows throughout temperate and arctic regions of the northern hemisphere and in many places on mountains in the tropics, often at considerable altitudes. In Britain it is confined to the hilly parts of Wales and the north but is widespread on well-drained heaths, moors and grassy upland areas. In other parts of the world it may be found in dry, often coniferous, woods.

The spores contain up to 50 % oil and were formerly used in herbal remedies and also as dry dressing for wounds. Because of their water-repellant properties they were at one time used to coat pills and to make flash-powder and fireworks.

FIR CLUBMOSS
Huperzia selago (L.) Bernh.

This species has a tufted habit, with stems which are erect and 5—30 cm. high and which have forking branches. Long wiry roots grow from the base of the stems.

The leaves are small and glossy, linear to lanceolate in shape and with sharply pointed tips. Small leafy buds (bulbils) are found at the tips of the stems; these fall off and develop as new plants. The sporangia are borne, not in cones, but in short fertiles zones which alternate with vegetative zones along the length of the stems.

It is found in similar regions to *L. clavatum* but in more mountainous areas. In Britain it grows on mountain summits. It is usually a plant of rocky or grassy slopes, but sometimes grows in damp conifer woods.

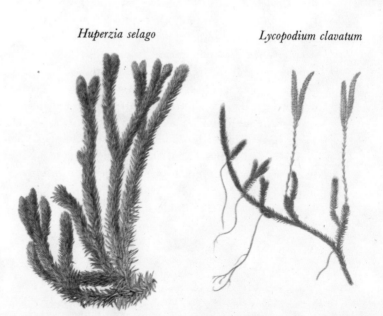

Huperzia selago   *Lycopodium clavatum*

The firlike habit of the leafy stems gives it its name. The Horsetails are an ancient group consisting of the sole genus *Equisetum* in the family Equisetaceae.

WOOD HORSETAIL
Equisetum sylvaticum L.

This is a handsome perennial 10—80 cm. high with rhizomes which grow at a depth of up to 50 cm. As in Lycopodiaceae, *Equisetum* has two plants in its life history — the chief plant producing spores. Each spring unbranched fertile pale pinkish or greenish erect stems grow up, which become dark green and branched after the spores are shed. They bear sporangia in terminal cones 1.5—2.5 cm. long. The vegetative stems are more conspicuous, and are 1—4 mm. in diameter, grooved and with numerous drooping branched laterals. On the ground beneath grow the minute sexual plants which develop from the spores. *E. sylvaticum* grows in damp woods on acid soils but sometimes in more open habitats. It is found throughout most of Europe (rarely in the Mediterranean region), also in temperate Asia and North America.

The following ferns provide a selection of woodland types. Authorities differ on their classification but many would group them in one family, Polypodiaceae.

MALE FERN
Dryopteris filix-mas (L.) Schott

A robust fern with one or more crowns of leaves, this has a stout upright brown rhizome covered with shrivelled leaf bases. The leaves (fronds) grow 30—130 cm. high and up to 25 cm. wide each with a pale brown scaly leaf-stalk. There are 20—35 pairs of deeply lobed tapering leaflets (pinnae), which grow smaller towards the top of the frond and which bear groups of sporangia (sori) on the lower side. Each sorus is protected by a characteristic stalked kidney-shaped scale— the indusium.
Ferns have a life-cycle similar to that of Clubmosses and Horsetails, the sexual stage being minute and heart-shaped. It is green and independent. Many ferns, including the familiar Male Fern, grow in damp often cool places. The Male Fern, so-called because of its robust habit, grows in woods and on hedgebanks and is common in Britain and in the rest of Europe, in both lowland and upland areas. It is also found in temperate and in tropical mountain areas of Asia, as well as in Morocco, North America and part of South America.

The rhizome is collected in many countries and used as a raw material in the pharmaceutical industry. In the past a tea was made from the rhizome and used as a household remedy against intestinal worms, and it is interesting that the plant is still used as source of of modern medicines for this purpose. Formerly it was also used for cleansing wounds, but its use has now been superseded by modern methods.

LADY-FERN
Athyrium filix-femina (L.) Roth

This rather tall fern has a short rhizome. The leaves are about 1 m high, with reddish-brown petioles. They have up to 30 pairs of subdivided leaflets, which are a fresh green colour. The leaflets may be subdivided again. They bear the sori on the underside, and these are covered by indusia which are whitish, toothed and sickle-shaped.
Lady-fern (with its much-divided dainty fronds) is relatively common in damp woods and hedgebanks but also in shady rocky areas and in marshes. It is found throughout the north temperate zone (and therefore throughout Europe), also in mountain areas of tropical America and Asia.

BRACKEN
Pteridium aquilinum (L.) Kuhn

This fern is up to 2 m. high and has a thick branching rhizome several metres long. From this every year grow up the long-stalked fronds singly — not in a crown — with a roughly triangular outline and pinnately divided two or three times. They are light green in colour but the petiole is often dark brown at the base. The leaflets are numerous, paired, lanceolate or oblong in shape, often with a lobed base and hairy beneath — at least on the main veins.
The sporangia are borne in continuous sori which run all round the margins of the leaflets and are protected

both by the inrolled margin and also by membranous indusium.

Bracken is a common, in fact dominant, fern found in woods, heaths, acid grassland and heaths. It is found mainly on light acid soils and may cover large areas. The fern is known in many parts of the world, but is not found in the Arctic nor in temperate South America. It does not tolerate deep shade nor yet exposure and thus it does not grow at high altitudes. Bracken is of no medicinal use and is of limited usefulness for food. The Maoris in New Zealand are reputed to eat the rhizome, and in several countries the young tops are sometimes boiled and eaten like spinach. It is rarely grazed by sheep or rabbits and this is why it spreads so extensively.

BEECH FERN
Thelypteris phegopteris (L.) Slosson

This fern has single fronds 10—50 cm. high, arising from a long rhizome. The petioles are long and yellowish, the leaf-blades are pinnate and yellowish-green, with small lance-shaped leaflets arranged as 10—20 pairs along each side of the axis, the longest in the middle. One of the characteristics of this plant is that the lowest leaves are bent backwards, and are as long as, or slightly shorter than, the pair of leaflets above.

The circular light brown sori appear on the underside of the leaflets and lack indusia. This handsome fern grows in damp shady woods and at the edges of springs and occurs in mountainous as well as lowland areas. It tends to prefer acid soils. It grows all over the northern temperate zone, as well as in temperate Asia (including Japan and the Himalayas), also in North America.

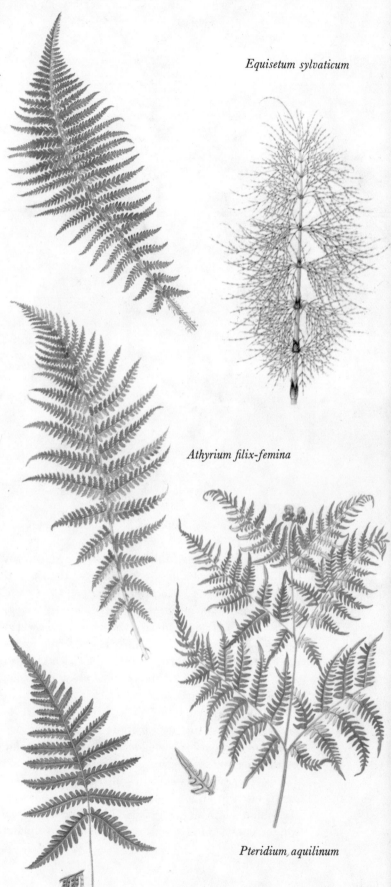

Dryopteris filix-mas

Equisetum sylvaticum

Athyrium filix-femina

Thelypteris phegopteris

Pteridium aquilinum

Blechnum spicant

Matteucia struthiopteris

HARD-FERN
Blechnum spicant (L.) Roth

This fern has a short, thick rhizome and numerous sterile, smooth, spreading pinnate leaves 10—50 cm. long. They are borne in a rather spreading crown, are leathery and dark green, and overwinter. In spring, in the centre of this crown, arise the fertile leaves which are 15—75 cm. high. The leaflets of the fertile leaves are linear or sickle shaped, inrolled and with a blackish axis. The sori form a continuous line along each side of the main vein of the leaflets.

These sori are on the underside of the fertile leaves and are so dense that they more or less cover the surface. The indusia are elongate and are pushed aside by the ripening sporangia.

Hard-fern grows in woods in hilly and mountainous areas, often in large clumps, and also on moors and heathland, on mountain grassland and in rocky areas, almost always on acid soils. It is common in upland

areas in Britain. It is found in Europe southwards from Iceland and Scandinavia, eastwards to Russia, the Caucasus and Japan, also in western North America.

OSTRICH FERN
Matteucia struthiopteris (L.) Tod.

This fern grows up to 150 cm. high and has a thick short underground rhizome. Its large leaves are lanceolate in outline, soft, bright green and pinnately divided into leaflets.

From the central crown of the vegetative leaves, shorter (50—60 cm. long) fertile leaves appear. These fertile leaves are also pinnate, at first green and tightly inrolled, later becoming brown and uncurled. These fertile leaves bear large sporangia and when these are mature, the fertile leaves look very much like ostrich feathers, and this gives the plant its common name.

This is a woodland fern which grows in the north temperate zone including North Africa nad North America, and is naturalised in parts of Europe. It is a very decorative and ornamental plant and is often cultivated in gardens. It is protected in many countries.

WOOD ANEMONE, WINDFLOWER
Anemone nemorosa L.
Family: *Ranunculaceae*

This is a perennial herb up to 30 cm. high with a thin brown creeping rhizome from which, very early in spring, develop long-stalked deeply-divided three-lobed leaves.

These are followed by flowering stems which bear 3 similar but smaller leaves. A solitary flower about 4 cm. across grows at the top of each stem. Each flower has 6—8 white sepals (or perianth members) which are tinged pink or violet on the outside and which surround numerous stamens and carpels. During periods of bad weather and rain the flowers close. The fruits are globular clusters of hairy nutlets.

The Wood Anemone grows in deciduous woods, in hedgerows and in upland meadows but never on very acid soils. It flowers between March and May, usually growing in large masses, and soon after the trees come into leaf the plants die down.

The Wood Anemone grows throughout most of Europe but is rare in the Mediterranean region. It is also found in the northern temperate zone of western Asia. Probably 3 subspecies populate the different regions. In Britain, the plant is found throughout the country, including Ireland and the Channel Islands, but is absent from the Outer Hebrides, Orkney and Shetland. It is a common and familiar springtime plant and takes its name from the movement of the somewhat drooping flowers in the March winds.

The plant, like many ranunculaceous species, contains the poisonous alkaloid proto-anemonin which is acid and can cause blisters. It has been established that thirty plants could kill a man and the plant causes inflammation of the intestines if eaten by animals. The dried plant however is not poisonous.

YELLOW WOOD ANEMONE
Anemone ranunculoides L.

This perennial has a slender brown rhizome from which grows a single basal leaf very like those of the *Anemone nemorosa*, or sometimes it has no basal leaves at all. The flower stem has 3 deeply-lobed leaves which are similar to the basal leaf. The flowers are solitary (but sometimes in clusters of 2—5) and are long-stalked and golden-yellow.

This species too flowers early in spring in woods, hedgerows or in meadows and grows in most of Europe except the north-west, in the Caucasus, Asia Minor, Siberia and possibly Tibet. It was introduced into England but is rare.

Yellow Wood Anemone is poisonous and contains proto-anemonin. In parts of Russia the poison was once used on the tips of arrows.

SNOWDROP WINDFLOWER
Anemone sylvestris L.

This perennial grows up to 50 cm. high and has a short rhizome. The plant spreads by root-buds. As with the other members of this genus, the leaves have deeply palmately three-lobed blades and long petioles. The flower stem has 3 stalked, palmate, five-lobed leaves with toothed segments. At the end of the stem grows a solitary flower of between 4 and 7 cm. across. The perianth members are white inside and out and also the outer surface bears silky hairs. The flowers have numerous yellow stamens and densely woolly-haired carpels. The fruits are a cluster of nutlets.

The plant flowers between April and June in open woods, along the edges of woods and on hedgebanks. It is found over large areas of Central and southern Europe, in western parts of Asia, in Mongolia, Manchuria, in east and northern Siberia as well as in the Caucasus.

This species too is poisonous.

LESSER CELANDINE, PILEWORT
Ranunculus ficaria L.
Family: *Ranunculaceae*

This perennial herb grows 5—30 cm. high and has a number of roots. Some of the roots become club-

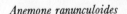

Anemone ranunculoides

Anemone nemorosa

Anemone sylvestris

shaped tubers which contain a great deal of starch. The basal leaves are long-stalked, heart or kidney-shaped, fleshy, glossy and slightly toothed. The glossiness of the leaves is caused by cells containing starch. The stem leaves are smaller and short-stalked. The flowers have 3 green sepals and between 8 and 12 shiny yellow petals.

The fruits are numerous one-seeded nutlets each with a persistent style. Propagation is also effected through the growth of new root tubers.

The plant flowers between March and May. At the end of May the flowering period is over and the plant dies. It grows in damp deciduous woods, in meadows, under hedges and by streams and forms large colonies. It grows all over Europe, the Caucasus and from western parts of Siberia to Central Asia.

Both the mature leaves and also the root tubers are very poisonous. They contain proto-anemonin (and also vitamin C) and taste sharp and bitter. The plant is avoided by grazing animals. In the past the sap has been used as a poison for arrows.

The name 'Celandine' probably derives from the Greek word *chelidon* (swallow), because this plant flowers when the swallows return in the spring.

WHITE BUTTERCUP
Ranunculus aconitifolius L.

This sturdy perennial is up to 50 cm. high and has a short rhizome and branching stems. The lower leaves are long stalked, palmate, with 3—5 deeply lobed segments. The middle segment is three-lobed; the segments on either side have two lobes. All segments are toothed. The stem leaves are similar, but are stalkless and become smaller towards the top. The flowers are white, 1—2 cm. across, with a violet calyx, and grow in loose clusters. The fruits are short-beaked nutlets.

The plant flowers between May and August and grows in woods, along the banks of rivers and lakes and in other damp places and in meadows. It is a mountain plant. It grows in sub-alpine regions and is never found in Britain. It is known in Central and southern Europe. The plant is poisonous and grazing animals will avoid it.

234

BANEBERRY, HERB CHRISTOPHER
Actaea spicata L.
Family: *Ranunculaceae*

This perennial grows 30—65 cm. high and exudes an unpleasant odour. It has a thick reddish-brown rhizome. The leaves are pinnately divided into 3 or 5 oval, toothed leaflets.

The flowers are small, white and grow in many-flowered clusters. The petals fall soon after flowering, leaving the numerous stamens and carpels exposed. The fruits are shiny black berries with brownish hemispherical seeds.

The plant flowers between May and June and grows in shady woods, particularly deciduous woods. The plant is found all over Europe, in the temperate zones of Asia and probably reaches China.

All parts of the plant contain the poisonous substance proto-anemonin, but in the past the rhizome was used for skin troubles and for cases of asthma. The berries have also been used to produce a black dye. The plant was formerly regarded as a 'magical plant' and was dedicated to St. Christopher.

In Britain the plant is confined to the northern counties and is found in ashwoods growing on limestone and, with other plants, on limestone rock-formations.

COLUMBINE
Aquilegia vulgaris L.
Family: *Ranunculaceae*

This perennial plant grows 30—60 cm. high. The stems are erect, thin, with a few branches above. The lower leaves are long-stalked with three long-stalked toothed leaflets which are further divided into three segments. The upper leaves are smaller, narrowly three-lobed and stalkless.

The flowers are long stalked, blue-violet, rarely white or pink, up to 5 cm. across and nodding. The sepals are also coloured. The petals each have a curved spur which is knob-like at its apex.

The flowers can only be pollinated by bumblebees or similar insects since the nectar is deep inside the petal spurs.

The fruits are 5 elongate and podlike follicles and contain numerous black shiny seeds.

The plant flowers between May and June and grows in woods, on hillsides and amongst hedges as well as in rocky places and in meadows. It grows in Central and southern Europe, in temperate zones of Asia right up to China and also in North Africa. It was introduced into North America. It grows in Britain but is not common.

Because of its conspicuous flower it used to be worn as an amulet during the Middle Ages and was thought to give protection against ghosts and spells.

Columbine is a poisonous plant. The leaves and young fruits contain an alkaloid as yet unidentified. Despite this the plant has in the past been used as a household remedy to relieve jaundice and skin diseases.

This is a very variable species. Cultivated varieties are long-spurred and are popular garden plants.

They thrive in rich soil and prefer light shade. The colour range is extensive and includes purple, mauve, red, pink and shades of yellow.

Unlike *Aquilegia vulgaris* which is self-coloured, the cultivated forms usually have petals and spurs of different colours.

In Britain two species of *Aquilegia* may be found but both are uncommon. *A. vulgaris* is native and grows in woods and wet places on calcareous soils in practically all of Britain. The rare Pyrenean Columbine *(A. pyrenaica* DC.*)* is native to the Pyrenees and is introduced in Britain.

A. vulgaris is grown in gardens but it is more usual to find the long-spurred types which are hybrids between three species — *A. coerulea* James which is pale blue and *A. chrysantha* A. Gray and *A. formosa* Fisch, both of which are yellow-petalled with red spurs.

The popular name 'Columbine' comes from the Latin *columba* (a dove) and the generic name *Aquilegia* derives from the Latin word *aquila* meaning an eagle. The reason for these birdlike names will be clear if one takes a flower and picks off three of the five sepals and four of the petals, leaving one petal between the two remaining sepals. The spur of this petal then bears a resemblance to the head and neck of a bird, the rest of the petal forming its tail, with the sepals on either side resembling spreading wings.

This fancied resemblance to a bird is less obvious in the cultivated long-spurred varieties which have straight spurs, unlike the sharply curved and knobbed spurs of *A. vulgaris*.

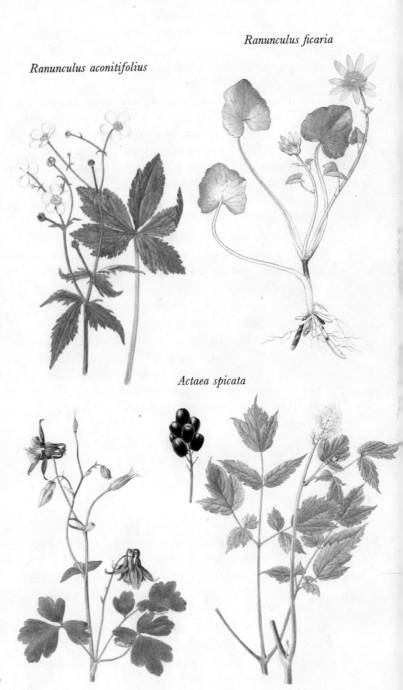

Ranunculus ficaria

Ranunculus aconitifolius

Actaea spicata

Aquilegia vulgaris

HEPATICA
Hepatica nobilis Miller
Family: *Ranunculaceae*

This perennial is 5—15 cm. high and has a short thick rhizome from which flowering stems grow in early spring (before the leaves come out). Ths stems carry solitary flowers and beneath each are 3 small bracts. The flowers have 6—9 blue, pink, red or even white perianth members. Each has numerous white stamens and numerous beaked carpels.

The leaves appear only after flowering and have three broad, rounded, shallow lobes which are hairy when the plant is young and later become smooth. The leaves are leathery and tough, dark green and tinged violet on the lower side; they overwinter.

The plant flowers between March and May and grows in shady deciduous woods and hedgerows, preferring calcareous soils and mountain regions. Hepatica resembles an *Anemone* and is often included in that genus. The plant is found in most of continental Europe, eastwards to Russia and southwards to Italy and Spain. It is never found wild in Britain.

All parts of the plant contain a small amount of poisonous proto-anemonin, tannins and other substances. The leaves and flowers were used as a household remedy for relieving liver and gall-bladder trouble, as well as for coughs and chest complaints.

The name derives from the Greek word *hepar* (meaning liver) which refers to the liver-like shape of the leaves as well as to its healing qualities.

GREATER MEADOW RUE
Thalictrum aquilegifolium L.
Family: *Ranunculaceae*

This perennial herb grows .5—1.5 m. high. The erect branched stems bear pinnate leaves with 3—7 oval deeply-toothed leaflets.

The flowers are pale lilac or greenish white with 4—5 perianth segments which quickly fall off. The flowers form fluffy-looking clusters. The stalks of the stamens are violet and almost wedge-shaped, often as wide as the anthers, and they make the stamens very conspicuous. The fruits are short-stalked, brown, 3-sided and winged nutlets.

The plant flowers between May and July and grows in damp woods and hedges, as well as on the banks of rivers and lakes. It is known over much of Europe, from the Balkans to Italy and Spain and in the north up to southern Sweden, but it is not found in Britain. This is a poisonous plant — the root is particularly dangerous. It is often grown as a garden plant for its decorative foliage and 'fluffy' flowers.

WOLFSBANE
Aconitum vulparia Riechenb.
Family: *Ranunculaceae*

This perennial herb grows .5—1 m. high and has erect branched stems. The leaves are deeply palmately divided into 3—5 narrow lobed wedge-shaped segments.

The yellow flowers have a tall erect hood and are borne in branched leafless spikes. The flowers are pollinated by long-tongued insects because the nectar-secreting spurs are deep in the hood. These spurs are characteristically spirally curved. The fruits are 3 hairless follicles and contain a number of dark three-sided seeds.

The plant flowers between June and August and grows in damp woods and meadows, and in rocky places. It is a mountain plant and, in the Alps, grows at 2,500 metres above sea level.

Wolfsbane is found in much of Europe and Asia; it is not found in Britain but extends eastwards and southwards from France and the Netherlands, to Rumania, Poland and Italy. Wolfsbane is a very poisonous plant containing several alkaloids including the extremely dangerous aconitine.

MONKSHOOD
Aconitum napellus L.

This perennial is up to 1 m. high and has a pair of blackish tuberous underground stems, one or both of which are formed each year,and which are up to 9 cm. long and 3 cm. across at the top. From these grow the erect stems.

The stem leaves are of two types. The upper leaves are small and stalkless. Like the lower ones they are soft and light green and are either smooth or covered with small downy hairs. The lower leaves are palmate, up to 15 cm. across, and cut to the base into 3—5 lobes which are further divided into linear and deeply-toothed segments.

The flowers are violet, blue, or sometimes white, and have a conspicuous helmet-like hood which is always broader than it is long, and which hides the 2 nectar-secreting spurs.

The fruits are 3 follicles containing winged seeds. The plant flowers between June and September and grows in damp woods and meadows, and on shady stream banks.

Aconitum napellus is known in mountainous regions of Europe, Caucasia and in Siberia and is also found in the Far East and in Central Asia. It grows at heights of 3,000 metres above sea level.

Monkshood is very variable and has affinities with other species. The plant is grown in gardens in Britain. The common name refers to the hooded shape of the perianth.

All parts of this plant, particularly the tubers, are very poisonous. The plant was recognised by Pliny as being extremely deadly. The tubers contain several alkaloids, particularly aconitine, a very quick-acting poison. Only 3 or 4 grams of aconitine are required to kill a man, since the poison paralyses the central nervous system.

Aconitine, and related alkaloids, are characteristic of all members of the genus *Aconitum*. Many authorities regard Monkshood as the most poisonous of all British plants. The tuber has often been mistaken for Horseradish *(Armoracia)* and has been made up into sauce and eaten, with fatal results. Monkshood is known in Greek, Roman and Scandinavian mythology.

The ancient Gauls and Slavs poisoned wolves and foxes with the sap of the plant; it was used as poison for deadly arrows. Despite its high poison content, the plant was used as a household remedy. Today it is still used in the pharmaceutical industry, but drugs containing aconitine can be obtained only on prescription.

ASARABACCA
Asarum europaeum
Family: *Aristolochiaceae*

This is an inconspicuous plant with a thick creeping rhizome and stems 2—10 cm. high. These bear usually 2—5 long-stalked overwintering leaves and

Hepatica nobilis

Thalictrum aquilegifolium

Aconitum vulparia

Aconitum napellus

2 brown scales. The leaves are leathery and tough, kidney-shaped, and have a deep incision at the junction with the stalk. They are dark green and shiny above — lighter below. They may reach 10 cm. across. The short-stalked rather unattractive flowers grow close to the ground, often hiding beneath dried leaves. They have a bell-shaped fleshy corolla which is 1.5 cm. across and brownish in colour. They smell of pepper when rubbed. The rhizome smells of camphor and has a burning taste.

The fruits are egg-shaped, hairy capsules. The seeds have fleshy appendages which are eaten by ants which in turn distribute the seeds.

The plant flowers between March and August forming large colonies in deciduous woods and shady hedges. It grows in Central and southern Europe, in Britain and southern parts of Sweden as well as in parts of Asia Minor and Siberia. It has a preference for calcareous soils. Although found in Britain it is rare, and only doubtfully native.

In ancient times and in the Middle Ages this plant was a well-known household remedy. The syrup made from this plant was used to help relieve coughs and induce vomiting. The dried and pulverised rhizomes were added to snuff.

The rhizome contains volatile oils and a poisonous substance which paralyses the central nervous system. It also contains tannins and starch. The plant is no longer of medicinal use.

Corydalis bulbosa (L.) DC.
Family: *Papaveraceae*

This perennial herb grows 10—35 cm. high and has a large rounded tuber which is at first solid and later becomes hollow. The tuber develops roots and also usually a single stem which is erect and bears 1—3 leaves.

This erect, fleshy, often red-brown stem differs from those of other species in lacking scales below the leaves. The leaves are bluish-green, broadly wedge-shaped and usually twice divided into three, with small irregular wedge-shaped segments.

The flowers are a dull pinkish purple, sometimes whitish in colour, and smell of resin. They have 2 sepals which are quickly lost and 4 petals. The upper

petal is spurred and curved at the apex. This spur contains the nectar which can be reached only by long-tongued insects. The flowers are in rather dense elongate inflorescences. The fruits are shining 2-valved capsules 2—2.5 cm. long and pendant when ripe.

The plant flowers between March and May and grows in light deciduous woods and hedges and prefers soils rich in humus. It always grows in large clumps and can also be found in meadows, orchards and in vineyards.

Corydalis bulbosa is known in Central and southern Europe as well as in parts of Russia and in Scandinavia. The roots have been used in the past as a household remedy.

The plant contains many substances which are still used in the pharmaceutical industry. The medicines made from this plant are used for treatment of the nervous system and for lowering the blood pressure. The plant is variable, with three subspecies.

PERENNIAL HONESTY
Lunaria rediviva L.
Family: *Cruciferae*

This species of Honesty is a perennial with hairy stems growing up to 1.5 m. high. The lower leaves are stalked, with pointed tips and are heart-shaped. The upper leaves are toothed, triangular and elongate and distinctly stalked, thus differing from Honesty *(L. annua)*. The pale violet (rarely white) flowers form dense clusters and have an aromatic scent. The fruits are very conspicuous since they form a broad elliptic pod, pointed at both ends, and they also have a silvery skin which later parts to release the seeds.

The plant flowers between April and July and grows in shady woods and in damp soil rich in humus. It is also found along the banks of streams that run through woods, and at up to 1,400 metres above sea level in the Alps. It is known in most of Europe except the extreme north and south. It is a rare garden-escape in Britain.

In some countries the plant is protected. It is often cultivated in gardens, as is *Lunaria annua*. The seeds were formerly used medicinally.

GARLIC MUSTARD
Alliaria petiolata (Bieb.) Cavara and Grande
Family: *Cruciferae*

This biennial plant smells of garlic when its leaves are rubbed or crushed. The stems are erect, usually without branches, and sparsely hairy. The lower long-stalked leaves are kidney-shaped, and coarsely toothed. The upper leaves have short stalks, are elongate and oval with a heart-shaped base. They are irregularly toothed. The plant grows up to 120 cm. high.

The white flowers are small, 6 mm. across, with the typical structure of the family. They are borne in terminal leafless clusters. The fruits are 6 cm. long pods on long stalks. The plant flowers between April and July and grows in open woods, in hedges, in shady gardens and on walls.

It is known throughout Europe southwards from 68° north. It is less common in the extreme south but is also found in the Caucasus, from Asia Minor to the Himalayas, and in North Africa.

The plant was used medicinally in the past.

SWEET VIOLET
Viola odorata L.
Family: *Violaceae*

This familiar perennial plant has a leafy rosette and numerous creeping, above-ground, over-wintering stems, which are up to 20 cm. long and which root at the tips. The basal leaves are dark green, rounded, kidney to heart-shaped, blunt or pointed at the tip and shallowly toothed. The blades are 1.5—6 cm. across.

The flowers grow on long stalks and are violet, or sometimes white, and are rarely pink. They have a sweet scent. The lower petal is spurred. The calyx has spreading appendages which are shorter than the petals. The fruits are hairy capsules with numerous seeds which are covered by a fleshy layer. This is eaten by ants and the seeds are spread in this way.

Since Sweet Violet begins to flower in March, when only a few insects are about, numerous flowers are not pollinated. It is for this reason that further flowers appear in the late summer. These flowers have closed calyces and stunted petals and are self-fertilising, forming capsules containing seeds.

Corydalis bulbosa

Asarum europaeum

Alliaria petiolata

Lunaria rediviva

Viola odorata

The Sweet Violet grows in meadows and hedgerows, in woods and gardens, often becoming naturalised. Originally this plant grew only in Mediterranean countries and the southern part of the Alps, the Atlas Mountains in North Africa, in Mesopotamia and Caucasia.

This is a medicinal plant which contains bitter substances, including salicylic acid, in the rhizome. The rhizomes are used to make drugs to treat whooping cough. A violet pigment can be extracted from the flowers and, if this is treated with an alkali, it changes to green. This colour change makes it an acceptable substitute for litmus. In France a precious green volatile oil is extracted from the plant which has an aromatic scent. In order to manufacture this perfume special subspecies have been cultivated.

According to an ancient Greek legend, Violet was the daughter of the giant Atlas. The girl was pursued by Phoebus (the sun) and she begged Zeus to change her into a Violet, so that she could hide from the rays of her pursuer.

COMMON DOG VIOLET
Viola riviniana Reichenb.

This perennial has a main axis ending in a leaf rosette. The stems are up to 15 cm. long. The rosette leaves are long-stalked, finely toothed and broadly heart-shaped. The stem leaves have lance-shaped stipules which also have finely toothed margins.

The large blue-violet flowers are white at the base and have broad petals. The calyx has appendages which are almost square. The white or pale violet spur of the flower is thick, blunt and furrowed. It is common throughout Europe except in the south-east. It also grows in Morocco and Madeira and flowers between April and June in light woods, hedges and pastures, on heaths and among mountain rocks.

GREATER STITCHWORT
Stellaria holostea L.
Family: *Caryophyllaceae*

This perennial herb has short non-flowering stems, and also longer flowering stems which are four-angled and up to 60 cm. high. Both types of stem grow from a creeping rhizome. The leaves are narrow, stiff and lance-shaped. They are bluish-green and taper to a point. They are rough along the margins and on the underside of the midrib.

The flowers are large and white with petals that are bilobed halfway to the base. They are in loose branched inflorescences. The fruits are capsules with warty seeds.

The plant flowers between April and June and grows in deciduous woods and in hedges, often on the heavier soils. It is found over almost all Europe and Asia Minor, from Armenia to Caucasia, and in Finland and Scandinavia, as well as in North Africa.

GOAT'S-BEARD SPIRAEA
Aruncus dioicus (Walter) Fernald
Family: *Rosaceae*

This perennial herb grows up to 2 m. high. The leaves are very large (up to 1 m. long), without stipules and are long-stalked. They are pinnately divided 2 or 3 times into long-pointed, toothed, oval leaflets. The plants are unisexual, sometimes bisexual. The male flowers are yellowish-white, the female ones are white. Both types of flower are clustered into long slender horizontal inflorescences. The poisonous fruits are brown capsules 3 mm. across and pendant.

The plant flowers between June and August and grows in damp mountainous woods, along the banks of mountain streams and in shady places. The male plants are the more handsome and are often grown in the moister shady parts of gardens. It is found in western, Central and eastern Europe, in the more temperate zones of Asia as well as in North Africa.

WILD STRAWBERRY
Fragaria vesca L.
Family: *Rosaceae*

This perennial herb spreads by producing long arching runners which root at the nodes and form new plants. It has a thick woody stem, with a rosette of trifoliate leaves and erect flower stems. The oval leaflets are bright green, coarsely toothed and 1—6 cm. long. The flower stems are up to 30 cm. high, about as long as the leaves, and bear clusters of white flowers. These flowers are about 1.5 cm. across, with a conspicuous epicalyx outside the sepals, and numerous stamens.

The fruits have a fleshy and juicy, red, sweet egg-shaped receptacle which is covered with small projecting brownish achenes (nutlets). Wild Strawberries resemble cultivated Strawberries but are smaller and the persistent sepals are bent back. The plant flowers between April and July and grows in coppices, light woods, along the edges of woods, in hedges and in dry grassy places, especially on limy soils.

The Wild Strawberry is known almost everywhere in Europe, and in temperate zones of Asia from Lake Baikal in the east to Iceland and north east Scandinavia in the north. It has been introduced into eastern parts of Asia, in Japan, all over America, in South Africa, southern Australia and in New Zealand. It is not found in Crete. This delicious edible fruit has been known since the Middle Ages and is used to make jams and beverages.

The leaves contain tannins and volatile oils; they smell of lemon and can be made into a tea. The plant was used medicinally to relieve infections; however some people are allergic to this plant and may develop nettle rash from handling it.

WHITE CINQUEFOIL
Potentilla alba L.
Family: *Rosaceae*

This is a slender, hairy perennial up to 15 cm. high. The basal leaves are palmate with five lance-shaped leaflets. They are elongate, dark green on the upper side and covered with silver-grey hairs beneath. The flowers are white, 2 cm. across, with up to 20 stamens. The petals are notched and longer than the sepals.

The fruits are smooth. The plant flowers between April and May and grows in poor pastures, in open woods (particularly of oak), on grassy hills and in rocky places. It is known all over eastern and Central Europe.

HERB BENNET, WOOD AVENS
Geum urbanum L.
Family: *Rosaceae*

This hairy perennial grows 20—60 cm. high. It has a short thick rhizome and thick branched stems. The stalked basal leaves are pinnate, with round to oval

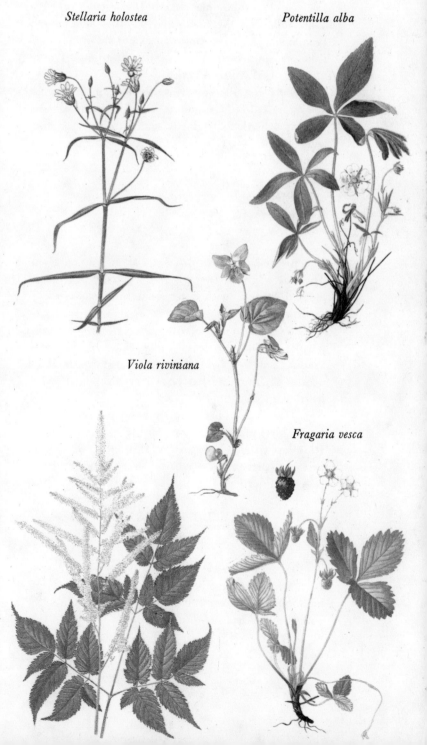

Stellaria holostea

Potentilla alba

Viola riviniana

Fragaria vesca

Aruncus dioicus

double-toothed leaflets. The terminal leaflet is three to five-lobed. The lower stem-leaves are three-lobed or pinnate; the upper leaves are simple. All have large leafy stipules. The flowers are 1—1.5 cm. across with yellow petals which fall off quickly, and small sepals which turn downwards after flowering. The fruits are a cluster of hairy nutlets, with long hook-like styles which stick to animal fur and to clothing. The plant grows in deciduous woods, hedgerows and scrub, and in shady places generally, usually on rich damp soils. It flowers between May and September. It is known all over the temperate zone of Europe, Asia and in North Africa. It was introduced into Australia and North America.

The roots contain starch, sugar and volatile oils. They smell like Carnations. Dried rhizomes were used as a household remedy and to make beer and wine. They were also used in the manufacture of mouthwashes.

SPRING PEA
Lathyrus vernus (L.) Bernh.
Family: *Leguminosae*

This perennial has angular stems about 40 cm. high. The leaves have between 2 and 4 pairs of oval long-pointed leaflets, with a terminal leaflet and not a tendril.
The flowers are nodding, with purple, violet or reddish-purple petals which fade to blue. The calyx is bell-shaped and the flowers are pollinated by bumble-bees. The fruits are flat brown or black pods with lentil-like seeds.
This plant flowers between April and June and grows in dry deciduous woods, preferring calcareous soils. It is known in most parts of Europe (but not in Britain, Portugal, Greece or Turkey) and in parts of Asia Minor.

NARROW-LEAVED EVERLASTING PEA
Lathyrus sylvestris L.

This smooth perennial has a long creeping rhizome from which numerous, up to 2 cm. long, low-lying or climbing angular stems appear. The stem is broadly winged; the leaf-stalks are narrowly winged. The leaves have a pair of linear lance-shaped leaflets. A branched tendril develops at the end of the leaf.
The pink or violet flowers are large, with a bell-shaped toothed calyx, and grow in long-stalked clusters in the leaf axils. The fruits are large brown pods containing 10—15 seeds.
The plant flowers between June and August and grows in light deciduous woods, in scrub and along the edges of woods. It prefers calcareous soils. It grows in south and Central Europe from Spain to the Black Sea, and northwards to France, Britain and Scandinavia.

MILK-VETCH
Astragalus glycyphyllos L.
Family: *Leguminosae*

This perennial fresh green plant has prostrate, sometimes woody stems 30—100 cm. long. The leaves are 10—20 cm. long, pinnate with 9—13 broad oval leaflets. The flowers have a bell-shaped calyx and creamy, tinged greenish-yellow petals. They are borne in dense long-stalked clusters. The fruits are pointed, cylindrical, slightly curved and almost hairless.
The plant flowers between June and August and grows in light woods, in grassy places and scrub, usually on chalk or limestone. It is known in most of Europe and in northern parts of Asia, but is rare in Mediterranean countries. It is native to Britain but is not common, and is never found in Ireland.

GARDEN LUPIN
Lupinus polyphyllus Lindley
Family: *Leguminosae*

This is a familiar perennial herb which can live for up to ten years. It grows about 1.5 m. high. During the first year a dense leafy rosette develops and only after the second year do the flower-stems appear. The leaves are long-stalked, decorative and distinctive. They are pinnate, with 9—17 lance-shaped leaflets which are silky-hairy below.
The large flowers have hairy calyces and blue, pink, rarely white, petals. They form beautiful dense erect spikes up to 50 cm. long. The large hairy pods contain 5—9 mottled seeds.

242

Lathyrus vernus

Geum urbanum

Lathyrus sylvestris

Astragalus glycyphyllos

Lupinus polyphyllus

This Lupin comes from the Pacific coast of North America. It is a plant which has been cultivated for a long time. Like all leguminous plants, it can enrich the soil by 'fixing' free soil nitrogen. The plant spreads very quickly and grows on poor, sandy soils. In some areas it is cultivated in fields as animal foodstuff and harvested twice a year. It is also ploughed in to enrich the soil.

The plant flowers between June and August and has become naturalised in light woods and on sunny slopes. All parts of the plant, particularly the seeds, contain glycosides as well as poisonous alkaloids. The plant is very familiar as the modern garden plant, the Russell Lupin, which has massive inflorescences and bright multicoloured flowers.

Lupinus perennis L.

This plant comes from the North American Atlantic coast. It is shorter and has fewer and smaller leaves than *L. polyphyllus*. It is planted as a fodder crop for domestic animals, and as a garden plant. It often becomes naturalised.

WOOD-SORREL
Oxalis acetosella L.
Family: *Oxalidaceae*

Wood-sorrel is a delicate perennial herb with a thin creeping rhizome covered in fleshy scales. From this arise scattered and solitary flowers.

The long-stalked, three-lobed leaves (up to 15 cm. long) are similar to clover leaves. The leaflets are wedge-shaped, yellowish-green and sometimes tinged red on the underside. In the rain and at night, the leaves take on a 'sleep' position, i. e. they fold up around the centre midrib. This can be seen if the plant is covered for a time.

The flowers have hairy calyces and white petals delicately veined with violet. The lower side of the petals is usually tinged violet and the flowers droop during bad weather and when it is dark. As well as the flowers there are often flower-like buds which are capable of self-pollination and which set copious seed. Such flowers are termed *cleistogamous* i. e. 'closed' flowers. The fruit of the Wood-sorrel is about 1 cm. long and is a capsule which splits at the top, throwing out the seeds.

Wood-sorrel flowers between April and May and grows in shady woods rich in humus. It often covers large areas and is found at a height of 2,000 metres above sea level in mountainous regions. The plant grows almost anywhere in the northern temperate zone; it also grows in northern and Central Asia across to Japan.

All parts of the plant have an astringent taste and contain oxalic acid. This is a poisonous substance and 4 or 5 grams can be fatal. If it is mixed with animal fodder it is dangerous to livestock.

DOG'S MERCURY
Mercurialis perennis L.
Family: *Euphorbiaceae*

This is a perennial plant with a long creeping branched rhizome which turns black-violet when dried. It has erect unbranched stems bearing leaves which are short-stalked, elliptical-oval, toothed and 2—8 cm. long. The leaves are reduced to scales at the base of the stem.

The plant has either male or female flowers. Male flowers have 3 greenish sepals and 8—15 stamens, and are borne in dense clusters on long axillary spikes. The long-stalked female flowers are also green, in groups of 1—3, and grow in the axils of the upper leaves. The hairy fruits are capsules divided into two lobes each containing one seed. These seeds are whitish-grey, rounded and wrinkled.

The plant flowers between February and April, often in large clumps, growing in shady deciduous woods with humus-rich soils and especially in oak and beech woods. It is found almost everywhere in Europe as well as in Algeria (where it is rare) and in South West Asia. All parts of the plant are poisonous and contain volatile oils and tannins. The seeds also contain oil. The plant is dangerous for both animals and humans to eat. In the past this plant was used medicinally to relieve constipation, kidney trouble and various infections as well as to heal burns and boils.

TOUCH-ME-NOT
Impatiens noli-tangere L.
Family: *Balsaminaceae*

This smooth annual herb grows 20—180 cm. high and has simple or branched erect stems. These stems are thick and swollen at the nodes. The plant is fleshy and quickly withers when cut. The leaves are alternate, oval-oblong, pointed and toothed with a glandular margin.

The flowers are pendant and up to 4 cm. across, with 3 sepals, the lateral ones being small and green, the lowest one large and yellow with a curved spur. The flowers are in loose clusters of 3—6 in the leaf axils. The fruits are capsules which burst open if touched when ripe — the wall splitting into 5 valves which coil like elastic and shoot out the seeds. This explains the common name, Touch-me-not, and the Latin name *Impatiens*.

The plant flowers between July and September and grows in wet ground in woods and also by shady streams. It is found in Central Europe and in parts of southern Europe, the Middle East and eastwards to China and Japan. In Britain it is very uncommon and is found mainly in the north.

SMALL BALSAM
Impatiens parviflora DC.

This plant is up to 1 m. high and has small yellow erect flowers with a straight conical spur. The leaves are oval, long-pointed and toothed.

It grows in eastern parts of Siberia, in Turkestan as well as in Mongolia, and was introduced from there into much of Europe and North America. It forms large colonies in damp deciduous woods and on cultivated ground. In Britain it is becoming more common in shady places generally.

This plant too has capsules which, when touched, spring open and so disperse the seeds.

Oxalis acetosella

Mercurialis perennis

Impatiens noli-tangere

Aegopodium podagraria

Epilobium angustifolium

ROSEBAY WILLOW-HERB, FIREWEED
Epilobium angustifolium L.
Family: *Onagraceae*

This perennial is up to 2.5 m. high and has long spreading roots which give rise to erect leafy stems. These stems are unbranched and bear numerous spirally arranged leaves. The leaves are elongate, linear to lance-shaped and pointed, bluish-green on the underside and conspicuously veined. They often have wavy margins.

The flowers are numerous with dark purple sepals and purplish-pink (rarely white) petals and are borne in large dense elongate inflorescences. The fruits are long, downy capsules with small seeds, each with a white plume.

This is a species which quickly covers an area and grows mostly in large colonies in light woods and along the edges of woods. It flowers between July and September and when ripe the downy seeds float over large areas, thus spreading rapidly. When they settle beside rivers and reservoirs, or on waste, burnt or bombed areas, they germinate. In mountainous areas the plant can be found at 2,000 m. above sea level.

It is known in most parts of the world — in Europe as far north as Iceland and the Shetland Islands, and in the most northern parts of Norway. It is also found in much of Asia, in North America and in Greenland. It is however totally absent from Africa. In Britain, this plant became abundant on bombsites in World War II. It was formerly named *Chamaenerion*.

GOUTWEED, GROUND ELDER
Aegopodium podagraria L.
Family: *Umbelliferae*

All green parts of this plant have an unpleasant odour. Ground Elder is a perennial which grows up

245

to 1 m. high. It spreads extensively by means of underground stems and is known as a difficult weed to eradicate from gardens. The erect stems are hollow, grooved and branched.

The leaves on the lower parts of the plant have long stalks and are cut into three oval segments. Above these leaves are pinnate ones with usually 5, often subdivided, leaflets. All leaflets are toothed and pointed and may be asymmetrical. The upper stem leaves are smaller and are often undivided, and they have inflated petioles.

The flowers are small, white or pink, and without sepals. They are borne in compound umbels. The fruits are light coloured, ovoid and ribbed.

The plant flowers between May and August and grows usually in large colonies in damp deciduous woods, on banks, in gardens and in shady places generally. It is found up to 3,100 metres above sea level in mountainous areas. It is known over most of Europe (except for parts of the south), in Asia Minor, Caucasia and Siberia. It was introduced into North America. If even a small part of the underground stem is planted, Ground Elder quickly establishes itself.

The plant was formerly used as a household remedy and an ointment made from it was applied to wounds. It was also used to relieve bee and other insect bites. In some countries the plant is still eaten as a vegetable or salad and is actually cultivated for this purpose.

SANICLE
Sanicula europaea L.
Family: *Umbelliferae*

This smooth perennial plant has erect stems 20—60 cm. high which grow from a short rhizome. The basal leaves have long stalks and are deeply palmately lobed, with 3—5 wedge-shaped segments which are coarsely toothed and which may also be lobed. Usually the leaves are basal only. Stem-leaves, if they are present at all, have no stalks and are less segmented.

The flowers are whitish or reddish, small, and with stamens protruding above the petals. The flowers are umbelliferous with male flowers at the outside and bisexual flowers to the inside of the umbels.

The fruits are egg-shaped, with numerous hooked bristles which cling to animal fur and so are dispersed. The plant flowers between May and September and grows in shady deciduous or mixed woods on loamy soils. It is a typical ground-layer woodland plant of oak or chalk beech woods. In warm countries it grows only in mountainous regions.

It grows throughout most of Europe, in Central, eastern and southern parts of Asia, in North Africa and in mountainous parts of tropical Africa. It grows at 2,500 metres above sea level in the Cameroons. The plant has been used as a household remedy and, in some countries, the volatile oils and tannins are still extracted from the leaves by boiling in hot water. This extract is said to relieve infections, to cleanse open wounds and to aid digestion.

GREAT MASTERWORT, MOUNTAIN SANICLE
Astrantia major L.
Family: *Umbelliferae*

This perennial herb has a short, woody, creeping rhizome from which grow usually unbranched stems up to 100 cm. high. The leaves are mostly in a loose basal rosette and are long-stalked, 6—15 cm. across, circular in outline and deeply palmately divided into 3—7 lanceolate and strongly toothed segments. Almost all of what appear to be stem-leaves are, in fact, leafy bracts.

The small flowers have white or pinkish petals, which are curved inwards, and long stamens. The flowers are borne in simple umbels and each of these inflorescences is surrounded by large whitish-green or reddish lance-shaped bracteoles. The fruits (like those of all umbellifers) are formed of 2 carpels and are almost cylindrical.

The plant flowers between June and September, and grows in light woods and meadows, preferring calcareous soils and moist, shaded situations. It is found in southern and Central Europe, eastwards as far as Caucasia, westwards as far as Spain. The plant was introduced in Britain and is naturalised in several localities.

This is a fairly variable plant with two subspecies, differing in the size of the bracteoles and in distribution. *Astrantia major* has long been cultivated in gardens in Britain and it is probably as a garden escape that it has become naturalised in a few places. The plant was formerly used medicinally and is still used in some countries as a tonic.

WILD ANGELICA, JACK-JUMP-ABOUT
Angelica sylvestris L.
Family: *Umbelliferae*

Wild Angelica is a robust perennial which grows to a height of about 2 m. It has a thick rhizome which tastes very bitter and smells faintly of carrots. The stems are erect, ridged and purplish in colour overlaid with a mealy bloom. They are branched only at the top. The leaf-stalks are deeply channelled with a semi-cylindrical inflated sheath at the base. The basal leaves are large, up to 60 cm. long and triangular in outline; they are pinnately divided 2 or 3 times into toothed, pointed, oval segments. The inflated sheaths of the upper leaves enclose both the young axillary branches as well as protecting the inflorescences. Rainwater often collects in the sheaths and sometimes small organisms live in it. The upper leaves are less segmented and the very top ones have no stalks.

The flowers are borne in compound, terminal and axillary umbels each of 20—35 heads and are small, white or pink, with minute sepals and small incurved petals. The fruits are flattened and ovoid, ridged and with papery marginal wings.

The plant flowers between July and September and grows in light damp woods, in hedges, damp meadows, in marshes and fens, and along the edges of rivers and lakes. It grows in most of Europe (but is not common in the south), in Asia Minor, the Caucasus and Siberia. This is a very ancient species, remains of which have been found in Stone Age settlements. In some areas the young leaves are eaten as a vegetable, and the roots were formerly used as a remedy for chest infections and stomach and kidney complaints.

COWSLIP, PAIGLE
Primula veris L.
Family: *Primulaceae*

This perennial herb has a short stout rhizome and a basal rosette of 5—20 wrinkled oval leaves 2—6 cm. long. These narrow at the base into the winged leaf-stalks.

From the leaf rosette flower-stems appear which

Sanicula europaea

Astrantia major

Angelica sylvestris

carry short-stalked clusters of sweet-smelling flowers. The notched petals are yellow, orange coloured at the base. The calyx is inflated, somewhat angular and greenish yellow. The flowerheads hang down to one side of the flower-stem and were thought to symbolise the keys of St. Peter.

The fruits are ovoid capsules which are shorter than the calyx. The plant flowers between April and June and grows in light woods, pastures and meadows, especially on clay, chalk or limestone soils and may be locally abundant.

The Cowslip is a familiar flower and grows in most of Europe (except in the extreme north and south), and also in temperate Asia.

The plant was formerly important medicinally, the dried flowers being used to relieve respiratory and kidney complaints. Although becoming slightly less common, the flowers are still collected to make a home-made wine.

The Cowslip forms a hybrid with the Primrose *(P. vulgaris)* and this hybrid *(P. veris* X *vulgaris)* has larger paler flowers and is a more hairy plant, known as False Oxlip.

OXLIP, PAIGLE
Primula elatior (L.) Hill

Also commonly known as Paigle (referring to the symbol of St. Peter's bunch of keys), the Oxlip also has a short rhizome and a basal rosette of oblong-oval leaves. As in the Primrose, the leaves (which are rather longer) are inrolled when young and, like the stems, are hairy.

The flowers are without scent and are pale yellow with orange marks at the base. The calyx is greenish-yellow with green veins, 3-sided and not inflated. The flowers of the Oxlip form nodding one-sided clusters.

The fruits are capsules, and are longer than the calyx. The plant flowers between April and May and grows in damp woods, in scrub, pastures and in hedges and is known to grow up to 2,600 metres above sea level in some mountain regions. In Britain it is found on chalky boulder clay from Suffolk to Bedfordshire.

It is a variable species, with 5 subspecies which differ in their distribution range. The Oxlip is found in most parts of Europe from southern Sweden to the Alps and southern Russia, and also in southern Spain, the Carpathians and the Urals and in parts of western Asia.

Old Norse mythology claimed that the flower was the favourite of fairies, elves and mermaids. The plant was formerly used as a household remedy, supposedly relieving many different illnesses, amongst them coughs, diphtheria, rheumatism and epilepsy. The plant is still used by the pharmaceutical industry, the products being taken for insomnia and migraine. The young leaves were at one time also made into soup or salad.

The Oxlip may be mistaken for the False Oxlip but it can be distinguished from it in several ways. The Oxlip grows taller — up to 30 cm. high — and the flowers are in a pendant cluster, instead of growing spreading and upright.

MOUNTAIN TASSEL-FLOWER
Soldanella montana Mikan
Family: *Primulaceae*

This plant is not found in Britain. It has a basal rosette of undivided, rounded to kidney-shaped, toothed leaves. Flower-stems of between 10 and 30 cm. high grow from the basal leaf rosette. Umbel-shaped clusters of 3—6 flowerheads appear on each flower-stem. Both flower-stems and leaf-stalks are densely covered in glandular hairs.

The flowers are 10—16 mm. across with a striking reddish-violet bell-shaped corolla. This is cut into a fringe of narrow outward-curving segments. The fruits of the Mountain Tassel-flower are egg-shaped capsules opening by 10 blunt teeth which are at first covered by a small lid.

The plant flowers between May and June and grows in humus-rich soil in mountain woods and pastures. It is essentially a plant of mountain regions. It is known in the western parts of the Pyrenees, the eastern parts of the Alps as well as in northern mountainous regions. It also grows in Czechoslovakia, in the Carpathian mountains and in mountainous areas of the Balkans.

Together with other species of *Soldanella*, this is a protected plant in some countries.

SOWBREAD
Cyclamen europaeum Aiton
Family: *Primulaceae*

Formerly known as *C. neapolitanum*, this perennial herb has a disc-shaped corm 2—10 cm. across from which grow flower-stalks, leaves and roots. These roots arise only from the upper surface of the corm; the leaves appear after the flowers and are oval to heart-shaped, with a toothed margin of 5—9 angles. The leaves are long-stalked and dark-green, mottled with white dots above and tinged purple beneath.

The flower-stalks are always longer than the leaf-stalks and bear attractive, solitary, pendant flowers 2.5 cm. across. These have pale pink or white petals which are blotched with dark purple at the base and are reflexed i. e. turned back.

The fruits are rounded capsules with large sticky seeds which become mature only in the following year. During the ripening period, the flower-stalks twist spirally so that the fruits reach the ground, where they open by valves which are also reflexed.

The plant flowers between August and October and grows in deciduous woods, bushy places and hedge-banks, preferring cool, rather shaded habitats on humus-rich soils. In mountainous areas it often grows in pastures and amongst rocks. It grows in France, Italy, Switzerland and Yugoslavia, Albania, Greece and Turkey. In Britain, the plant was introduced. It has become naturalised in a number of places but is extremely rare.

The corm contains the poisonous glycoside cyclamin which causes disorders of the kidneys and stomach. The poison is effective even in small doses and in Sicily the fishermen use the corm to stupefy fish. In ancient times the juice was used as poison on arrows. The corm was a favourite food of wild boars which were not affected by the poison; this gave rise to the name Sowbread. A tea made from the corm was formerly a household remedy to relieve consti-pation, and also to treat rheumatism, headaches, certain heart conditions and goitre. The plant is not

very common and is protected in several countries, but may occasionally be locally abundant.

ROUND-LEAVED OR LARGER WINTERGREEN
Pyrola rotundifolia L.
Family: *Pyrolaceae*

This perennial evergreen herb grows up to 40 cm.

Primula elatior

Primula veris

Soldanella montana

Cyclamen europaeum

high, with a thin, creeping, branched rhizome and erect angular stems. The stems bear oblong scales at the base. The dark green leaves are broadly oval, leathery and long-stalked, and grow in a basal rosette. The flower-stems are leafless and end in an open elongate inflorescence.

The flowers are bell-shaped with pure white petals, and a short 5-lobed calyx. There are 10 stamens. A long curved style protrudes from the centre of each flower. The fruits are capsules. The plant flowers between June and August and grows in a variety of habitats, including woods, fens and bogs, damp rocky places and even dune-slacks.

It is known in the greater part of Europe (from Iceland to Central Spain, northern Italy and Bulgaria), Asia Minor and northern Asia to the Altai Mountains. In Britain the plant is not common.

The leaves were used as a household remedy against epilepsy and to cleanse wounds and are still, in some countries, used even today for kidney-trouble.

ONE-FLOWERED WINTERGREEN
Moneses uniflora (L.) A. Gray
Family: *Pyrolaceae*

Formerly known as *Pyrola uniflora* this small plant is perennial and up to 15 cm. high. It has a rhizome with thread-like roots and erect angular flower-stems. The evergreen leaves form a basal rosette and are short-stalked, light green and leathery, round and finely-toothed.

Each flower-stem has a large, often drooping, pleasantly scented white flower with spreading petals 1.5 cm. across. The fruits are erect capsules opening by valves. The plant flowers between May and August and grows in damp mountain woods, especially pine woods. It is known in much of Europe (but not in the extreme south), in Asia Minor and eastwards to Japan, also in North America. In Central Europe the leaves have been used to treat eye infections.

COMMON CENTAURY
Centaurium erythraea Rafn.
Family: *Gentianaceae*

This is a highly variable plant with at least six sub-

species. The plant is annual or biennial with a basal rosette of spoon-shaped leaves 1—5 cm. long, with 3—7 prominent veins. The stems are 2—50 cm. high, usually solitary and branched above. The stems leaves are smaller, narrower and with 3 veins. The flowers vary in size and are pinkish-purple or pure pink (rarely white), and are borne in dense terminal clusters.

The fruits are small capsules with numerous seeds. The plant flowers between June and September and grows in open woods, at the edges of woods, in meadows and dry grassland and on mountain slopes. It is known over most of Europe and in western and Central Asia. It was introduced into North America. This is an ancient medicinal plant and was also used as a 'magical' plant to guard against evil spirits, to ward off lightning and to protect animals against black magic. If carried in the purse it was thought to guarantee the owner money all the year round.

It was used as a household remedy to cleanse wounds and to clear eye infections. A tea made from the leaves was used to relieve stomach and liver complaints. The plant has been used successfully to treat fevers since classical times.

The flowers yield a bright yellowish-green dye which is extremely long-lasting.

The unusual name (Centaury) is said to derive from the Centaurs of Greek mythology, who were supposed to have used the plant.

LESSER PERIWINKLE
Vinca minor L.
Family: *Apocynaceae*

This small Periwinkle is a perennial shrublet with slender, trailing, non-flowering stems 1 m. or more long, which root at intervals at the nodes. The flower-stems are erect and often woody at the base.

The leaves are short-stalked, smooth, leathery and evergreen, 1.5—4.5 cm. long. They are oval, elliptical or lanceolate. The flowers are long-stalked, with a spreading blue, bluish-violet, mauve or white corolla. The petals are joined at the base with 5 wedge-shaped lobes. The flowers are solitary in the leaf axils. The fruits have brownish seeds and are formed of two spreading carpels which are fused at the base.

The plant flowers between February and May and usually forms large colonies. It grows in woods, hedges and often also amongst rocks and in vineyards. It is frequently cultivated in gardens, especially as ground-cover, but is rather invasive. It is known in Central, western and southern Europe, (but in Britain is only doubtfully native), in Asia Minor, in Caucasia and in western Asia.

This is an evergreen plant which, in the Middle Ages was used as a 'magical' plant. It was said to predict death and was the centre of many superstitions. In some cultures the leaves and flowers were wound into a bride's wreath or a death wreath, and the name 'Periwinkle' can be derived from the Latin words for its use in wreaths and garlands.

LUNGWORT
Pulmonaria officinalis L.
Family: *Boraginaceae*

Lungwort is a hairy perennial with a creeping rhizome. From this arise simple, rather weak stems up to 30 cm. high. Basal leaves appear in the autumn, and again in spring and summer, during flowering and fruiting. They are oval, heart-shaped at the base and narrowing into long leaf-stalks winged at the top. They are usually white spotted. The stem-leaves are oval and clasp the stem.

The flowers have short stalks and are pink, turning blue after pollination. The corolla is about 1 cm. across joined at the base with 5 pointed lobes which are hairy at the throat. The flowers are in short dense clusters. The fruits are dark brown nutlets.

The plant flowers between March and June and grows in shady thickets, hedgebanks and damp, open woods. It is known over most of Europe north to 68° and also in Asia eastwards to North India, in North Africa and North America.

TUBEROUS COMFREY
Symphytum tuberosum L.
Family: *Boraginaceae*

This is a perennial herb with an intermittently thickened, tuberous, creeping rhizome. From it arise leafy flower-stems 15—50 cm. high. The stem-leaves are

Centaurium erythraea

Moneses uniflora

Pyrola rotundifolia

Symphytum tuberosum

Vinca minor

Pulmonaria officinalis

broad, lance-shaped and — except the upper ones — stalked. The basal leaves die at flowering time. All leaves are bristly-haired.

The bell-shaped flowers are pale yellow, with a deeply lobed calyx, and are borne in few-flowered nodding clusters. The fruits are warty nutlets.

The plant flowers between April and July and grows in damp woods, hedgerows, and in damp, shady places generally.

It grows in Central, western and southern Europe and eastwards to south west Russia and Turkey. It is not common in Britain but is found more often in the north. It is a garden escape in Ireland.

YELLOW ARCHANGEL
Lamium galeobdolon (L.) Ehrend. and Polatschek
Family: *Labiatae*

Formerly known as *Galeobdolon luteum* or *Lamium galeobdolon*, Yellow Archangel is a common English plant.

The stems are 15—60 cm. high and bear stalked leaves which are irregularly toothed, oval and sharply pointed and 3—8 cm. long. In addition the plant has long leafy creeping stems. Both stems and leaves are hairy.

The flowers are bright yellow with a 2-lipped corolla, the lower lip divided into 3 almost equal brown-streaked lobes. The flowers are borne in whorls in the axils of leafy bracts and form long leafy spikes. The fruits are divided into four black nutlets within the calyx.

Yellow Archangel flowers between April and July and grows in damp woods and hedges, especially on heavier soils. It is known almost all over Europe, eastwards to Russia and Iran, but is rare in the north and Mediterranean regions.

This is a very variable plant, particularly in the formation of its flowers and leaves.

BASTARD BALM
Melittis melissophyllum L.
Family: *Labiatae*

This perennial is 20—70 cm. high with erect stems covered in soft hairs and usually unbranched. The leaves are stalked, up to 15 cm. long, oval, pointed, with a heart-shaped base and a coarsely rounded-toothed margin. When dried they have a very pleasant odour.

Whorls of 2—6 large pink, purple, white or variagated flowers appear in the leaf axils. The corolla is funnel-shaped with a small upper lip and the lower broad with 3 rounded spreading lobes. The calyx is bell-shaped, papery and 10-veined. The flowers are pollinated by bumblebees and hawkmoths. The fruits are 4 nutlets within the calyx.

The plant flowers between May and July and grows in deciduous woods, on hedgebanks, in ravines and among shady rocks. It prefers calcareous soil. It grows in Central and southern Europe and is sometimes cultivated in gardens. In Britain it is a rare plant confined to Wales and southern England. The plant is protected in some countries.

HEDGE WOUNDWORT
Stachys sylvatica L.
Family: *Labiatae*

This perennial herb has four-angled stems 30—120 cm. high. The plant also has a long creeping rhizome which gives off a strong odour when bruised. The leaves are long-stalked, 4—14 cm. long, oval to heart-shaped, toothed and, like the stems, covered in rough hairs. The flowers have a reddish-purple corolla with white markings but are sometimes pink or white. They are 2-lipped and both corolla and the 5-toothed calyx are hairy. The flowers are borne in whorls of 3—6, in the axils of leafy bracts. The fruits are 3-sided nutlets.

The plant flowers between June and September and grows on hedgebanks, in mixed woods, and in waste and shady places. It is known almost all over Europe, except in Iceland and the Mediterranean countries. It is a common plant in England and Wales and was formerly used for poultices.

LARGE-FLOWERED HEMP-NETTLE
Galeopsis speciosa Miller
Family: *Labiatae*

This annual herb has erect stems up to 1 m. high

Atropa belladonna

Stachys sylvatica

Galeopsis speciosa

which have swellings below the nodes covered with yellow-tipped glandular hairs. The long-stalked leaves are 2.5—10 cm. long, broadly lanceolate, pointed and toothed.

The large flowers are pale yellow, 2-lipped and usually with a conspicuous violet blotch on the lower lip. The calyx is sparsely hairy and shorter than the corolla tube.

The fruits are angular nutlets. The flowers are insect-pollinated. The plant probably hybridised with *Galeopsis pubescens* to give rise to the Common Hemp-nettle *(Galeopsis tetrahit)*. The plant flowers between July and September and may be found at the edges of woods, but is more often a weed of cultivation and waste places, especially on black peaty soils. It is widespread in Europe, but is rare in the south. In Britain the plant is scattered in distribution.

This is a very variable species, showing particularly variations in markings on the flower.

DEADLY NIGHTSHADE
Atropa belladonna L.
Family: *Solanaceae*

Deadly Nightshade is a large perennial herb 1.5—2 m. high. The smooth or slightly hairy stems bear oval pointed leaves up to 20 cm. long.

The flowers are 2.5—3 cm. across, solitary and droop-ing, with a pointed, somewhat enlarged calyx which spreads its lobes in a star shape. The corolla is bell-shaped, brownish-purple on the outside and greyish-yellow with red veins on the inside.

The fruits are large, shining black berries, 1.5—2 cm. across, which grow within the enlarged calyx. They contain a highly poisonous reddish-purple pulp and numerous kidney-shaped seeds.

The plant flowers between June and September and grows in deciduous woods, particularly on chalky soils. It is also found in thickets and on waste ground. It is known almost all over Europe, in western Asia to Iran, and also in North Africa. It has long been cultivated in various parts of the world and has subsequently become naturalised. It is thus sometimes found near old buildings and ruins.

All parts of the plant contain poisonous alkaloids. These stimulate the nervous system and dilate the

253

pupils of the eyes. They also dry up internal secretion including saliva. The symptoms of poisoning are a dry mouth, dilation of the pupils and increase in the heart beat, hallucinations, a narcotic sleep followed sometimes by death. Ten mgm. or less of this poison is enough to cause death in children but the fatal dose for adults is unknown.

Since ancient times the plant has been used and misused. During the Middle Ages an ointment made from the plant was said to be used by witches at their 'sabbath'. When rubbed on the skin the ointment made them sleepy and induced hallucinations. Nowadays the alkaloids are used in ophthalmic surgery and treatment, also as part of pre-operative injections. The plant is an important raw material in the pharmaceutical industry and for this reason has been cultivated in England and the U.S.A. The Latin name *Atropa* comes from the Greek *atropos* meaning inflexible. Atropos was one of the Fates in Greek legend who cut off the thread of life. *Belladonna* means 'beautiful woman', which refers to the fact that women used to put the juice of the berries into their eyes to make themselves appear more attractive through their pupils becoming large and black.

COMMON SPEEDWELL
Veronica officinalis L.
Family: *Scrophulariaceae*

This is a common perennial herb 10—50 cm. high with creeping rooting stems which form large mats. The ends of the stems grow upwards, each ending in a flower-spike. The leaves are 1.5—5 cm. long, oval to elliptical, almost stalkless, and toothed. Both stems and leaves are softly hairy. The flowers are small, pale blue to blue-lilac, on short stalks and in rather dense spikes of 15—25 flowers, each flower being borne in the axil of a linear bract.

Pollination is effected by a variety of bees and flies, which have easy access to the almost flat flowers. The fruits are inverted heart-shaped capsules with minute seeds.

The plant flowers between May and July and grows in dry open woods, on heaths and dry grassland. It is therefore sometimes called Heath Speedwell. It is known almost throughout Europe, the Middle East and also North America (where it was probably introduced).

This plant was used as a household remedy during the Middle Ages and in some areas a tea is still made from it to relieve catarrh and also to cleanse open wounds.

LARGE YELLOW FOXGLOVE
Digitalis grandiflora Miller
Family: *Scrophulariaceae*

This handsome Foxglove is a biennial or perennial with unbranched, glandular-hairy stems 60—100 cm. high. The leaves are 7—25 cm. long, stalkless, and are borne alternately along the stems. They are oval to lance-shaped, with a finely toothed margin, and are smooth and shining above and hairy below.

The flowers are large, pale yellow on the outside and mottled brown on the inside, and borne in a long slender spike. The corolla is tubular and slightly lobed. Within are four stamens, two of which are longer than the others.

The fruits are enclosed by the calyx and are ovoid or conical capsules. The plant flowers between June and September and grows in open woods and clearings, as well as among rocks on mountain sides.

It is known over much of Europe from Belgium and southern central France to southern parts of Russia, western parts of Siberia as well as in Asia Minor.

All parts of the plant, particularly the leaves, contain a number of poisnonous glycosides including digitalin, and this makes it an especially valuable medicinal plant. These glycosides affect the heart (by slowing down the rate of heart-beat) and circulation. They are contained in many commercial medicines but an overdose can have serious or fatal consequences. All species of *Digitalis* have varying amounts of these glycosides.

FOXGLOVE
Digitalis purpurea L.

This is a biennial or perennial species with rather larger leaves which grows up to 180 cm. high. The flowers are tubular, 4—5 cm. long, pinkish-purple or white, and spotted within. It grows in open woods, clearings and scrub, also on heaths, in lowland and

mountainous areas, especially on acid soils.
Foxglove grows in western, South West and Central Europe and also in Morocco. It is widely naturalised elsewhere. This is the only species of Foxglove in Britain and has been valued as a medicinal plant here since 500 A. D. but was not recognised until the 11th century in the rest of Europe.

TOOTHWORT
Lathraea squamaria L.
Family: *Orobanchaceae*

Like all species in this family, Toothwort is a root-parasite with a creeping fleshy rhizome covered in white fleshy scales. From this eventually develop stout, erect, pink or cream stems 15—30 cm. high and this takes approximately ten years from the germination of the seed. All parts of the plant lack chlorophyll.
The flowers are 14—17 mm. long, tubular and pink, and both calyx and corolla are 2-lipped. The flowers develop in the axils of scaly bracts and form stout, drooping, one-sided spikes. The fruits are rounded capsules with numerous seeds.
This strange plant flowers between March and May and grows in damp deciduous woods and in hedge-rows, especially on the richer soils. It is a total parasite, drawing its nourishment from the roots of the trees on which it grows. It is found most often on hazel, poplar, elm, beech and alder. It often appears in vineyards where it causes much damage. The plant is known almost all over Europe as well as in temperate parts of Asia to the Himalayas.

SWEET WOODRUFF
Galium odoratum (L.) Scop.
Family: *Rubiaceae*

Sweet Woodruff was formerly known as *Asperula*. It is a sweet-smelling perennial herb giving off the scent of new-mown hay when crushed. The 4-angled stems grow 15—45 cm. high and bear a whorl of 6—8 leaves at each node. These leaves are lanceolate-elliptical, 2.5—4 cm. long, with prickly margins.
The flowers are small, scented and have deeply lobed, white corollas. They form terminal, umbel-like clusters 3—4 cm. across. The small fruits are covered in hooked bristles.

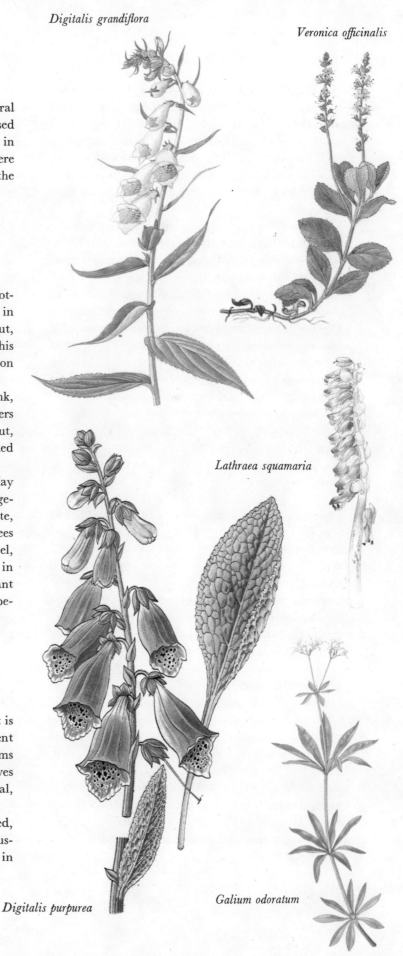

Digitalis grandiflora

Veronica officinalis

Lathraea squamaria

Digitalis purpurea

Galium odoratum

The plant flowers between April and June and grows in damp deciduous woods, particularly those on limy soils. It is found at up to 1,600 m. above sea level in mountainous areas. It grows in Central and northern Europe; in southern Europe it is found only in mountainous areas. It also grows in Siberia and in North Africa. The plant is found in almost all parts of Britain.

All parts of the plant contain coumarin, the smell of which is particularly noticeable when the plant is dry. It also contains tannins and bitter substances as well as a glycoside. This plant has, since ancient times, been used as a household remedy to relieve jaundice, heart conditions, and also to alleviate stones in the bladder. The coumarin it contains could make it valuable in treating excessive blood-clotting conditions. Its use for other ailments, like its use as a crude bedding material, is a thing of the past. In some countries a tea is still made from the leaves and these, and the stems, are used to flavour wines and liqueurs.

DANEWORT
Sambucus ebulus L.
Family: *Caprifoliaceae*

This is a strong-smelling perennial herb 60—120 cm. high. It has a creeping rhizome and numerous erect unbranched stems. The stipulate leaves are pinnate, with 7—13 oblong or lance-shaped, sharply toothed leaflets 5—15 cm. long.

The small white or pink flowers have nearly flat 5-lobed corollas and reddish-violet, later black, stamens. They are borne in flat-topped inflorescences 7—10 cm. across and with 3 primary branches, and often smell of bitter almonds.

The stalked black fruits contain seeds which are usually eaten by birds and so spread in and around towns and villages. It may thus become a weed of roadsides and waste places but it is also found in clearings in woods, hedgerows and scrub.

The plant flowers between June and August. It is doubtfully native in Britain, never common, and scattered over much of the country but mainly in the south. It is found in Central and southern Europe, in western parts of Asia to the Himalayas, also in Madeira.

Danewort has often been thought to be poisonous. This has no justification for it contains only a very small amount of glycosides. It does contain tannins and bitter substances, also volatile oils. The fruits have always been made into a dye with which, even today, leather and threads are dyed. In the past, ink was made from the fruit and in Rumania wines are coloured with it.

The fruits and rhizomes are collected, dried and made into a tea to relieve infections of the urinary tract. It is also a purgative and can cause vomiting. The fruits are not made into wines and jellies as are those of the related Elder *(Sambucus nigra)*.

NARROW-LEAVED BELLFLOWER
Campanula persicifolia L.
Family: *Campanulaceae*

This familiar plant is widely grown in gardens in Britain. In the wild it grows up to 1 m. high. It usually has unbranched stems and narrow elongate leaves. Both stems and leaves are smooth and contain latex. The flowers are up to 4 cm. across, bluish-violet, rarely white. The corolla is broad, bell-shaped and has 5 shallow triangular lobes. The flowers are borne in a stalked spike of 2—8 or more flowers, each flower developing in the axil of a bract. Further small inflorescences may develop in these axils. The fruits are capsules which open by three valves, expelling brownish seeds.

The plant flowers between June and September and grows in open woods, thickets and hedges. It is known in almost all of Europe and in western and northern Asia.

Senecio nemorensis L.
Family: *Compositae*

This plant is not found in Britain. It is a robust perennial which grows up to 2 m. high and has erect leafy stems terminating in flat-topped clusters of flowerheads. The leaves are oval or lance-shaped, toothed and half-clasp the stem. When dried they emit a very strong and unusual scent.

The flowers are yellow and are borne in heads 1.5—2.5 cm. across. The ray florets are few (4—8), the disc

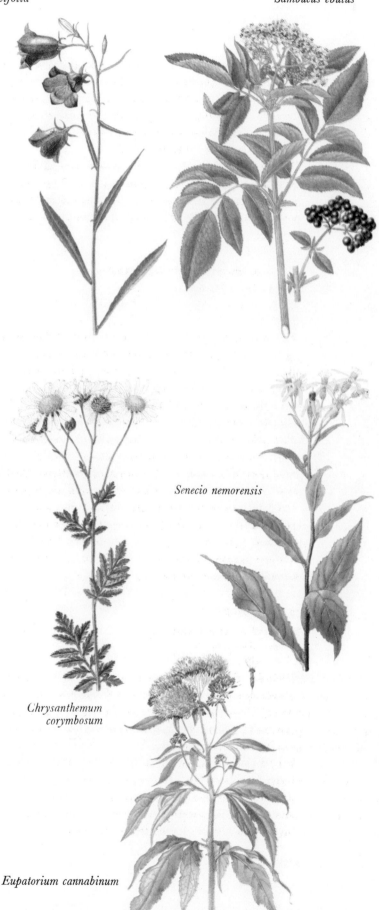

florets are tubular and the flowerheads have a bell-shaped involucre. The fruits bear a pappus of several rows of hairs.

The plant flowers between July and August and grows in damp woods and ravines among hills. It is widespread in southern and Central Europe.

This is a very variable species. It was used as a household remedy from the time of the Middle Ages and it is at present still used in some countries to cleanse wounds. Ointments were made in the past from the sap of the leaves.

Chrysanthemum corymbosum L.
Family: *Compositae*

This perennial herb is not found in Britain. It grows up to about 60 cm. high with a number of leafy branched stems. The leaves are yellowish-green and pinnate, with 7—15 much lobed, toothed leaflets.

The flowerheads have yellow tubular disc florets and white strap-shaped ray florets, and are 2.5—4 cm. across; they are grouped, 3—10 together, in flat-topped clusters. The fruits are flattened and ribbed, and have no pappus.

The plant flowers between July and August and grows in light woods and waysides and on sunny overgrown hillsides. It prefers calcareous soils and a warm position. It is known in Central and southern Europe, in Asia Minor and in Caucasia.

Chrysanthemum corymbosum resembles Feverfew *(Chrysanthemum parthenium)* in many features, but differs particularly in its total lack of aromatic oils.

HEMP AGRIMONY
Eupatorium cannabinum L.
Family: *Compositae*

This is a robust perennial up to 160 cm. high. It has a short woody rhizome and erect, softly hairy stems which are leafy and often reddish in colour. All leaves are paired, hairy and glandular. The lower leaves are simple, and the stem-leaves are deeply 3-lobed. The flowerheads have purple-tipped involucral bracts. There are no ray florets and only 5—6 disc florets which are mauve, reddish or white. The heads are in dense, flat-topped clusters.

Senecio nemorensis

*Chrysanthemum
corymbosum*

Eupatorium cannabinum

The fruits are blackish, 5-angled and gland-dotted, with a simple pappus. The plant flowers from July to September and grows in damp woods, beside streams, in marshes and fens. It grows throughout Europe, Asia Minor and Caucasia, in western and Central Asia and in North Africa.

Both the root and leaves have a bitter taste and have been used as a household remedy. Hemp Agrimony has an unusual appearance for a member of the Compositae; it is allied to the small garden plant called *Ageratum*.

WOOD OR HEATH CUDWEED
Gnaphalium sylvaticum L.
Family: *Compositae*

This is an erect perennial 8—60 cm. high. The stems are branched only at the base and bear rather well-spaced linear leaves 2—8 cm. long, which become progressively smaller higher up the stem. All leaves are hairless above, with white woolly hairs beneath. The flowerheads have pale brown florets which are all disc florets; the 3 or 4 central ones are bisexual, the more numerous outer florets are female. The flowerheads are borne singly or in clusters of 2—8 in the leaf-axils. The fruits are cylindrical with a reddish pappus. The plant flowers between July and September and grows in dry woods, heaths and on dry pastures usually on acid soils. It is known practically throughout Europe (except in Portugal and Turkey), also in the Caucasus and North America.

CAT'S-FOOT
Antennaria dioica (L.) Gaertner
Family: *Compositae*

Cat's-foot is a low growing perennial with a short woody rhizome from which grow creeping, rooting stems. These stems produce leafy rosettes, which can give rise to new plants, and also erect leafy flower-stems 5—20 cm. high.

The flower-stems, and also the lower surfaces of the leaves, are covered with white woolly hairs. The rosette leaves are spoon-shaped; the upper stem-leaves being narrower and linear. The smooth green upper leaf surface belies the common name of the plant, which refers to the softly hairy appearance below.

This is a unisexual plant. The flowerheads are short-stalked and in terminal clusters of 2—8. Male plants have flowerheads which are 6 mm. across, surrounded by white or pink, blunt, oval, involucral bracts and containing sterile bisexual and also male florets. Female plants of Cat's-foot have flowerheads which are 12 mm. across with rose-pink linear involucral bracts.

The plant flowers between May and July and usually grows in large clumps. It is chiefly a plant of mountain grassland, heaths and dry pastures but may also be found on the fringes of adjacent woods. It grows in northern and Central Europe (but not the Mediterranean region), in Siberia, western Asia and North America. It is mainly a mountain plant.

The leaves were used in the past as a household remedy for throat infections. The flowers were made into wreaths.

ALPINE OR PURPLE COLTSFOOT
Homogyne alpina (L.) Cass.
Family: *Compositae*

This perennial grows 10—40 cm. high. It has a thin rhizome covered with woolly scales. From the rhizome grow leafy creeping stems and erect flower-stems (tinged reddish-brown), which bear a few oval scales (reduced leaves) and hairs which are cottony near the base of the stems, glandular above. The green leaves form a basal rosette and are up to 4 cm. across, leathery, round or kidney-shaped with a heart-shaped base and toothed. They are often purplish beneath. The flowerheads are solitary, 1—1.5 cm. across, consisting of a number of pale violet disc florets surrounded by an involucre of linear purple-tipped cottony bracts. The fruits bear a pappus of simple white hairs.

The plant flowers from May to September, in open mountain woods and clearings, in damp pastures and on mountain pastures above the tree line, sometimes near springs. It grows in mountainous regions of Central and South East Europe. It is a great rarity in Britain.

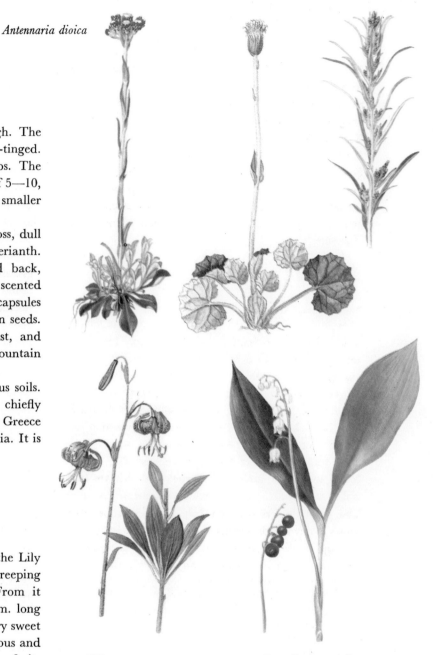

Antennaria dioica

MARTAGON LILY
Lilium martagon L.
Family: *Liliaceae*

This handsome lily grows up to 1.5 m. high. The erect stems are leafy and usually reddish-tinged. They grow singly from yellowish scaly bulbs. The leaves are 7—20 cm. long, mostly in whorls of 5—10, and lanceolate. Those at the top of the stem are smaller and single.

The long-stalked flowers are about 4 cm. across, dull purple with darker purple spots within the perianth. The long lobes of the perianth are curled back, exposing the long stamens and style. The scented flowers are pollinated by moths. The fruits are capsules opening by 3 valves and containing flat brown seeds. The plant flowers between June and August, and grows in deciduous woods, in scrub and in mountain pastures.

The Martagon Lily is said to prefer calcareous soils. The plant is known over much of Europe, chiefly in mountain regions from France and Spain to Greece and Russia. It also grows in northern Mongolia. It is naturalised in Scandinavia and Britain.

LILY-OF-THE-VALLEY
Convallaria majalis L.
Family: *Liliaceae*

This is one of the most familiar members of the Lily family. It has a long, much-branched and creeping rhizome which bears roots at the nodes. From it develop pairs of lance-shaped leaves 8—20 cm. long with obvious parallel veins. The flowers are very sweet scented, white or cream, bell-shaped, pendulous and borne in a 1-sided elongate inflorescence. The fruits are scarlet berries containing 12—24 round seeds. The plant flowers between April and June, growing in large clusters in dry deciduous woods and clearings, also in thickets. It is commonly cultivated in gardens. It is known almost all over Europe, except for the most southern and most northern areas. It also grows in northern parts of Asia, eastern parts of China and in Japan. It has been introduced in other temperate areas.

The plant contains poisonous glycosides as well as the

Lilium martagon   *Convallaria majalis*

alkaloid majalin and volatile oils. The leaves yield a green dye and this was formerly used to dye household articles. It has been of medicinal use and was formerly used to treat heart diseases and epilepsy. The leaves, roots and particularly the flowers are collected and used as a raw material in the pharmaceutical industry. The medicinal compounds present in Lily-of-the-valley have a similar effect on the action

259

of the heart to that of digitalin, although the action is less marked.

The flowerheads used to be dried and added to snuff. The strongly scented volatile oils obtained from the flowerheads were, and still are, used in the manufacture of perfume and to scent lotions, soaps, talcum powder and other toilet preparations.

HERB PARIS
Paris quadrifolia L.
Family: *Liliaceae*

This unusual plant has stems 15—40 cm. high which grow from a creeping rhizome. Each stem has a group of usually 4 leaves in a whorl on an otherwise leafless stem — hence the specific name.

The flowers are borne above the leaves on a long solitary stalk. The 4 outer perianth segments are 2.5—3.5 cm. long, lance-shaped, spreading and greenish; the inner 4 are linear and shorter. There are 8 prominent stamens and 4 purplish-black carpels. The fruit is a kind of large, shiny, black berry containing numerous brown seeds.

The plant flowers between April and July, growing in damp woods on limy soils. It is known in northern, Central and much of southern Europe; it is also found in the Caucasus and parts of Siberia.

All parts of the plant, particularly the berries are very poisonous, containing an unpleasant, bitter-tasting compound as well as citric acid. The seeds are fatty.

A red dye was made from the berries and the juice from the leaves used to cleanse wounds. In the past the plant was also used as a household remedy for infectious diseases.

Some authorities place *Paris* in the family Trilliaceae.

SOLOMON'S SEAL
Polygonatum multiflorum (L.) All.
Family: *Liliaceae*

This perennial plant has a stout, creeping rhizome from which grow erect, arching stems up to 80 cm. high. The smooth, stalkless leaves are borne on either side along the length of the stem and are 5—12 cm. long and oval to elliptical in shape.

The flowers are without scent and have a narrow, tubular white perianth — somewhat constricted in the middle — with six greenish-tipped teeth. They are borne in stalked clusters of 2—5 flowers in the axil of each leaf. The fruits are bluish-black berries, with rounded seeds which have an unpleasant and sickly flavour.

This plant flowers between May and June and grows in shady woods, in scrub and in shady places generally. The garden variety of Solomon's Seal is a hybrid between *P. multiflorum* and the sweet-scented *P. odoratum*. It grows over most of Europe and in the temperate zones of Asia to Japan.

The plant takes its name from the prominent circular stem scars on the subterranean rhizome, one being formed each year. They bear some resemblance to a document seal.

SWEET-SCENTED SOLOMON'S SEAL
Polygonatum odoratum (Miller) Druce

This species differs in having angular stems bearing solitary or paired flowers. These flowers are larger than those of *P. multiflorum* and are sweetly scented.

RAMSONS
Allium ursinum L.
Family: *Liliaceae*

This perennial plant forms a small slender bulb which exudes a strong garlicky smell. The plant has a basal rosette of usually 2 bright green, broad, elliptical or oval leaves, 10—25 cm. long. Each leaf narrows into a stalk which is twisted through 180° and is as long as the blade.

The flowers are also long-stalked and are 8—10 mm. across. They have white, star-shaped, spreading or reflexed perianths and form flat-topped umbels. The fruits are capsules and contain seeds which are spread by ants. The seeds do not usually begin to germinate until they are at least fourteen months old. The plant flowers between April and July, often growing in large colonies, and preferring shady places including damp woods and hedgebanks. It is known in almost all of Europe, also in Asia Minor, Caucasia and Siberia.

Both leaves and bulbs were used medicinally in the past. It is interesting that its intense garlic flavour can be tasted in the milk of cows which have eaten the plant.

MAY LILY
Maianthemum bifolium (L.) Schmidt
Family: *Liliaceae*

The May Lily is extremely rare in Britain. It has a slender creeping rhizome from which grow stems 8—20 cm. high, each bearing 2 leaves. There are also 1—3 long-stalked basal leaves. The stem-leaves are pointed and oval, with a heart-shaped base. When dried they smell of coumarin. The basal leaves usually die before flowering begins.

The flowers are short-stalked, 1—2 cm. across with a white, star-shaped, spreading perianth. They are borne in dense clusters of 8—15 flowers. The fruits are at first pink — developing into red berries about 6 mm. across.

The plant flowers between May and July and is a woodland plant. It tolerates quite high altitues and will grow in mountainous areas at up to 2,100 m. above sea level. It is widespread in Europe and is also found in northern temperate parts of Asia eastwards to Korea.

SNOWDROP
Galanthus nivalis L.
Family: *Amaryllidaceae*

The Snowdrop is one of the best-known spring plants. It has a small bulb from which grow 2 linear, bluish-green basal leaves and later an erect flower-stem up to 25 cm. high. At the top of this stem is a membranous green bilobed bract known as a *sphathe*. In the axil of the spathe develops the single long-stalked pendant flower. This has 3 outer pure white perianth segments and 3 inner shorter ones, which are deeply notched and have a green margin or spot.

The fruits are ovoid capsules. They contain numerous seeds which have a horn-shaped appendage. This is often eaten by ants and thus the seeds are dispersed.

Paris quadrifolia

Polygonatum multiflorum

Allium ursinum

Galanthus nivalis

Maianthemum bifolium

The plant dies down shortly after flowering. As suggested by its name, the Snowdrop flowers from January to March. It is found in damp woods and meadows, and by shady streamsides. It is commonly cultivated. It is known over most of Europe as far south as Sicily, and also in south east Russia, northern Syria, Caucasia and Asia Minor.

261

SPRING SNOWFLAKE
Leucojum vernum L.
Family: *Amaryllidaceae*

This spring-flowering plant has a bulb about 2 cm. across from which grow 3 or 4 bright green linear leaves. A leafless flower-stem grows from between these leaves up to 15—40 cm. high; it has a papery green bilobed spathe 3—4 cm. long. In the axil of this is a pendulous stalk bearing 1 (sometimes 2) flowers. These flowers are not unlike those of the Snowdrop but differ essentially in the longer inner perianth. The perianth is white or yellowish with 6 segments all of which are tipped with yellowish-green.

The plant flowers between February and April and grows in damp woods, and thickets, on hedgebanks and in meadows. It is essentially a hill plant of southern and Central Europe except for the warmer parts of the Mediterranean region. It is extremely rare in Britain, where it has possibly been introduced. This is a popular plant often cultivated in gardens and protected in several countries, since it is becoming rather scarce.

BUSHGRASS
Calamagrostis epigejos (L.) Roth.
Family: *Gramineae*

This is a rather stout perennial grass which grows 60—200 cm. high. The leaves are greyish-green, rough, flat and long-pointed with a long torn ligule. The brown, green or violet-tinged spikelets are borne in a spreading much-branched inflorescence 15—30 cm. long. Each spikelet consists of 1 floret only and this has a number of silky hairs at the base and a single short awn.

This grass flowers between June and August and usually covers large areas in damp woods, fens and ditches. It is abundant in England but rare in the rest of Britain. It is known in most of Europe, and also throughout the whole of temperate Asia.

Calamagrostis arundinacea (L.) Roth.

This is a stiff, hairless, perennial grass which has

erect stems .5—1.5 m. high and also underground creeping stems. The purplish spikelets of the inflorescence have 1 hairy, fertile floret and a single rudimentary one. The plant grows in mountain woods and scrub in much of Europe and in temperate parts of Asia. It is not found in Britain.

Calamagrostis is a large genus of grasses with about 120 species growing in temperate regions. Britain has 4 native species, one of which, *C. scotica* is very rare.

LADY'S SLIPPER ORCHID
Cypripedium calceolus L.
Family: *Orchidaceae*

This particular orchid has a most handsome flower. It is a perennial, with a short, scaly, creeping rhizome and leafy green stems 15—50 cm. high. The leaves are sheathing, lanceolate and strongly veined.

The flowers are usually solitary, occasionally 2 on a stem, in the axils of leafy bracts. The perianth is large and spreading and is 6—9 cm. across. Like those of all orchids it shows bilateral symmetry with the lower and inner perianth segment enlarged to form the lip or *labellum*. In *Cypripedium* the labellum is especially large, forming an inflated slipper-shaped sac. In this species the labellum is yellow, veined and spotted on the inside with red. The other perianth segments are maroon. In the centre of the flower is the *column*, formed by the 2 fertile anthers and the stigmas. The fruits are elongate capsules.

Insects pollinate the flower when they crawl from the labellum, inside which they collect, to the column. The plant flowers in May and June, growing in woods and thickets on limestone soils. It is nearly extinct in Britain but still grows in much of Central and northern Europe, also in northern Asia.

WHITE HELLEBORINE
Cephalanthera damasonium (Miller) Druce
Family: *Orchidaceae*

This Helleborine is perennial, 15—50 cm. high, and has a creeping rhizome with narrow leafy stems which are scaly at the base. The leaves are alternate, 5—10 cm. long, oval to lance-shaped and clasp the stem. Higher up the stem they become smaller, finally

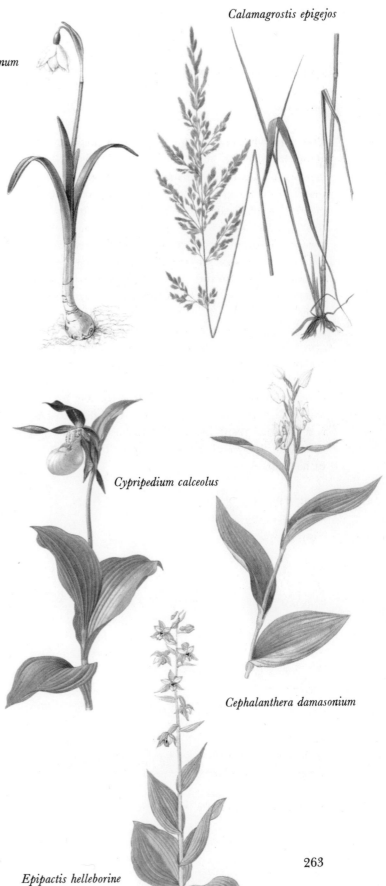

Leucojum vernum

Calamagrostis epigejos

Cypripedium calceolus

Cephalanthera damasonium

Epipactis helleborine

becoming leafy bracts. The flowers are 3—12 on a stem and have a tubular creamy-white perianth. The flowers are usually self-pollinated.

The plant flowers in May and June and grows in woods and in shady bushy places on chalky soils, especially near beech trees. It is known in most of Europe (including England), in Central Russia and Caucasia, in Asia Minor and North Africa.

RED HELLEBORINE
Cephalanthera rubra (L.) Richard

This species has hairy stems 20—50 cm. high which bear 3—10 bright rose-red flowers.

BROAD HELLEBORINE
Epipactis helleborine (L.) Crantz
Family: *Orchidaceae*

This is another genus of Helleborines. The plant has a thick short rhizome with 1—3 leafy stems. These stems are 25—80 cm. high, with 2 or more basal scales, and are hairy above and violet-tinged below. The characteristic broad, oval, almost round leaves are 5—17 cm. long, the lower ones clasping the stem, the upper ones grading into leaf-like bracts.

The flowers are greenish or purple and unscented. The labellum is short, with 2 smooth basal bosses. The 15—50 drooping flowers are borne in a long, one-sided spike. The plant flowers between July and September and grows in woods, hedges and meadows and also in rocky and grassy places.

The plant is known all over Europe, in temperate parts of Asia eastwards to the Himalayas and Japan, also in North Africa.

It is variable in both floral and vegetative features.

DARK RED HELLEBORINE
Epipactis atrorubens (Hoffm.) Schultes

This rare British plant is not found in southern counties. It has dark wine-red flowers which are vanilla-

263

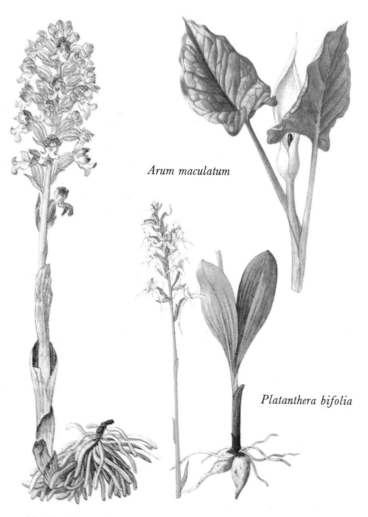

Arum maculatum

Platanthera bifolia

Neottia nidus-avis

green leaves and the plant lives as a *saprophyte* in humus-rich soils, absorbing soluble carbohydrates and proteins by means of *mycorrhiza*. These are literally 'fungal roots' and are roots which are in intimate association with a soil fungus. A number of other plants (not necessarily lacking chlorophyll) form similar associations.

The flowers are honey-brown and smell of honey. They have a large two-lobed labellum and are borne in inflorescences 5—20 cm. long.

It grows in shady woods especially beech woods. It prefers calcareous soils and is found almost throughout Europe and also in Siberia and the Caucasus.

LESSER BUTTERFLY ORCHID
Platanthera bifolia (L.) Richard
Family: *Orchidaceae*

This Orchid has 2 tapering root-tubers from which grows a stem 15—45 cm. high with 2 or 3 sheathing basal scales, 2 large elliptical basal leaves 3—9 cm. long, and smaller leaves which grade into bracts. The flowers are large, greenish-white and vanilla-scented, with a spreading perianth including a long, narrow, spurred and green-tipped labellum. The inflorescence is a rather open one containing up to 20 flowers.

The plant flowers between May and July and grows in open woods, in marshes, and on grassy hillsides and especially on calcareous soils. It may be found at up to 2,000 m. above sea level and grows almost throughout Europe (except in Iceland), also in Caucasia, North Africa and northern Asia.

GREATER BUTTERFLY ORCHID
Platanthera chlorantha (Cust.) Reichenb.

This species resembles *P. bifolia* in most respects but is larger (up to 60 cm. tall) and with more greenish flowers — these have thick-lipped spurs.

LORDS-AND-LADIES, CUCKOO-PINT
Arum maculatum L.
Family: *Araceae*

This perennial plant is up to 50 cm. high and has

scented. It grows in woods and grassy places, also among rocks and in screes but almost always in limestone areas. Occasionally, however, it may be found among dunes. It grows virtually throughout Europe, in the Caucasus and in Iran.

BIRD'S-NEST ORCHID
Neottia nidus-avis (L.) Richard
Family: *Orchidaceae*

This plant is a fairly widely distributed orchid in Britain. It takes its common name (Bird's-nest Orchid) from the tangled mass of short fleshy roots which surround the short rhizome and which resemble a bird's nest.

The erect stems develop from the rhizome and are 20—50 cm. high, brownish, glandular and with numerous sheathing scales at the base. There are no

264

a tuberous rhizome, a new one being formed each year. The leaves are long-stalked with net-veined, dark-spotted, arrow-shaped blades. In April—May, a stout flower-stem appears which has a rather complex structure.

This specialised stem is known as a *spadix*; it enlarges at the tip and becomes purple in colour. Below this are numerous small flowers which are almost entirely enclosed by a leafy sheath known as a *spathe*. This is 15—25 cm. long, pale green and often blotched with purple, and longer than the spadix. The flowers are arranged in 4 zones — fertile female flowers at the base, sterile female flowers above, fertile male flowers above these and sterile male flowers uppermost.

The flowers exude an unpleasant smell which attracts small flies and midges. These are trapped deep inside the spathe because the sterile flowers form downward-pointing hairs and prevent the insects from escaping. The flowers are pollinated in a very specialised way. The female flowers ripen first and are pollinated by pollen carried into the spathe by the insects. Meanwhile the male flowers are maturing. The sterile flowers now shrivel, thus allowing the insects to escape and, as they crawl over the ripe stamens, to carry away more pollen.

By July, a number of scarlet fleshy berries will have developed, and they form a spike 3—5 cm. long. The plant grows in damp, shady woods and hedges. It prefers calcareous soils and tolerates shade very well. It grows in Central and southern Europe, and part of northern Europe, also in North Africa.

All parts of the plant, particularly the rhizome and the berries, contain poisonous substances, chiefly glycosides. These have a marked effect on the heart. The poison can be inactivated by heat i.e. if the plant is dried, boiled or roasted. The rhizome contains up to 70 % starch but has a bitter taste. This can be destroyed by boiling. In some countries when times were hard the boiled rhizomes were eaten.

Lords-and-ladies has been known in the past as a 'magical' plant to scare evil ghosts. It was also put in the cradle of any new born child to protect it against evil spells.

This is a familiar British plant and one which has acquired a variety of names in different parts of the country.

NORWAY SPRUCE
Picea abies (L.) Karsten
Family: *Pinaceae*

This conifer grows 30—60 m. high and has a flat, shallow root system without a tap root. It is therefore easily uprooted. The tree is slender and pyramidal in shape. The leaves are dark green sharp-pointed needles which last up to 7 years and are 1—2 cm. long. They are 4-angled, with 2 or 3 faint lines of stomata externally and usually 2 resin-canals internally. The leaves are borne directly on the stems (not on short shoots as in, for example, *Pinus*). The twigs are usually brown and the twiglets pendulous. The cones emerge in May to June. The male cones develop in the axils of the previous year's leaves. The female cones grow at the tips of the branches and towards the upper part of the tree. They are at first pink, but after pollination become brownish and pendant. They ripen in one year and are cylindrical and 10—15 cm. long, with thin irregularly toothed scales. The seeds are winged.

This Spruce is native to northern and Central Europe from Scandinavia and Russia to the Pyrenees, Alps and Macedonia. Nowadays it is extensively planted for forestry and, although a mountain tree, is grown in both lowland and upland areas.

Norway Spruce yields a strong timber which is used

Picea abies

Pinus sylvestris

for a variety of construction purposes. The bark yields
a useful resin and is also a source of tannins.

SILVER FIR
Abies alba Miller
Family: *Pinaceae*

This is a handsome conifer which may grow to
a height of 50 m. It has a stout trunk and a pyramidal
crown, becoming flatter with age. The bark is smooth
and greyish-white and the young twigs are downy.
The leaves are 1.5—3 cm. long and are borne directly
on the stems, in 2 sets along each side of the stems.
The upper rows are upright, the lower are horizontal.
The leaf surface is dark green and shining above and
bears 2 white waxy stomatal lines below. Internally
they have resin-canals.
The cones appear in May and June. The male cones
develop in leaf axils on the lower side of twigs. The
male cones develop on the upper side. They mature
in one year and are erect, cylindrical and 10—20 cm.
long. The ripe scales drop off the axis.
Silver Fir forms natural mountain forest in Central
and southern Europe from southern Germany to the
Pyrenees, southern Italy and Macedonia but is also
extensively planted. It is grown for timber in northern
and western Europe. The wood is used in construction
work and also papermaking and the bark yields
turpentine and tannins.

SCOTS PINE
Pinus sylvestris L.
Family: *Pinaceae*

This familiar conifer grows up to 40 cm. high and
is pyramidal when young but becomes flat-topped
with age. The bark on the upper trunk is bright
reddish-brown but becomes dark brown below. The
needles are between 3 and 7 cm. long, bluish-green
and twisted. They grow in pairs on short shoots.
Internally, as in all species of *Pinus*, there are a number
of resin-canals.
The male cones are about 6 mm. long, and are borne
in large clusters in place of the short shoots at the
base of the new season's growth. The pink female
cones are at first upright, solitary or sometimes in

Abies alba

clusters of 2 or 3, at the ends of the new season's
growth. After pollination the cones turn down.
The cones are at first green, turning brown after
fertilisation in the second year. They are sharp-
pointed, 3—6 cm. long and pendulous, and take 2—3
years to mature. The young cones appear between
May and June and the ripe female cones shed their
winged seeds in autumn. Scots Pine is found growing
naturally in sandy soils, on heaths, on hillsides and
amongst rocks.
This is one of the most common pine trees growing in
Central and northern Europe as well as in northern
parts of Asia. It is commonly grown in plantations.
The wood is light, soft and rich in resin and is thus
less affected by dampness. This makes it a multi-
purpose wood used for construction work and furniture, and also in paper manufacture. Resin, creosote
and turpentine are obtained from wood and bark.
The buds contain volatile oils and vitamin C; they
were used medicinally for bronchial catarrh and
rheumatism.

BLACK PINE
Pinus nigra Arnold

This pine grows up to 50 m. high and is pyramidal
in shape with blackish-grey bark. There are 5 subspecies of varying appearance. The dark green rigid

Pinus nigra

Pinus mugo

Larix decidua

needles are 4—19 cm. long and grow in pairs on short shoots, remaining on the tree for about 4—5 years.

The male cones are borne in a similar fashion to those of *P. sylvestris* but are somewhat larger. The female cones grow at the tips of the branches and are at first reddish. All the cones grow at right angles to the stem and are 3—8 cm. long, shiny and light brown. They ripen during the third year and shortly afterwards fall off.

The tree produces new cones in May and June and grows naturally in mountainous areas in Spain, Italy, Corsica, Sicily, Austria, the Balkans and the Crimea, and also in Asia Minor and Morocco. The subspecies vary somewhat in distribution.

Pinus nigra is planted on dry soils in Central and northern Europe and is often grown for ornament. The wood is rich in resin and is used to produce resin and turpentine.

MOUNTAIN PINE
Pinus mugo Turra

Usually this pine develops into a dense spreading shrub 3.5 m. high. It has a short thick straight trunk and a number of low-growing branches ending in upturned twigs. The bark of the Mountain Pine is dark grey and scaly.

The needles are bright green, somewhat curved and finely toothed and 3—8 cm. long. They are borne in pairs on short shoots and remain 3—9 years on the tree.

The male cones are clustered; the female cones are purple or violet and are solitary or in pairs at the ends of the new shoots. The young cones are upright but bend downwards or horizontally after pollination. They grow 2—5 cm. long, becoming brown and glossy and ripening in the third year.

This species grows in mountainous areas of Europe. It appears either as a small 'knee pine' above the usual tree line or as a low-growing pyramidal shrub, in the variety known as *uncinata*, which grows below the tree line.

The cones are produced in May to June and the tree grows in mountainous areas of Central and South East Europe, including the Pyrenees, the Apennines and in the Carpathians.

It can grow at 2,500 metres above sea level and may form large colonies above the general tree line.

The needles and young shoots contain volatile oils which are obtained through distillation and which were formerly used to manufacture inhalants. The needles were also made into a syrup which was supposed to relieve coughs. Nowadays the tree may be planted to form shelter-belts.

COMMON LARCH
Larix decidua Miller
Family: *Pinaceae*

This tree grows up to 50 m. high and has a long tap root, an erect trunk and a pyramidal shape. The crown becomes irregular in older trees. Large trees are said to live for up to 500 years.

The branches are irregular and the twigs thin and pendulous. The old bark is flaking and greyish-brown. The soft, light green needles are borne singly directly on the young shoots and also in tufts of 30—40 on stumpy short shoots. They are 2—3 cm. long, have 2 resin-canals and are deciduous.

The male cones are yellow, rounded and solitary; the female cones are bright red, sometimes pinkish-purple, ripening in autumn of the same year as ovoid erect brown cones 2—3.5 cm. long. The Larch produces cones between April and June and grows naturally only in the Swiss and Bavarian Alps, and in the northern Carpathians. Ancient woods confirm that Larch trees must, in the past, have spread widely east and north.

Today it is planted all over Central and northern Europe. It is a variable species but is basically a light-demanding mountain forest tree.

The wood is very flexible, but tough. It is not affected adversely by damp and can be used for a variety of construction purposes.

The resin of Common Larch is soft and looks like honey. In the past it was used as a household remedy to relieve catarrh and to make ointments.

FLUTTERING ELM
Ulmus laevis Pallas
Family: *Ulmaceae*

This species of elm has a broad crown and grows up to 35 m. high. The buds are pointed and up to 1 cm. long. The leaves are short-stalked and rounded or oval in shape. They are softly hairy or smooth beneath and doubly-toothed along the margins.

The flowers are small with 8—10 red stamens and 2 stigmas hang in clusters on long stalks. They are pollinated by the wind. The fruits are elliptical and long-stalked, with a single seed in the centre of a papery hairy-rimmed wing.

The tree flowers between March and April before the leaves appear and grows in damp woods in river valleys in Central, eastern and south eastern Europe, but not in Britain.

The wood is heavy, hard and resistant to water and is therefore used, for example, for farm buildings, wooden piles, coffins and boats, and also to make furniture and for flooring.

Ulmus laevis

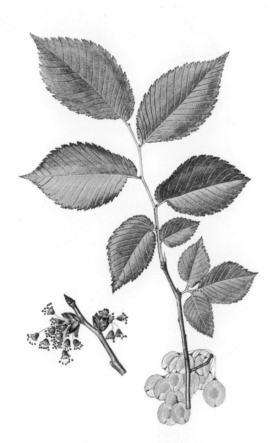

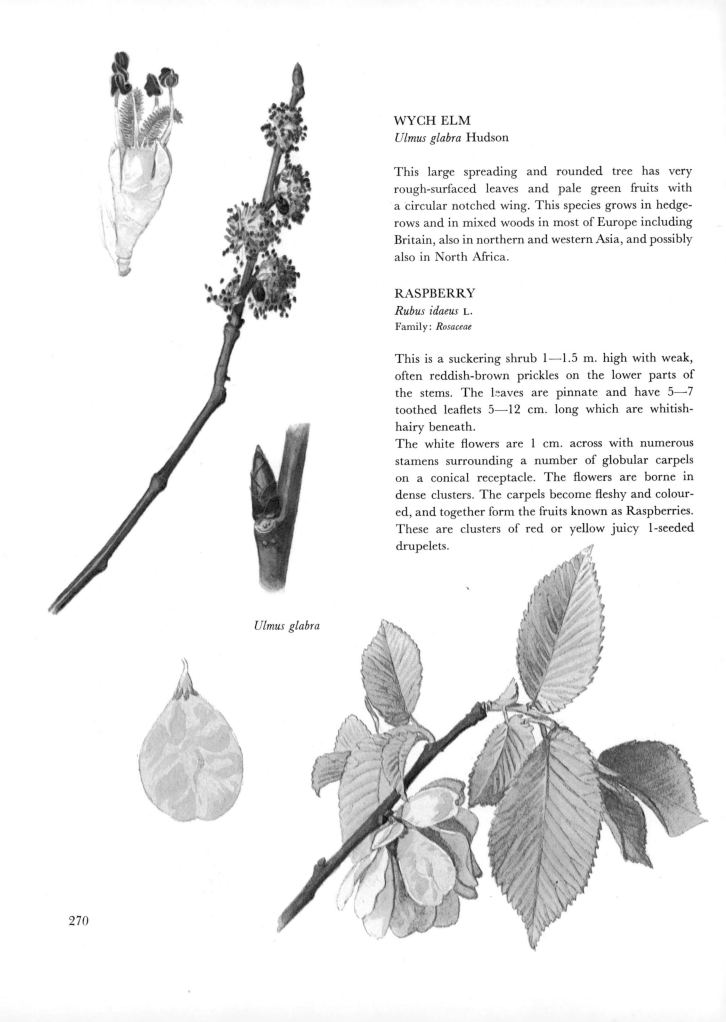

WYCH ELM
Ulmus glabra Hudson

This large spreading and rounded tree has very rough-surfaced leaves and pale green fruits with a circular notched wing. This species grows in hedgerows and in mixed woods in most of Europe including Britain, also in northern and western Asia, and possibly also in North Africa.

RASPBERRY
Rubus idaeus L.
Family: *Rosaceae*

This is a suckering shrub 1—1.5 m. high with weak, often reddish-brown prickles on the lower parts of the stems. The leaves are pinnate and have 5—7 toothed leaflets 5—12 cm. long which are whitish-hairy beneath.
The white flowers are 1 cm. across with numerous stamens surrounding a number of globular carpels on a conical receptacle. The flowers are borne in dense clusters. The carpels become fleshy and coloured, and together form the fruits known as Raspberries. These are clusters of red or yellow juicy 1-seeded drupelets.

Ulmus glabra

The shrub flowers in June—August and grows wild in groups in woods and clearings, at the edges of woods and on heaths, especially in hilly areas.

It is known virtually all over Europe (but in southern areas only in the mountains), in Asia Minor, and in North and Central Asia.

Raspberries have a very pleasant scent and flavour and are an edible fruit which can be made into wines, syrups and jams. Seeds have been found during excavations of Stone Age sites indicating ancient usage. The Raspberry has been cultivated since the Middle Ages.

John Gerard mentioned in his book 'The Herbal or General History of Plants' in 1598, that large plantations of Raspberries were established near Moscow and the plant appears to tolerate cold, but not arctic, conditions very well. In Scotland the fruit is grown on a large commercial scale.

Raspberry canes have been grown in France and England since the 17th century, and later also in North America. Several subspecies and varieties with particularly large fruits are cultivated, but the most pleasant flavour is still found in the wild fruit. The leaves contain a glycoside which affects muscle action and they are still made into a tea which, if taken during pregnancy, makes for easier childbirth.

BLACKBERRY
Rubus fruticosus L.

This is a very variable plant and is best regarded as an aggregate species. It has angled prickly stems which later become woody. They often root at the tips.

The leaves are pinnate, with 3—5 oval toothed leaflets 5—12 cm. long. The main veins and the leaf-stalks are prickly. The leaves usually overwinter. The flowers are borne in branched terminal clusters and are white or pink and 2—3 cm. across. The 5 petals surround the numerous stamens and the conical receptacle which bears the carpels. The fruits are at first red, turning shiny black and, like the Raspberry, are a collection of drupelets.

The Blackberry flowers between May and October and grows in open woods and clearings, at the edges of woods, in scrub and in hedgerows, also on heaths

and in waste places. This is an extremely variable species with several hundred varieties which are still being classified. The fruits are collected and have a pleasant sweet to sour taste. Syrups, wines, jams and jellies are made from the fruits.

This is a plant long known to man, and its seeds have been found in Stone Age settlements. It was also known in ancient Greece both as a fruit and as a medicinal plant.

The leaves contain a large amount of tannin and were often dried and made into a tea, and were also used in herbal remedies. It grows throughout Europe, including the Mediterranean region, and also in the Far East.

Rubus idaeus

Rubus fruticosus

271

Prunus padus

BIRD-CHERRY
Prunus padus L.
Family: *Rosaceae*

This small tree or shrub is 3—15 m. high and has spreading branches covered in a strong-smelling reddish-brown bark. The leaves are elliptical, 6—10 cm. long and finely toothed.

The white flowers, like the leaves, smell of almonds. They are borne in long pendulous clusters of 15—35 flowers. The fruits are black and bitter and resemble small cherries. They are eaten by birds and the seeds are thus dispersed. The roots and also rooting branches can spread over a large area and may also propagate the shrub.

Bird-cherry flowers between April and May and grows in woods and hedgerows chiefly in upland areas. In mountainous areas it can grow at a level of 1,500 metres above sea level. In Britain it is a plant of the more northern counties but is sometimes cultivated in the south.

Bird-cherry grows in most of Europe except in the Mediterranean area. It grows in Portugal and western parts of Spain, in the Alps, the Balkans, Armenia, Afghanistan, the Himalayas, Central Asia, Siberia and also in the Atlas mountains of Morocco.

Vegetative parts, but not the fruits, contain the poisonous glycoside amygdalin. The non-poisonous fruits have, since ancient times, been used to make syrups and conserves. In some areas the fruits are fermented to make alcoholic drinks.

The bark has been used in the past as a household remedy against rheumatism and gout, against stomach complaints and even against syphilis. A dye was obtained from the inner green bark. The soft wood smells of almonds and was formerly used for making gun butts. The straight branches are used to make the stems of tobacco pipes — the so-called cherry-wood pipes.

ROWAN, MOUNTAIN ASH
Sorbus aucuparia L.
Family: *Rosaceae*

This slender tree grows 15—20 m. high and has downy twigs and smooth greyish-brown branches. The leaves are pinnate and have 11—15 oblong, pointed, sharply saw-toothed leaflets which are 2.5—9 cm. long and somewhat hairy beneath. The small white flowers are in dense flat-topped clusters and have a downy calyx, 20 cream stamens and 3—4 styles.

The fruits are ovoid scarlet berries and are eaten by birds. The tree flowers between May and July and grows in open woods and clearings, in scrub and among mountain rocks. It prefers the lighter soils and is rare on clay.

It is often found close to the tree-line in mountain areas. It is also a commonly planted tree. It grows in most parts of Europe, particularly in northern areas; in Asia Minor, in western parts of Siberia, in the Caucasus and in Morocco. In Britain, the Rowan is more common in northern and western counties and grows at higher altitudes than other trees.

The fruits contain tannins and other substances. The seeds contain oil and also small amounts of the poisonous glycoside amygdalin. The fruit is used to make jam, vinegar and alcoholic beverages.

It has in the past been used as a household remedy against tuberculosis and even today the fruit is used as a mild laxative. If however the fruit is eaten in large quantities poisoning may follow.

The wood is used for carving and for making small

272

Sorbus aucuparia

1

Rosa pendulina

items of furniture. The bark has been used for its tannin and for dyeing and oil has been extracted from the seeds.

ALPINE ROSE
Rosa pendulina L.
Family: *Rosaceae*

This is a dwarf spreading shrub .5—2 m. high. The leaves are dark green, and pinnately divided into 7—11 leaflets which are 2—6 cm. long, sharply saw-toothed, and sparsely hairy beneath. The stems are purplish or green.

The flowers are large and solitary, bright carmine and borne on hairy flower-stalks. The red bottle-shaped fruit is pendulous and often glandular-hairy. This species prefers shady and damp places and flowers between May and July. It grows in mountainous areas, preferring woods, hedgerows and among rocks. In such upland areas it grows up to a height of 2,600 metres above sea level.

The Alpine Rose is known in South eastern and Central Europe; it is never found in Britain. This species and *R. blanda* are the only European ones which are thornless.

FALSE ACACIA, LOCUST
Robinia pseudoacacia L.
Family: *Leguminosae*

This grows either as a tree up to 25 m. high or as a wide-spreading and suckering shrub. The young branches have strong, shiny, reddish-brown stipular thorns. The leaves are stalked, 15—25 cm. long, pinnate, and with 7—21 stalked, oval or elliptical leaflets; they have a rounded tip and entire margin. The pea-like flowers appear in April—June and are white (rarely pink) with a yellow basal blotch. They are 1.5—2.5 cm. across, with a strong sweet scent and are borne in drooping clusters up to 20 cm. long. The fruits are large reddish-brown pods.

It originated in North America where it grew wild in deciduous woods from Virginia to South Carolina. It spread to the warm areas of northern America and was introduced into Europe in 1601 by a Monsieur Jean Robin — hence its name. Today it is known in most parts of Europe, in North Africa, eastern parts of Asia, the Middle East and in New Zealand. When this tree is in blossom it is often admired, but it is not a popular tree. This is because it is a tree which can grow on very poor soil and yet can spread quickly forming thickets. It is difficult to eradicate because of the abundance of suckers; these also spread and impoverish the soil, making it unsuitable for most other plants.

The leaves are rich in tannin and thus decompose slowly and do not readily form humus. The dead leaves also contain deleterious substances which percolate into the soil. These, together with the undecomposed leaves, seem to inhibit the germination of seeds and the growth of other plants. The roots, bark and seeds contain other substances including a poisonous glycoside.

The bark of young branches was formerly made up into a herbal remedy and used against fever and migraine. The bark also contains tannins and a yellow dye and was used to make paper and also as a substitute for silk and wool. The sweet-smelling flowers are popular with bees for their nectar and are still used commercially in the making of perfume.

From the skins of the fruit a strong narcotic and intoxicating syrup in made in America. The wood is yellow, hard and very durable. It is resistant to decay and is used for fence-posts, wheels and flooring.

Robinia pseudoacacia

HAZEL, COB-NUT
Corylus avellana L.
Family: *Corylaceae*

This bushy shrub sometimes grows into a small tree up to 6 cm. high. It has glandular hairy twigs and branches with smooth brown bark. The leaves are hairy, stalked, toothed, rounded and long-pointed, with a heart-shaped base.
The flowers are unisexual and the male flowers are borne in catkins. These appear as small greenish-brown buds which elongate into 8 cm. long catkins in the following spring. The female flowers are incon-spicuous and are in groups of 4 in leaf-like buds, but with 2 long red styles to each flower. The flowers are wind-pollinated. The fruits are nuts which are sheathed by a *cupule* formed of deeply-lobed, toothed bracts. The nuts are brown, 1.5—2 cm. across and have a hard woody shell.
The shrub flowers between January and April — before the leaves appear. It grows in light woods, at the edges of woods, in clearings and in hedgerows. It is known in Central and southern Europe, as well as in Caucasia where formerly the Hazel was a very common shrub. However in that part of the world it has now been nearly exterminated. It also grows in the Crimea, and in Asia Minor. It is native to Britain where it is common everywhere.
The nut contains 60 % oil, also protein and sugars. It is rich in calories and is a useful food.
The shrub was known to the ancient Greeks and Romans and was cultivated by them. The nuts are nowadays used as fillings for chocolates. The oil is used in the manufacture of oil paints, cosmetics and cooking oil. The wood is used to make hurdles and wattles and the branches lend themselves to being bent and made into walking sticks.

Corylus avellana

HORNBEAM
Carpinus betulus L.
Family: *Corylaceae*

The Hornbeam is a less well known tree which may

Carpinus betulus

be pollarded, but grows naturally to a height of 25 m. Pollarding is the topping of the tree about 1.5—2 m. from the ground to encourage the growth of a number of upright branches. The trunk is fluted with smooth grey bark. The leaves are 4—10 cm. long, oval and long-pointed and doubly toothed. The leaves of the Hornbeam are roughly hairy on the veins below.

The male flowers, although they form in the autumn, grow into catkins only in spring. The female flowers are also in catkins. Both catkins appear with the leaves and are pendant; the female catkins elongate to 14 cm. when in fruit. The fruits are nutlets which are hidden in three-lobed bracts (cupules) which have the middle lobe much longer than the lateral ones.

This tree flowers between April and May and grows in mixed and in oak woods, but occasionally grows as a pure stand. It is a tree found typically in European deciduous woods, mostly growing in flat areas, and not demanding much light. It tends to grow on sandy or loamy clays.

When the tree is cut, i. e. pollarded, new shoots grow very quickly from the tree stump.

The Hornbeam is cultivated in many parks. It grows in Central, southern and eastern parts of Europe, in Caucasia, Asia Minor and Iran.

The white wood is heavy and close-grained and therefore very durable. It is used for flooring and other constructional purposes. Tannin is extracted from the bark.

SILVER BIRCH
Betula pendula Roth
Family: *Betulaceae*

This is a small to medium sized tree up to 30 m. high with a slender trunk and silvery white bark. The white colouring comes from the cells in the bark which contain a substance called betulin. The twigs are brown and covered in flat-topped resin-glands. The bark at the base of the trunk is fissured and black. The main branches are erect but most of the others are pendant.

The leaves are stalked, oval or broadly triangular with a double-toothed margin. They are 2—7 cm.

long. The young leaves are covered in downy hairs but the mature leaves are smooth.

The male and female flowers are borne in separate pendant catkins. The male catkins have flowers with brown bracts and yellow stamens. The female flowers have light green bracts and purple stigmas. The fruits are winged nutlets, the wing being formed from fused bracts.

The tree flowers between April and May and grows in deciduous and mixed woods as well as in clearings. It also grows on rocky slopes and will colonise heathland. It is found all over Europe, as well as in the Caucasus, in Siberia and Asia Minor. It forms large forests in Finland and in Russia.

The leaves contain a variety of substances including volatile oils, tannins and vitamin C. They are therefore collected and used as a herbal tea. From the charcoal of the bark, material for painters and printers is made. The bark is also a source of tannins.

Birch Tar Oil is obtained from the white bark and is used for the preparation of Russian leather to which it gives its characteristic smell. It is also a fungal and insect repellant. The sap, which is obtained from the tree in spring, is made into alcoholic beverages and is also used in cosmetics. The white wood is soft and light but durable. It is used in the manufacture of furniture, also of tool-handles, and in wood carving. The twigs are used for thatching and for making brooms.

BEECH
Fagus sylvatica L.
Family: *Fagaceae*

This familiar and handsome tree grows up to 40 m. high. The leaf-buds are long pointed, with reddish-brown overlapping scales. The trunk is straight, with smooth grey bark. The leaves are a delicate light green in spring, turning to coppery-orange in autumn. They are smooth but fringed with silky hairs and are oval to elliptical with a pointed tip.

The male flowers are reddish-brown and borne in long-stalked globular pendulous catkins. The female flowers are usually in pairs and surrounded by a 4-lobed scaly cupule. This becomes woody as the fruit, which is a nut, develops. It is termed the 'mast' and

Betula pendula

277

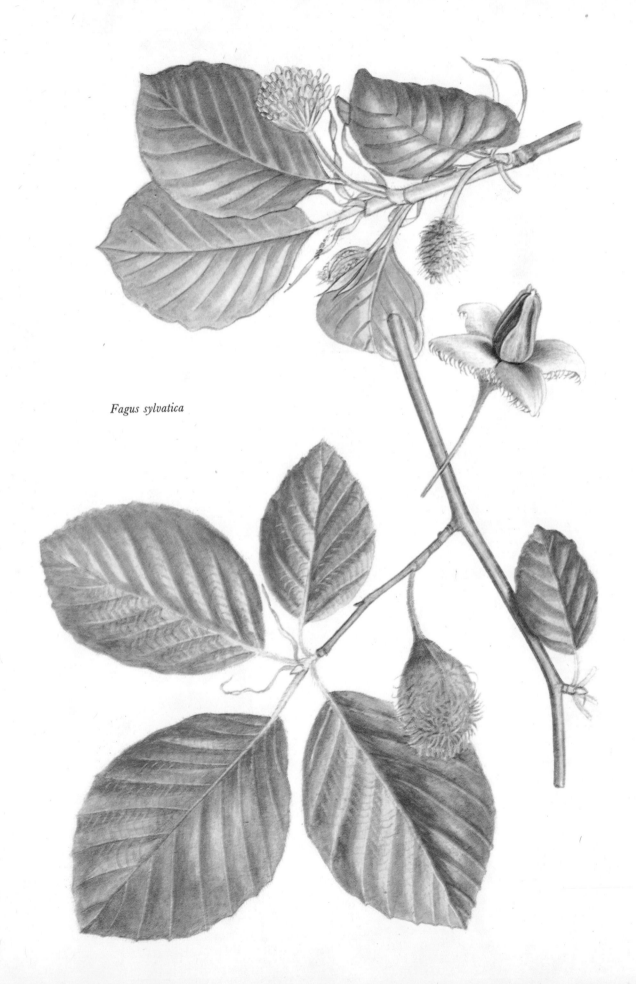

Fagus sylvatica

a good fruiting season is called a 'mast year'.

The tree flowers between April and May and grows in woods, on hills and on mountain-sides. Beech is a characteristic plant of chalk and limestone soils and also of well-drained loams and sands. It is often the dominant tree in a wood. It is often planted. It grows naturally in much of Europe, eastwards to the Crimea and southwards to Sicily and Greece. The light brown, fine-grained wood is very durable and is used for many purposes, including the making of furniture. The nuts contain 20 % oil and are eaten both by animals and man. They yield cooking, lighting and lubricating oil. Beech is a tree which casts a deep shade because its leaf canopy is particularly dense. It thus tends to exclude other plants.

COMMON OAK, PEDUNCULATE OAK
Quercus robur L.
Family: *Fagaceae*

The Common Oak is a large deciduous tree which grows up to 45 m. high and has a large spreading crown. The bark is smooth when young but later becomes deeply fissured. The leaves are short-stalked and leathery, hairy when young. They are deeply pinnately lobed, with 5—7 pairs of lobes. At the base of the blade is a pair of reflexed ear-like lobes.

The male flowers have a yellowish-green perianth and are borne in slender pendulous catkins up to 4 cm. long. The female flowers are borne in long-stalked clusters of 1—5 flowers. They are pollinated by the wind. The fruits are the familiar acorns which take 2 years to form and are half-surrounded by the small scaly cup or cupule. They grow in long-stalked clusters.

The tree flowers between April and May, growing in hedgerows and woods — where it may be the dominant tree — particularly on the heavier soils. It is also planted in parks and on large estates. It is native to Britain and grows in most of Europe (except the extreme north and the Mediterranean), in the Crimea and Caucasia.

The wood is of superb quality, being particularly hard and durable, and is used in the furniture and the building industries, but was formerly very important for building ships and timber-framed houses. The bark contains a great deal of tannin and is used in tanning leather and also as a dyestuff. The young bark contains many substances used medicinally. A tea is made from it and was used to relieve catarrh, diarrhoea and various infections, and as a lotion for frostbite and burns. It was also used as an antidote against poisoning by alkaloids. The familiar pink oak-apples (galls) also contain tannins and are used in the manufacture of ink.

In ancient times, people ate acorns. They have been roasted and used as a coffee substitute and are eaten by many animals, especially pigs, but are poisonous to cattle.

DURMAST OAK, SESSILE OAK
Quercus petraea (Mattuschka) Liebl.

This too is a familiar species of Oak in Britain. It is a large tree branching higher up than *Q. robur* and with a narrower crown. It grows up to 40 m high. It

Quercus robur

has leaves with longer stalks than those of *Q. robur*; they lack the reflexed basal lobes but have large hairs on the underside of the midrib and main veins.

The male flowers are in long catkins. The female flowers grow in clusters of 2—7 and are short-stalked. The tree flowers between April and May and grows in mixed woods preferring non-calcareous soils. It often grows in more upland areas than does *Q. robur*. Its distribution range is similar but it is found in the more mountainous parts.

This is a tree which is often crossed with other species and is also cultivated.

The wood, like that of all Oaks, is hard and durable and is used for furniture and house construction and for any other purpose requiring durability and strength. All Oaks are slow-growing and extremely long-lived.

Quercus petraea

GREAT SALLOW, GOAT WILLOW
Salix caprea L.
Family: *Salicaceae*

This shrub or small tree has smooth brownish branches with long-stalked broadly oval pointed leaves. They are rounded at the base, with a toothed margin, and are shiny above and covered in greyish hairs beneath. The lateral veins are prominent. They appear after the catkins.

Willows are unisexual. The numerous male flowers each have 2 conspicuous projecting yellow stamens and are borne in erect catkins covered in long silky hairs. Female catkins elongate to 10 cm. when fruiting. The fruits contain long-haired seeds.

The catkins appear in March-April. Goat Willow grows in woods, scrub and hedgerows, also by fresh water. In mountains it can grow up to 2,000 metres above sea level.

It is known almost everywhere in Europe (but is absent from the extreme north and south), also in temperate zones of Asia eastwards as far as Syria and Turkestan.

Willows flower very early and, because the flowers have nectaries, bees are provided with a good source of nectar.

The bark contains salicine which was used medicinally before the discovery of quinine and aspirin.

ASPEN
Populus tremula L.
Family: *Salicaceae*

The Aspen is a tree reaching 20 m. in height. It produces suckers freely so that, although short-lived, it may form quite dense thickets. The bark is smooth and greyish-white, later becoming dark and fissured. The buds are slightly sticky and produce toothed, rounded but pointed-tipped leaves with flattened leaf-stalks. These permit the leaves to tremble in the slightest breeze (hence the specific name *tremula*). The male flowers have 5—12 red stamens; the female flowers have 2 purple stigmas. Both types of flower, together with brownish hairy deeply cut bracts, are borne in long pendant catkins. The fruits are smooth capsules, containing numerous white hairy seeds.

The tree flowers in February and March and grows in damp mixed woods, also on heaths and moorland. It tolerates poor sandy soils where it may become locally abundant. It is known almost everywhere in Europe (but in the south only on mountains), in Caucasia, Siberia, Japan and North Africa. Growing beside the river Volga in Russia these trees, together with pine, birch and oak, form large forest areas.

The wood is very soft and is used for the manufacture of matches, and also high-quality paper. In some areas the buds were collected and made into a herbal tea which was used to sooth burns.

SPINDLE-TREE
Euonymus europaeus L.
Family: *Celastraceae*

This is a much-branched deciduous shrub or small tree. It grows 2—6 m. high, with stiff green 4-angled stems which develop a smooth grey bark.

The leaves are stalked, smooth, lance-shaped and pointed, with a toothed margin and narrowing considerably towards the stalk. They turn red in autumn. Both leaves and green twigs have an unpleasant odour. The flowers are yellowish-green and are borne in long-stalked clusters of 3—8 in the leaf axils. The fruits are deep pink with a wall of 4 rounded segments. These split open to reveal a bright orange fleshy layer known as an *aril* which encircles the seed. After the capsule has opened the seeds hang on long threads. The fruits are eaten by birds which excrete and so disperse the seeds. The seeds are slow to germinate and need to be subjected to frost before they can sprout.

The plant flowers between April and June and grows in woods, scrub and hedges, usually on calcareous soils in lowland and upland areas. It grows in most of Europe (except in the extreme north and south), also in the Caucasus and in western Asia.

Salix caprea

Populus tremula

Euonymus europaeus

281

The wood is pale yellow and hard and can be easily split into strips. It can then be used to make small wooden items such as pegs, skewers and spindles (hence the common name). The bark, fruit and roots are poisonous and emetic. They contain the glycoside euonymin which affects the heart. It has not so far been used medicinally. A volatile oil which is also present in all parts of the plant, was formerly used in the manufacture of soap.

NORWAY MAPLE
Acer platanoides L.
Family: *Aceraceae*

This tree grows up to 30 m. high and has a spreading crown. The trunk and branches have a grey fissured bark. The leaves are deeply palmately lobed, 5—15 cm. across, with a toothed margin. The petioles are long and, if cut, exude latex. The flowers are yellowish-green and are borne in large erect clusters on short leafy branches. The fruits are the familiar paired winged 'keys'.

The tree flowers between April and May and grows in mixed woods, hedgerows and plantations. It is also planted in parks and along roadsides. It grows in much of Europe (but not in the extreme north and west), also in Asia Minor, the Caucasus and Iran.

The Norway Maple was introduced in Britain but is planted less frequently than the related Sycamore (*A. pseudoplatanus*). In warmer areas *A. platanoides* is confined to the mountains.

The wood is hard and is used to make small items of furniture.

SYCAMORE
Acer pseudoplatanus L.

This tree has a spreading irregular crown and a characteristic scaly bark. It grows up to 30 m. high. The leaves are long-stalked and palmately divided. The blades are 7—16 cm. long with 5 coarsely toothed lobes. The leaf-stalks of *A. pseudoplatanus* are 10—20 cm. long, reddish in colour and, unlike *A. platanoides*, without latex.

The yellowish-green flowers are borne in narrow many-flowered inflorescences on short leafy branches.

The fruits are paired winged keys, the wings being spread and often with incurved tips.

The tree flowers between April and June and grows in mixed woods, hedgerows and plantations. It prefers rich, deep, well-drained soils but is tolerant of poor soils, salt spray and other demanding conditions. It grows naturally in mountainous areas of Central and southern Europe as well as in Asia Minor and the Caucasus. It is planted in other parts of the world including America. It is very common throughout Britain, where it was introduced in the 15th or 16th century.

The wood is hard, close-grained and durable. It makes excellent decorative veneers and is also used in wood carving and in the furniture trade. Utensils made from this wood have been found buried in Stone Age settlements. The sweet sap is sometimes made into a syrup although that of the Sugar Maple (*A. saccharinum*) is better.

COMMON MAPLE
Acer campestre L.

This is a small tree or shrub rarely more than 20 cm. high. The bark is light grey and scaly. The leaves are tough and long-stalked and palmately divided for about half their width into 3 or 5 lobes. These lobes are blunt and with few or no teeth.

Erect downy flowerheads (with 10—20 pale green flowers in each) are borne on short leafy branches. Unlike most other species of *Acer* the flowers appear with the leaves. The fruits are paired winged keys with wings which spread horizontally.

The Common Maple flowers between April and June and grows in open deciduous woods, at the edges of woods, in hedgerows and in scrub, mainly on limy soils. It is frequently planted. It grows in most parts of Europe (but is rare in Mediterranean countries), also in Asia Minor, Iran and Turkestan.

The wood of the Common Maple is hard yet easy to work. It is used in the furniture industry and also for making musical instruments. It makes excellent veneers. In the 16th century both bark and wood were made into a household remedy and used against poisonous snakebites, toothache and a variety of other complaints.

Acer platanoides

ALDER BUCKTHORN
Frangula alnus Miller
Family: *Rhamnaceae*

This is a small tree or shrub growing 4—5 m. high. It has slender, upright branches with a smooth greyish-black bark with areas of lemon-yellow. The short-stalked leaves are broadly elliptical with conspicuous lateral veins, and turn yellow or red in autumn.

The flowers are small, on thick stalks, and with greenish-white petals. Between 2 and 10 flowers are borne in clusters which are borne in the leaf axils. The fruits are 6—10 mm. in diameter, rounded and fleshy. As they ripen they change from green to red and then to black. The 2—4 seeds contain oil.

The shrub flowers between April and July and grows in damp woods and heathland, in scrub, on fen peat, and at the margins of bogs. It is known over most of Europe (but is rare in the Mediterranean region), in Siberia and in North Africa. In Britain it is native but is absent from Scotland and Ireland.

The wood is used to make charcoal of excellent quality which is used by artists. The bark, leaves and

Acer pseudoplatanus

Acer campestre

berries provide a source of natural dyestuffs. The dried bark was taken as a laxative or purgative. It also relieved toothache and skin irritations. The young bark is still used in the pharmaceutical industry.

Species of *Frangula* were formerly grouped with *Rhamnus* and the old name for this plant was *Rhamnus frangula*. *Frangula* differs from *Rhamnus* in lacking thorns and having buds without scales.

SMALL-LEAVED LIME
Tilia cordata Miller
Family: *Tiliaceae*

This is a large tree which grows to a height of 25 m. It has spreading branches with smooth dark-brown bark. The leaves are 3—9 cm. long, stalked, toothed and heart-shaped, with pointed tips. The flowers are yellowish-white, in pendant long-stalked clusters of 4—10 flowers. The stalk of each cluster is joined along its lower half to a large membranous bract.

The fruits are smooth nutlets which are wind-dispersed. The clusters are carried through the air, the bract acting as a wing.

The tree flowers between June and July and grows in deciduous woods on a wide range of soils, but especially limestone. It is often planted along roadsides. It is known over most of Europe (except in the extreme north and south), in Scandinavia, the Crimea and the Caucasus. It is native to Britain, but north of Perth it is not indigenous and is planted. It forms large forests in eastern Europe.

The Small-leaved Lime has for a long time been regarded as a favoured tree and has been a symbol in many legends and poems. It has also figured in folklore and various superstitions.

The wood is soft and white and very suitable for wood carving. The inner bark produces fibres which, in eastern Europe, are used to make baskets and ropes. Other species of Lime are used for the same purpose. Because of its abundant nectar the flowers are much visited by bees. The flowers are well-known as a household remedy. They contain a glycoside as well as volatile oils and are made into a tea which relieves infections, cramp and catarrh. It was also used for disorders of the kidneys and urinary tracts, and also for stomach upsets.

LARGE-LEAVED LIME
Tilia platyphyllos Scop.

This is a tall tree (up to 40 m. high) with much larger leaves (6—12 cm. long) than the Small-leaved Lime. The tertiary veins are very prominent and the leaves are noticeably darker.

The fragrant flowers are yellowish-white. There are 3 (sometimes 2—5) flowers in each pendulous cluster. The nutlets are downy and strongly 5-ribbed.

This tree flowers between June and July — before *T. cordata* — and grows in woods on good calcareous soils. It is often planted and grows naturally in Central and southern Europe. In Russia it forms huge forests together with beech and other trees. This species and the Small-leaved Lime have crossed to produce the Common Lime *T.* x *vulgaris*.

MEZEREON
Daphne mezereum L.
Family: *Thymelaeaceae*

Mezereon is a bushy deciduous shrub 25—200 cm. high. The leaves are oblong to lance-shaped, 3—10 cm. long, and short-stalked. They are bright green above and bluish-green beneath, and usually appear after the shrub has flowered.

The stalkless flowers are pinkish-purple, rarely white, with a strong sweet fragrance. They are borne in clusters at the upper part of the branches. There are no petals, the coloured parts being the 4 sepals. The fruits are usually bright red but, if the flowers have been white, then the fruits are yellow. They are 8-12 mm. across and are very fleshy.

This shrub flowers between February and May — even in January in a mild winter. It grows in open deciduous woods on calcareous soils. Mezereon grows in most of Europe and also in temperate Asia as far east as the Altai Mountains.

It is a very poisonous shrub. The leaves, fruit and bark are bitter and contain the poisonous glycosides mezerein and daphnin. The latter is also present in the flowers. The plant can irritate the skin and, if eaten, can cause malfunctioning of the kidneys and intestines, sometimes with fatal results.

The fruits are very poisonous, but seem to be eaten by

284

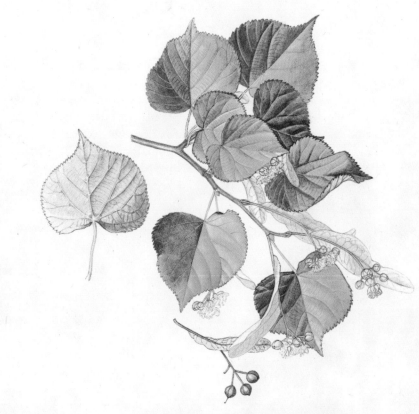

Tilia cordata

Tilia platyphyllos

Frangula alnus

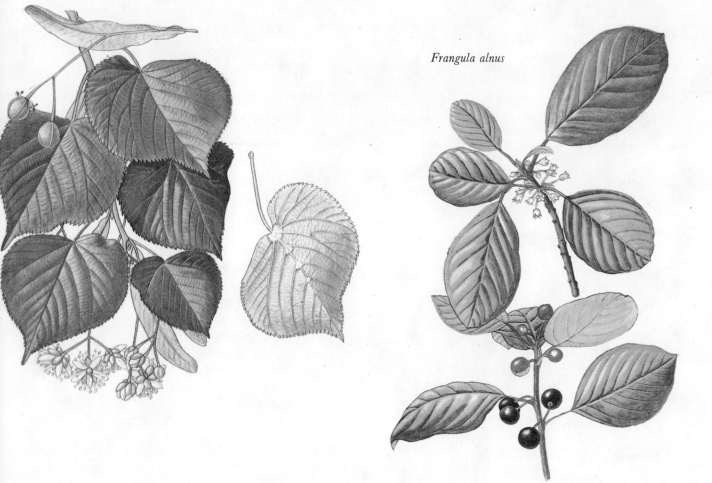

birds without any serious consequences, and it is birds that spread the seeds of this shrub.

The bark has, in the past, been used to treat many illnesses and is today still contained in certain ointments. If the leaves, fruit and bark are boiled a pale yellow to greenish-brown dye is obtained.

Mezereon is often cultivated in gardens but is usually rare in the wild. It is therefore protected in some countries.

Daphne mezereum

DOGWOOD
Cornus sanguinea L.
Family: *Cornaceae*

This erect shrub grows up to 4 m. high and has reddish-brown twigs which are particularly attractive in autumn. The stalked leaves are broadly elliptical. The flowers are white and are borne in dense flat-topped clusters 4—5 cm. across. The fruits are bluish-black and fleshy and contain 1—2 seeds.

Dogwood flowers between May and July and grows in mixed woods, scrub and hedgerows on calcareous soils. It may be the dominant shrub in chalk scrub. It grows in most of Europe except the extreme north. The fruits contain a greyish-blue dye which is used for leather. Oil from the seeds had, particularly in the past, been used for lighting and also in soap-making. The twigs are pliable and are sometimes used in basket-making. Dogwood, especially when variegated, is often grown in gardens.

BILBERRY, WHORTLEBERRY, HUCKLEBERRY
Vaccinium myrtillus L.
Family: *Ericaceae*

This is a much-branched shrublet which grows up to 60 cm. high, with a creeping rhizome and numerous erect stems. The twigs are green and strongly three-angled.

The bright green leaves are shed in winter and are oval and 1—3 cm. long. They are conspicuously veined and have a finely toothed margin. The solitary (sometimes paired) flowers have a globular greenish-pink corolla. The fruits are the well-known bluish-black Bilberries. They are sweet and fleshy and contain many small seeds.

The Bilberry flowers between April and July. It grows, usually in large groups, in open woods and on heaths and moors on acid soils. It grows above the tree-line in mountainous areas. The plant is known in most of Europe, and in northern Asia. In southern Europe it is confined to mountain areas. It is found in North America but was introduced.

The fruits are well-known. They are edible and contain sugar and tannins and are used to make jams and

286

Cornus sanguinea

liqueurs. They also yield a blue or black dye which is used in foodstuffs and to colour wine. In Roman times this dye was used for the clothes of slaves. It continued in use as a dye for several hundred years.

The dried berries were a household remedy and have in the past been used to cure diarrhoea.

The leaves were also used as a raw material in the pharmaceutical industry since they contain tannins, vitamin C and the glycoside neomyrtillin. This substance is supposed to lower the sugar content of the blood and was therefore administered to diabetics.

COWBERRY
Vaccinium vitis-idaea L.

This is a spreading, much-branched shrublet with numerous root-forming, creeping rhizomes, and erect arching branches not exceeding 30 cm. in height.

The twigs are smooth and covered in short hairs. The leaves are in two ranks and are bluntly oval with inrolled margins. They are evergreen, 1—3 cm. long, shiny, dark green above with brownish glandular dots beneath. The flowers are white or pink, 5—8 mm. across, and bell-shaped with a short reddish calyx. They are borne in short terminal drooping clusters. The fruits are greenish at first, turning bright red later, and are in small clusters to one side of the stem. The reddish or greenish flesh of the fruit tastes acid but is edible. Is some areas two crops of berries may be borne in a year.

The shrub flowers between May and August and usually covers large areas in open woods, especially pine woods. It also grows on moors, heaths, bogs, alpine meadows and tundra, preferring acid soils. In the Alps it can be found at up to 3,000 metres above sea level. It grows in Central but more often in northern Europe, and reaches sub-arctic regions. Towards the east it is found all over Russia. A sub-

Vaccinium myrtillus

Vaccinium vitis-idaea

species grows in Japan, Greenland and North America. The fruits contain sugar, citric and other organic acids and are sometimes used as a dessert. However they are said to be injurious to people suffering from kidney diseases. The fruits are also used to make jam and are sometimes distilled to make liqueurs.

In some countries the leaves are used as a raw material in the pharmaceutical industry.

ASH
Fraxinus excelsior L.
Family: *Oleaceae*

This is a tall tree — up to 40 m. high — with smooth greenish-grey branches and conspicuous swollen black buds. The terminal buds can reach 1 cm. in length. The paired leaves are stalked and pinnate with 7—15 lance-shaped, pointed and toothed leaflets. The leaves appear only after the tree has flowered.

The flowers are small and brownish-purple and are bisexual or unisexual. There is no calyx or corolla. They are borne in branched drooping axillary clusters and are wind-pollinated. The fruits are 3—4 cm. long, and are brown, winged nutlets i. e. keys. They grow in dense clusters.

The tree flowers between April and May and grows in damp woods, in scrub and hedgerows, and even on stony ground. It is known in most of Europe and eastwards to the Crimea, Caucasia and Iran.

This is a variable species with two European subspecies. The timber is hard yet light and flexible, and is used in the furniture industry and for making skis and other sports equipment, wooden floors, tool handles and walking sticks. The leaves contain sugars and volatile oils, and like the fruits are poisonous to livestock.

The tree is still used as a household remedy, as a laxative and also as a drug to control kidney function. A tea made from the leaves is taken for these purposes; it was formerly used for compresses for boils and to cleanse open wounds. The bark is also collected, since it is a good source of tannin. The tree is hardy and decorative and is often planted.

GUELDER ROSE
Viburnum opulus L.
Family: *Caprifoliaceae*

This deciduous shrub grows up to 4 m. in height, sometimes forming a small tree. The leaves grow in stalked pairs. They are undivided but may have 3—5 irregularly toothed lobes. Some of the leaf-stalks have small red glands. It is possible that these glands, which only appear when the shrub is not flowering, attract ants and insects which extract nectar from them and which may then be attracted to and pollinate the flowers.

These flowers are small and white and are borne in loose flat-topped clusters. There are two types of flower. The inner ones are small (6 mm. across) and bisexual; the outer ones are larger (1.5—2 cm. across) with 5 irregular petals, but are sterile. The fruits are shiny and red and during the winter months provide food for birds.

The shrub flowers between May and July and grows in damp woods, scrub, hedgerows and fens. It is known almost everwhere in Europe, and also in northern and western parts of Asia. It occasionally grows in Algeria.

Fraxinus excelsior

Sambucus nigra

Sambucus racemosa

Viburnum opulus

290

The bark contains a glycoside as well as tannins and sugars and is still used as a herbal medicine. The fruits contain a red dye. Although they can cause vomiting when fresh, they can be made into jam or wine.

ELDER
Sambucus nigra L.
Family: *Caprifoliaceae*

This shrub or small tree grows up to 10 m. high. The young branches are green, later turning grey, and have conspicuous lenticels.

The leaves are stalked and pinnate, with 3—9 oval or lance-shaped, long-pointed toothed leaflets which are 3—9 cm. long. If the leaves are crushed or rubbed they exude an unpleasant odour. The flowers are small and creamy-white and form large, dense, flat-topped clusters. These flowers have a strong rather sickly scent. The fruits are shiny black fleshy berries (which are occasionally green, pink or white) with small seeds and purple juice.

The plant flowers between June and July and grows in light deciduous woods, in clearings and scrub, by roadsides and in waste places. The seeds are distributed by birds. Elder grows virtually all over Europe (except in Iceland), in Caucasia, Asia Minor, Siberia, western Asia, North Africa and the Azores.

During excavation of Stone Age settlements seeds of the plant have been found, indicating it was used as food. It has been used as a herbal remedy since ancient times and it was also believed to have "magical" powers. The juice of the berries was used to dye cloth, and to dye the faces of goods carved in wood.

The plant contains alkaloids and other medicinal substances and all parts, except the roots, were used as lotions, inhalants and purgatives. Both the leaves and dried flowers are used to make teas which are laxative and also reduce fevers. The fruits contain much vitamin C and must, in former times, have been of some use in preventing scurvy. They are used today to make jams, jellies and wines.

The wood is hard and is used to make small items such as toys. The pith in the stems is large and white and was formerly important in the sectioning of plant material.

ALPINE (RED) ELDER
Sambucus racemosa L.

This species of Elder resembles *S. nigra* in many respects but is smaller (up to 4 m. high) with dark brown bark and cinnamon-brown pith.

The yellowish-green leaves are stalked and paired and have 5—7 oval or elliptical finely-toothed leaflets. The stipules are in the form of large glands. The small greenish-white flowers are grouped in dense ovoid clusters 3—6 cm. across and appear shortly after the leaves. The fruits are shiny scarlet berries and are borne in drooping clusters.

The plant flowers between April and May and grows in shady woods on hills and mountainsides. In Britain it is naturalised and grows mainly in Scotland. It is known in Central and southern Europe and in western Asia.

This species too was used medicinally and the fruits are also used for wine-making.

HOW TO USE THIS BOOK

Throughout this book use has been made of both common and Latin names for any particular plant. Although the common name may be easier to remember it often varies in different parts of the country, whereas the Latin name is universally known throughout the civilised world. Changes in the Latin (or proper) name can only be made at International Congress level and are subject to strict scientific scrutiny.

The Latin name is in two parts (this is the *binomial* system of nomenclature introduced by the famous Swedish botanist, Linnaeus (1707—1778)). The first name is that of the *genus* and it can be likened to a surname; the second name is that of the *species* and can be likened to a forename or Christian name. Most genera have a number of different species although the size of this number varies enormously.

The specific name may be commemorative or descriptive, and is often very informative e. g. *officinalis* indicates past or present use as a herbal plant, *sylvestris* indicates living in woods, *villosus* indicates a hairy plant, *alba* indicates white, *rubra* red.

Genera are grouped according to similarities between plants into *families*, and these larger units of classification can in turn be grouped into *orders*, the members of which may have certain features in common. The size (i. e. the number of members) of a family or an order may vary immensely. The majority of family names end in — aceae and order names in — ales.

GLOSSARY

achene a small, dry, indehiscent 1-seeded fruit.

actinomorphic regular, having 2 or more planes of symmetry (applied only to flowers).

anther that part of the stamen in which pollen is produced.

apetalous without a corolla.

apothecium an open, cup-like fruit-body in lichens and some fungi.

aril a fleshy appendage or coat developed by some seeds.

axil the junction between the stem and (any type of) leaf.

berry a fleshy fruit with numerous hard-skinned seeds.

bract a leaf-like organ (often reduced) with a flower or an inflorescence in its axil.

bulb an enlarged underground bud with fleshy scale leaves.

calyx the outer perianth, consisting of sepals which are usually green.

capsule a dry fruit opening by teeth, slits or pores; also the spore containing body of mosses and liverworts.

carpel a structure of variable shape, containing 1 or more ovules and which is (a) solitary or (b) grouped but free or (c) joined with others to form a compound ovary.

catkin an elongate, often pendulous inflorescence of unisexual apetalous flowers.

column applied to the central structure in an orchid flower and which bears stigmas and anthers.

compound (of a leaf) divided into separate leaflets.

corm a flattened, swollen, underground stem with enveloping papery scale-leaves.

cupule a cup-like structure surrounding an ovary and formed of free or joined bracts.

deciduous applied to any plant structure which falls off within a year.

dehiscence the bursting open of anther or fruit.

dentate toothed.

drupe a fleshy (sometimes leathery) fruit with a single seed which is surrounded by a hard coat.

entire simple, undivided.

epicalyx a whorl of small, leafy structures borne outside the calyx.

epidermis the outermost layer of leaves and green stems.

exstipulate without stipules.

filament the stalk of the stamen.

floret a small or reduced flower; usually applied to flowers of Compositae, Cyperaceae and Gramineae.

follicle a dry, pod-like structure, formed from one carpel, which contains several seeds and which dehisces along one side only.

gill a vertical spore-bearing plate borne with many others on the underside of cap-and-stalk or bracket fungi.

glandular secretory.

herb (herbaceous) applied to plants which die, or which die down, in one season and which never become woody.

hyphae the fine threads which form the absorptive part of a fungus (collectively, the mycelium).

inferior term applied to an ovary which bears sepals, petals and stamens above it.

inflorescence the mode of grouping of flowers on a flowering stem.

internode a length of stem between two nodes.

involucre a number of usually overlapping bracts surrounding an inflorescence.

leaflet a separate segment of a leaf — often resembling a leaf but it has no bud in its axil.

legume a dry pod, containing several seeds, which dehisces along one side (characteristic of Leguminosae).

ligule an outgrowth or scale borne at the junction of leaf-sheath and blade (as in grasses) or borne on a petal at the throat of the corolla.

linear narrow and elongate, at least 12 times longer than broad.

membranous thin and almost transparent.

mericarp a single-seeded portion of a schizocarpous fruit.

nut a 1-seeded fruit with a hard coat.

nutlet an achene or small nut.

ovary strictly, the structure which contains the ovules; often applied collectively to the carpels.

ovule the structure which, after fertilisation, becomes a seed.

palmate applied to leaves which are divided into radiating leaflets.

panicle a much-branched inflorescence (as in some grasses).

pappus a ring of hairs or scales (representing a calyx) at the top of the ovary of flowers in Compositae.

perianth the outer whorls of a flower, leafy and/or petaloid, often developing as calyx and corolla.

petal a segment of the corolla, often brightly coloured.

petaloid resembling a petal in colour and texture.

petiole leaf-stalk.

pinnate the bearing of leaflets along each side of the leaf axis.

raceme an elongate inflorescence of stalked flowers which is capable of indefinite apical extension.

receptacle the elongate, compressed or cup-like axis of the flower which bears the floral organs.

reduced applied to any organ or structure which is smaller or simpler than the basic type.

rhizome a (usually) underground stem bearing roots and scale leaves, and which serves both for vegetative reproduction and overwintering.

samara a dry, winged nutlet.

schizocarp a fruit splitting into indehiscent mericarps.

sepal a segment of the calyx, usually green.

serrate with sharp teeth, usually regular, like a saw.

sessile without a stalk.

seta the stalk of a moss or liverwort capsule (literally, a bristle).

spadix a markedly fleshy axis which bears numerous small flowers.

spathe a large bract enveloping a spadix or other inflorescence.

spike strictly a raceme of sessile flowers but often loosely applied to any elongate inflorescence.

spikelet a small cluster of flowers, with bracts, which is part of a larger inflorescence.

spur a long, usually nectar-secreting, projection from any member of a perianth.

stigma the receptive part of the carpel(s) — of variable form — on which the pollen germinates.

stipe the stalk of one of the larger fungi.

stipulate possessing stipules.

stipule paired, lateral outgrowths of variable form which develop from the leaf base.

style the usually elongate part of the carpel(s) which bears the stigma.

superior applied to an ovary which is above or at the same level as the bases of other flower parts.

tendril an elongate sensitive organ, often formed from a leaf or leaf part, which coils around any object it may touch.

thallus a simple plant body, not differentiated into stem, leaves and roots, characteristic of fungi, lichens, mosses and liverworts.

trifoliate with three leaflets.

umbel a usually flat-topped inflorescence in which all the flower-stalks spring from a common point.

velum the thin membrane which may cover the gills of a young cap-and-stalk fungus.

zygomorphic irregular, with only one plane of symmetry.

INDEX OF SCIENTIFIC NAMES

Abies alba 267
Acer campestre 282, 283
  platanoides 282, 283
  pseudoplatanus 282, 283
Achillea millefolium 124—125
  ptarmica 44, 45
Aconitum napellus 236—237
  vulparia 236, 237
Acorus calamus 37
Actaea spicata 234, 235
Adonis aestivalis 171, 173
  flammea 171
  vernalis 105—106, 171
Eegopodium podagraria 245—246
Agrimonia eupatoria 108, 109
Agropyron junceiforme 64, 65
  repens 65, 182
Agrostemma githago 174—175
Ajuga reptans 116, 117
Alchemilla vulgaris 141—142
Alisma plantago-aquatica 33
Alliaria petiolata 239
Allium ursinum 260—261
Alnus glutinosa 46—48
  incana 47
Alopecurus pratensis 152, 153
Allyssum alpestre 89
  montanum 89
  saxatile 88—89
Amanita citrina 222, 223
  muscaria 221—222
  pantherina 222, 223
  phalloides 223—224
  rubescens 222, 223
  virosa 223
Ammophila arenaria 63—64, 65
Anagallis arvensis 176—177
  tenella 176, 177
Anchusa officinalis 115—116, 117
Andromeda polifolia 78—79
Anemone nemorosa 232—233
  ranunculoides 233
  sylvestris 233
Angelica sylvestris 247
Anisantha sterilis 205
  tectorum 205
Antennaria dioica 258, 259
Anthemis arvensis 181
Anthoxanthum odoratum 152, 153
Anthyllis vulneraria 110, 111
Aquilegia chrysantha 235
  coerulea 235
  formosa 235
  pyrenaica 235
  vulgaris 234—235
Arctium lappa 203, 204
  minus 202—203
  tomentosum 204
Armillaria mellea 220, 221
Armoracia rusticana 40, 41, 237
Artemisia absinthium 200
  dracunculus 200
  vulgaris 199—200, 201

Arum maculatum 264—265
Aruncus dioicus 240, 241
Asarum europaeum 237—238, 239
Asplenium ruta-muraria 88, 89
  septentrionale 87
  trichomanes 87
  virida 87
Aster alpinus 94, 95
  tripolium 62, 63
Astragalus glycophyllos 242, 243
Astrantia major 246—247
Athyrium filix-femina 230, 231
Atriplex nitens 190, 191
Atropa belladonna 195, 253—254
Avena fatua 171
  sativa 170—171

Baldellia ranunculoides 34
Ballota nigra 194, 195
Berberis vulgaris 126—127
Beta vulgaris 162, 163
Betula nana 77—78, 79
  pendula 276, 277
Bidens cernua 44—45
  tripartita 44, 45
Blechnum spicant 232
Boletus aurantiacus 214, 215
  badius 214, 215
  chrysenteron 214, 215
  edulis 216, 217
  elegans 213
  erythropus 216, 217
  felleus 216, 217
  granulatus 215—216, 217
  luridus 216, 217
  luteus 214, 215
  rubellus 214
  satanas 217—218
  scaber 214—215
Brassica napus 162, 163
Briza media 150, 151
Butomus umbellatus 32

Cakile maritima 57
Calamagrostis arundinacea 36, 262
  epigejos 262, 263
Calla palustris 38
Callitriche palustris 15
Caltha palustris 29
Campanula glomerata 122, 123
  patula 145—146, 147
  persicifolia 256, 257
Cantharellus cibarius 218, 219
Capsella bursa-pastoris 173—174, 175
Cardamine pratensis 139—140
Cardaria draba 189—190
Carduus acanthoides 198—199
  nutans 198, 199
Carex arenaria 62
Carlina acaulis 123—124
  vulgaris 124, 125
Carpinus betulus 275—276
Centaurea cyanus 180, 181
  jacea 124, 125
  scabiosa 124
Centaurium erythraea 250, 251
Cephalanthera damasonium 262—263

rubra 262
Cerastium arvense 106, 107
Cerinthe minor 178, 179
Cetraria islandica 226, 227
Chamaemelum nobile 202
Chelidonium majus 189
Chenopodium album 190, 191
  bonus-henricus 190
Chrysanthemum cinerariifolium 201
  corymbosum 257
  leucanthemum 146, 147
  parthenium 257
  vulgare 200—201
Cichorium intybus 200, 201
Cicuta virosa 30, 31
Cirsium arvense 180, 181
  oleraceum 45—46, 47
  palustre 45
  tuberosum 45
Cladonia coccifera 226
  digitata 226, 227
  fimbriata 226, 227
  rangiferina 226, 227
Colchicum autumnale 148, 149—150
Convallaria majalis 259—260
Convolvulus arvensis 177—178, 179
Cornus mas 131—132
  sanguinea 286, 287
Coronilla varia 109—110, 111
Corydalis bulbosa 238, 239
Corylus avellana 275
Cotoneaster integerrimus 95
  nebrodensis 95
  niger 95
Crataegus laevigata 129
  monogyna 129, 130
Cyclamen europeum 249
Cynosurus cristatus 150—151
Cypripedium calceolus 262, 263
Cystopteris fragilis 88, 89
Cytisus ardoinii 130
  battandieri 130
  decumbens 130
  multiflorus 130
  purpureus 130
  scoparius 129—130, 131

Dactylis glomerata 150, 151
Dactylorhiza incarnata 154
Daphne mezereum 284 286
Datura stramonium 196, 197
Daucus carota 114, 115
Deschampsia caespitosa 152, 153
Dianthus carthusianorum 106, 107
  deltoides 106, 107
  gratianopolitanus 89—90
Dicranum scoparium 226, 227
Dictamnus albus 111—112
Digitalis grandiflora 254, 255
  purpurea 254—255
Dipsacus fullonum 198, 199
Drosera rotundifolia 75—76
Dryas octopetala 78, 97—98
Dryopteris filix-mas 230, 231

Echinops sphaerocephalus 204, 205
Echium vulgare 115, 117

Elodea canadensis 20
Elymus arenarius 64—65
Epilobium angustifolium 245
Epipactis atrorubens 263—264
    helleborine 263
Equisetum sylvaticum 230, 231
Erigeron canadensis 202, 203
Eriophorum angustifolium 76, 77
    latifolium 76—77
    vaginatum 77
Erodium cicutarium 176, 177
Eryngium campestre 113—114, 115
    maritimum 58, 60, 61
Euonymus europaeus 281—282
Eupatorium cannabinum 257—258
Euphorbia cyparissias 112, 113
    helioscopia 176, 177

Fagus sylvatica 276, 278, 279
Falcaria vulgaris 114, 115
Festuca pratensis 150, 151
Filipendula ulmaria 40—41
Fragaria vesca 240—241
Frangula alnus 283—284, 285
Fraxinus excelsior 288, 289

Galanthus nivalis 261
Galeopsis speciosa 252—253
    tetrahit 253
Galinsoga ciliata 204
    parviflora 204, 205
Galium aparine 197—198, 199
    mollugo 122, 123
    odoratum 255—256
    verum 122, 123
Gentiana clusii 93
    verna 93—94
Geranium sanguineum 110, 111
Geum rivale 41—42, 43
    urbanum 241—242, 243
Glaux maritima 60
Gnaphalium sylvaticum 258, 259
Groenlandia densa 21
Gymnadenia conopsea 154

Helianthemum nummularium 106, 107
Hepatica nobilis 236, 237
Heracleum sphondylium 144, 145
Hieracium pilosella 124, 125
Hippophaë rhamnoides 66—67
Holcus lanatus 152, 153
Homogyne alpina 258, 259
Hordeum distichon 169—170
    murinum 206
    spontaneum 169
    vulgare 169, 170
Hottonia palustris 17, 177
Huperzia selago 229—230
Hydrocharis morsus-ranae 18, 19
Hylocomium splendens 228—229
Hyoscyamus niger 194—196
Hypericum calycinum 113
    imperforatum 112
    montanum 112
    perforatum 112—113

Impatiens glandulifera 34

noli-tangere 244, 245
    parviflora 244
Iris pseudacorus 34, 35

Jovibarba sobolifera 91
Juncus effusus 35—36

Laburnocytisus adami 130, 131
Lactarius deliciosus 218, 219
    volemus 218, 219
Lactuca sativa 202
    serriola 202, 203
Lamium galeobdolon 252, 253
Lamium album 194, 195
Larix decidua 268, 269
Lathraea squamaria 255
Lathyrus pratensis 142—143
    sylvestris 242, 243
    tuberosus 175—176, 177
    vernus 242, 243
Ledum palustre 78, 79
Leontodon autumnalis 147—148
    hispidus 148
    taraxacoides 148
Leontopodium alpinum 94, 95
Lepiota procera 224, 225
Leucobryum glaucum 226, 227
Leucojum vernum 262, 263
Lilium martagon 259
Linaria vulgaris 121
Linum usitatissimum 164—165
Lithospermum arvense 178, 179
Lolium multiflorum 151
    perenne 151
Lotus corniculatus 144, 145
Lunaria annua 238
    rediviva 238, 239
Lupinus perennis 243
    polyphyllus 242—243
Luronium natans 34
Luzula campestris 125
Lychnis flos-cuculi 140, 141
Lycoperdon nigrescens 224
    perlatum 224, 225
Lycopodium clavatum 229
Lysimachia vulgaris 42, 43
Lythrum salicaria 42, 43

Maianthemum bifolium 261
Malva neglecta 193—194, 195
Matricaria matricarioides 201—202, 203
    recutita 180—181
Matteucia struthiopteris 232
Medicago sativa 164, 165
Melilotus alba 193
    officinalis 192—193
Melittis melissophyllum 252, 253
Menyanthes trifoliata 30—31
Mercurialis perennis 244, 245
Mnium hornum 228
    punctatum 226—228
    undulatum 228
Moneses uniflora 250, 251
Mutinus caninus 225
Myosotis scorpioides 31
Myriophyllum spicatum 16
    verticillatum 16, 17

Neottia nidus-avis 264
Nonea pulla 116, 117
Nuphar lutea 13, 14
Nymphaea alba 13
Nymphoides peltata 17—18

Oenanthe aquatica 29—30
Onobrychis viciifolia 109
Ononis spinosa 131
Orchis morio 153—154
Origanum vulgare 119
Oxalis acetosella 243—244, 245
Oxytropis pilosa 110, 111

Papaver rhoeas 171—172, 173
    setigerum 161
    somniferum 161
Paris quadrifolia 260, 261
Parmelia physodes 226, 227
Peltigera canina 225—226, 227
Petasites albus 46, 47
    fragrans 46
    hybridus 46, 47
Phalaris arundinacea 36, 37
Phallus impudicus 224—225
Phleum arenarium 64, 66
    pratense 153
Phragmites communis 35, 36
Picea abies 265—267
Pimpinella saxifraga 114—115
Pinguicula vulgaris 76, 77
Pinus mugo 78, 80, 268—269
    nigra 267—268
    sylvestris 266, 267, 268
Pisum sativum 162—164
Plantago coronopus 60
    lanceolata 145
    major 197
    maritima 60, 62, 63
Platanthera bifolia 264
    chlorantha 264
Pleurozium schreberi 228
Poa annua 204, 205
    pratensis 150, 151
    trivialis 199
Polygonatum multiflorum 260, 261
    odoratum 260
Polygonum amphibium 14—15
    bistorta 140—141
    convolvulus 175
Polypodium vulgare 88, 89
Polytrichum commune 228
Populus alba 50
    nigra 50
    tremula 280—281
Potamogeton crispus 22
    lucens 21
    natans 20—21
    perfoliatus 21
Potentilla alba 241
    anserina 192, 193
    palustris 76, 77
    tabernaemontani 108, 109
Poterium sanguisorba 142
Primula elatior 248, 249
    veris 247—248, 249
    vulgaris 248

Prunella vulgaris 118, 119
Prunus avium 127—128
  padus 272
  spinosa 128—129
Pteridium aquilinum 230—231
Puccinellia maritima 64
Pulmonaria officinalis 251
Pulsatilla pratensis 105
Pyrola rotundifolia 249—250, 251

Quercus petraea 279—280
  robur 279

Ramaria botrytis 213
  flava 213
  formosa 213
Ranunculus aconitifolius 234, 235
  acris 139
  aquatilis 14, 15
  ficaria 233—234, 235
  lingua 29
  repens 38, 39
Raphanus raphanistrum 172, 173
Rhinanthus minor 144, 145
Rhododendron ferrugineum 97, 98
Rhytidiadelphus triquetrus 228, 229
Robinia pseudoacacia 274—275
Rosa canina 127
  pendulina 274
Rubus fruticosus 271
  idaeus 270—271
Rumex acetosa 140, 141
Russula cyanoxantha 219—220, 221
  vesca 218—219
  virescens 218, 219

Sagittaria sagittifolia 33
Salicornia europaea 59
Salix alba 48, 49
  babylonica 47
  caprea 280, 281
  fragilis 49
  purpurea 49, 50
  viminalis 49—50
Salsola kali 58—59
Salvia officinalis 118
  pratensis 118, 119
  verticillata 118, 119
Sambucus ebulus 256, 257
  nigra 256, 290, 291
  racemosa 290, 291

Sanguisorba officinalis 115, 142, 143
Sanicula europaea 246, 247
Saponaria officinalis 40, 41
Saxifraga granulata 108, 109
  azoon 92—93
Schoenoplectus lacustris 35, 36
Scirpus maritimus 62, 63
  sylvaticus 35
Scleroderma aurantium 224, 225
Secale cereale 168—169
Sedum acre 92, 93
  album 92, 93
  telephium 91—92
Sempervivum tectorum 90—91
Senecio nemorensis 256—257
Sesleria caerulea 94—95
Sherardia arvensis 178, 179
Silene acaulis 90
  alba 140, 141
  maritima 107
  nutans 107—108, 109
  vulgaris 107
Sinapis arvensis 172—173
Solanum dulcamara 43—44, 45
  nigrum 196, 197
  tuberosum 165—167
Soldanella montana 248, 249
Sonchus oleraceus 179—180
Sorbus aria 95—97
  aucuparia 272—274
Sparganium erectum 38
Spartina alternifolia 66
  maritima 66
  townsendii 66
Spergularia marina 57—58
Sphagnum spp. 75
Stachys sylvatica 252, 253
Stellaria holostea 240, 241
Stipa capillata 125—126
  pennata 126
Stratiotes aloides 19—20
Suaeda maritima 58, 59
Symphytum officinale 42—43
  tuberosum 251—252

Taraxacum laevigatum 146, 147
  officinale 146—147
  palustre 147
  spectabile 147
Thalictrum aquilegifolium 236, 237
Thelypteris phegopteris 231

Thlaspi arvense 173
Thymus drucei 116
  serpyllum 116—117
  vulgaris 116, 117
Tilia cordata 284, 285
  platyphyllos 284, 285
Tragopogon dubium 149
  pratensis 148—149
Trapa natans 16, 17
Tricholoma flavovirens 220, 221
  portentosum 220, 221
Trifolium pratense 164, 165
  repens 142, 143
Triticum aestivum 168, 169
Trollius europaeus 139
Tussilago farfara 181—182
Typha angustifolia 38, 39
  latifolia 39

Ulmus glabra 270
  laevis 269
Urtica dioica 190, 191—192, 194, 199
  urens 192, 193
Utricularia intermedia 19
  minor 19
  neglecta 19
  vulgaris 18—19

Vaccinium myrtillus 286—287
  oxycoccos 80
  uliginosum 79
  vitis-idaea 287—288
Valerianella dentata 178—179
Verbascum lychnitis 120—121
  phoenicum 120, 121
  thapsiforme 120
  thapsus 119—120
Veronica beccabunga 31—32
  chamaedrys 121—122
  officinalis 254, 255
  spicata 122, 123
Viburnum opulus 288, 290, 291
Vicia cracca 143
  sepium 143—144, 145
Vinca minor 250—251
Viola odorata 239—240
  riviniana 240, 241
  tricolor 174, 175

Zea mays 167—168

INDEX OF COMMON NAMES

Aaron's Rod see Mullein, Common
Acacia, False 274—275
Adonis, Yellow 105—106, 171
Agrimony, 108, 109
    Hemp 281—282
Alder, 46—47
    Buckthorn see Buckthorn, Alder
    Grey 47
Alfalfa see Lucerne
Alison, Mountain 89
Alkanet, True 115—116, 117
Alpenrose 97, 98
Alyssum, Golden 88—89
Andromeda, Marsh 78—79
Angelica, Wild 247
Archangel, Yellow 252, 253
Arrowhead 33
Arum, Bog 38
Asarabacca 237—238, 239
Ash 288, 289
Aspen 280—281
Aster, Alpine 94, 95
    Sea 62, 63
Avens, Mountain 78, 97—98
    Water 41—42, 43
    Wood see Herb Bennet

Balsam, Himalayan see Policeman's Helmet
    Small 244
Baneberry 234, 235
Barberry 126—127
Barley, Six-rowed 169—170
    Two-rowed 169—170
    Wall 206
Bastard Balm 252, 253
Bedstraw, Hedge 122
    Lady's 122
Beech 276, 278, 279
Beech-fern 231
Beet 162, 163
Bellflower, Clustered 122, 123
    Narrow-leaved 256, 257
    Spreading 145—146, 147
Bilberry 286—287
Bindweed, Black 175
    Field 177—178, 179
Birch, Dwarf 77—78, 79
    Silver 276, 277
Birdsfoot-trefoil 144, 145
Bistort, 140—141
    Amphibious 14—15
Bittersweet see Nightshade, Woody
Blackberry 271
Blackthorn 128—129
Bladder-fern, Brittle 88, 89
Bladderwort, Greater 18—19
    Lesser 19
Bluebottle see Cornflower
Blusher, False, The 222, 223
Bog Arum 38
Bogbean 30—31
Bogmosses 75
Bog Whortleberry 79
Boletus, Bitter 216, 217

Brown-ring 214, 215
    Chestnut 214, 215
    Red-foot 214, 215
    Yellow Ring 213
Bouncing Bett see Soapwort
Bracken 230—231
Brandy-bottle see Water-lily, Yellow
Bread Wheat see Wheat
Brome, Barren 205
    Drooping 205
Brooklime 31—32
Broom, 129—130, 131
    Purple 130
Buckthorn, Alder 283—284, 285
    Sea 66—67
Bugle, Common 116, 117
Bugloss, Viper's 115, 117
Bulrush, 35, 36
    False see Reedmace
Burdock, Great 203, 204
    Lesser 202—203
    Woolly 204
Bur-marigold, Nodding 44—45
    Tripartite 44
Burnet, Great 142, 143
    Salad 142
    Saxifrage 114—115
Burning Bush 111—112
Bur-reed, Branched 38
Bushgrass 262, 263
Butterbur, 46, 47
    White 46, 47
Buttercup, Creeping 38, 39
    Meadow 139
    White 234, 235
Butterwort, Common 76, 77

Campion, Bladder 107
    Moss 90
    White 140, 141
Canadian Pondweed 20
Carrot, Wild 114, 115
Cat's-foot 258, 259
Cat's-tail, Sand 64, 66
Celandine, Greater 189
    Lesser 233—234, 235
Centaury, Common 250, 251
Cèpe 216, 217
Chamomile, 202
    Corn 181
    Wild 180—181
Chanterelle 218, 219
Charlock, 172—173
    White 172, 173
Cherry, Bird 272
    Cornelian 131—132
    Wild see Gean
Chickweed, Field Mouse-ear 106, 107
Chicory 200, 201
Cinquefoil, Marsh 76, 77
    Spring 108, 109
    White 241
Clary, Meadow 118, 119
    Whorled 118, 119
Cleavers see Goosegrass
Clover, Dutch or White 142, 143
    Red 164, 165

Clubmoss, Common or Stag's-horn 229
    Fir 229—230
Club-rush, Sea 62, 63
    Wood 35
Cob-nut see Hazel
Cocks-foot 150, 151
Coltsfoot, 181—182
    Alpine or Purple 258, 259
Columbine 234—235
    Pyrenean, 235
Comfrey, 42—43
    Tuberous 251—252
Coral Fungus, 213
    Yellow 213
Cord-grass, Townsend's 66
Corn 168
Corn Cockle 174—175
Cornflower 180, 181
Cotton-grass, Broad-leaved 76—77
    Common 76, 77
    Hare's Tail 77
Couch-grass, 64, 182
    Sand 64, 65
Cowbane 30, 31
Cowberry 287—288
Cow Parsnip see Hogweed
Cowslip 247—248, 249
Crab's Claw see Water Soldier
Cranberry 80
Cranesbill, Bloody 110, 111
Cress, Hoary see Pepperwort, Hoary
Crocus, Autumn 148, 149—150
Cuckoo Flower see Lady's Smock
Cuckoo-pint 264—265
Cudweed, Heath or Wood 258, 259

Daisy, Ox-eye 146, 147
Dandelion, 146—147
    Broad-leaved Marsh 147
    Lesser 146, 147
    Narrow-leaved Marsh 147
Danewort 256, 257
Dead-nettle, White 194, 195
Death Cap, 223—224
    False 222, 223
Dock 192
Dog's Mercury 244, 245
Dog's-tail, Crested 150—151
Dogwood 286, 287
Dropwort see Meadowsweet

Earth Ball 224, 225
Edelweiss 93, 94, 95
Elder, 256, 290, 291
    Alpine or Red 290, 291
    Ground 245—246
Elm, Fluttering 269
    Wych 270
Eryngo, Field 113—114, 115

Fat Hen 190, 191
Feather Grass 126
Fescue, Meadow 150, 151
Feverfew 257
Fir, Silver 267
Fireweed see Willow-herb, Rosebay
Flag, Sweet 37

Yellow 34, 35
Flax, Cultivated 164—165
Fleabane, Canadian 202, 203
Fly Agaric 221—222
Forget-me-not, Water 31
Foxglove, 254—255
   Large Yellow 254, 255
Foxtail, Meadow 152, 153
Frogbit 18, 19

Garlic Mustard 239
Gean 127—128
Gentian, Spring 93—94
   Stemless Trumpet 93
Glasswort 58
Globe Flower 139
Globe Thistle, Pale 204, 205
Goat's-beard 148—149
Good King Henry 190
Goosegrass 197—198
Goutweed see Elder, Ground
Great Masterwort 246—247
Gromwell, Corn 178, 179
Guelder Rose 288, 290, 291

Hair-grass, Tufted 152, 153
Hard-fern 232
Hawkbit, Autumn 147—148
   Hairy 148
   Rough 148
Hawkweed, Mouse-ear 124, 125
Hawthorn, Midland 129
Hazel 275
Heartsease see Pansy, Wild
Heliotrope, Winter 46
Helleborine, Broad 263
   Dark Red 263—264
   Red 263
   White 262—263
Hemlock 30
Hemp-nettle, Common 253
   Large-flowered 252—253
Henbane 194—196
Hepatica 236, 237
Herb Bennet 241—242, 243
Herb Christopher see Baneberry
Herb Paris 260, 261
Hogweed 144, 145
Honesty, 238
   Perennial 238, 239
Honey Fungus or Honey Agaric 220, 221
Honeywort, Lesser 178, 179
Horehound, Black 194, 195
Hornbeam 275—276
Horseradish 40, 41, 237
Horsetail, Wood 230, 231
Houseleek, 90—91
   Hen-and-chicken's 91
Huckleberry see Bilberry

Jack-go-to-bed-at-noon see Goat's-beard
Jack-jump-about see Angelica, Wild

Knapweed, Brown-rayed 124, 125
   Greater 124

Laburnum, Purple 130—131

Ladies' Fingers see Vetch, Kidney
Lady-fern 230, 231
Lady's Mantle 141—142
Lady's Smock 139—140
Larch, Common 268, 269
Ledum 78, 79
Lettuce, Garden 202
   Prickly 202, 203
Lily, Martagon 259
   May 261
Lily-of-the-valley 259—260
Lime, Large-leaved 284, 285
   Small-leaved 284, 285
Livelong see Orpine
Locust see Acacia, False
Longleaf 114, 115
Loosestrife, Purple 42, 43
   Yellow 42, 43
Lords-and-ladies see Cuckoo-pint
Lucerne 164, 165
Lungwort 251
Lupin, Garden 242—243
Lyme-grass 64

Madder, Field 178, 179
Maize 167—168
Male Fern 230, 231
Mallow, Dwarf 193—194, 195
Maple, Common 282, 283
   Norway 282, 283
Marjoram 119
Marram Grass 63—64, 65
Marsh Marigold 29
Mayweed, Rayless see Pineapple Weed
Meadow-grass, 150, 151
   Annual 204, 205
   Sea 64
Meadow Rue, Greater 236, 237
Meadow Saffron see Crocus, Autumn
Meadowsweet 40—41
Melilot, Common 192—193
   White 193
Mezereon 284—286
Milfoil see Yarrow
Milk-vetch, 242, 243
   Meadow Beaked or Yellow 110, 111
Milkwort, Sea 60
Monkshood 236—237
Moor-grass, Blue 94—95
Moss, Hair 228
   Iceland 226
   Reindeer 226, 227
Mountain Ash see Rowan
Mountain Sanicle see Great Masterwort
Mountain Tassel-flower 248, 249
Mugwort 199—200, 201
Mullein, Common 119—120
   Purple 120, 121
   White 120—121

Nettle, Small 192, 193
   Stinging 190, 191—192, 194, 199
Nightshade, Black 196, 197
   Deadly 195, 196, 253—254
   Woody 43—44, 45
Nonea 116, 117
Nottingham Catchfly 107—108, 109

Oak, Common or Pedunculate 279
   Sessile or Durmast 279—280
Oat, 170—171
   Common Wild 171
Orchid, Bird's-nest 264
   Early Marsh 154
   Fragrant 154
   Greater Butterfly 264
   Green-winged 153—154
   Lady's Slipper 262, 263
   Lesser Butterfly 264
Orpine 91—92
Osier, Common 49—50
   Purple 49, 50
Ostrich Fern 232
Oxlip 248, 249

Paigle see Cowslip and Oxlip
Pansy, Wild 174, 175
Panther see Blusher, False
Parasol Mushroom 224, 225
Pasque Flower, Small 105
Pea, Earth-nut or Tuberous 175—176, 177
   Field or Garden 162—164
   Narrow-leaved Everlasting 242, 243
   Spring 242, 243
Pennycress, Field 173
Pepperwort, Hoary 189—190
Periwinkle, Lesser 250—251
Pheasant's-eye, Summer 171, 173
   Yellow 105—106
Pilewort see Celandine, Lesser
Pimpernel, Bog 176—177
   Scarlet 176—177
Pine, Black 267—268
   Mountain 78, 80, 268—269
   Scots 266, 267, 268
Pineapple Weed 201—202, 203
Pink, Carthusian 106, 107
   Cheddar 89—90
   Maiden 106, 107
Plantain, Buck's-horn 60
   Great 197
   Ribwort 145, 197
   Sea 60, 62, 63
Policeman's Helmet 34
Polypody 88, 89
Pondweed, Broad-leaved 20—21
   Canadian 20
   Curled 22
   Perfoliate 21
   Shining 21
Poor Man's Weather-glass see Pimpernel,
   Scarlet
Poplar, Black 50
   White 50
Poppy, Corn or Field 171—172, 173
   Opium 161
Potato 165—167, 173
Primrose 248
Puff-ball, Common 224, 225
Pyrethrum, Dalmatian 201

Quaking Grass 150, 151

Radish, Wild see Charlock, White
Ragged Robin 140, 141

Ramsons 260—261
Rape 162, 163
Raspberry 270—271
Reed, Common 35, 36, 39
Reed-grass 36, 37
Reedmace, 39
   Lesser 38, 39
Restharrow, Spiny 131
Rocket, Sea 57
Rockrose, Common 106, 107
Rose, Alpine, 274
   Dog 127
Rose of Sharon 113
Rowan 272—274
Rush, Flowering 32, 33
   Soft 35—36
Rye 168—169
Rye-grass, 151
   Italian 151

Saffron Milk-cap 218, 219
Sage 118
Sainfoin 109
St. John's Wort, Common 112—113
   Imperforate 112
   Mountain 112
Sallow, Great 280, 281
Saltwort, Prickly 58—59
Sanicle 246, 247
Saxifrage, Burnet 114—115
   Livelong 92—93
   Meadow 108, 109
Seablite, Annual 58, 59
Sea-holly 58, 60, 61
Sea Spurrey, Lesser 57—58
Sedge, Sand 62
Self-heal, Common 118, 119
Shepherd's Purse 173—174, 175
Silverweed 192, 193
Sloe see Blackthorn
Smallreed 36
Snake-root see Bistort
Sneezewort 44, 45
Snowdrop 261
Snowflake, Spring 262, 263
Soapwort 40, 41
Soldier, Gallant 204, 205
   Shaggy 204
   Water 19—20
Solomon's Seal, 260, 261
   Sweet-scented 260
Sorrel, Common 140, 141

Sowbread 249
Sow-thistle, Common or Smooth 179—180
Spearwort, Greater 29
Speedwell, Common 254, 255
   Germander 121—122
   Spiked 122, 123
Spindle-tree 281—282
Spiraea, Goat's-beard 240, 241
Spleenwort, Forked 87
   Green 87
   Maidenhair 87
Spruce, Norway 265—267
Spurge, Cypress 112, 113
   Sun 176, 177
Starwort 15
Stinkhorn 224—225
Stitchwort, Greater 240, 241
Stonecrop, White 92, 93
   Yellow 92, 93
Storksbill, Common 176, 177
Strawberry, Wild 240—241
Succory, Wild see Chicory
Sundew, Common 75—76
Swede see Rape
Sweep's Brush see Woodrush, Field
Sweet Vernal-grass 152, 153
Sycamore 282, 283

Tansy 200—201
Tarragon 200
Teasel, Fuller's 198
   Wild 198, 199
Thistle, Cabbage 45—46, 47
   Carline 124, 125
   Creeping 180, 181
   Marsh 45
   Musk 198, 199
   Stemless Carline 124
   Tuberous 45
   Welted 198—199
Thorn-apple 196, 197
Thyme, Wild 116—117
Timothy Grass 153
Toadflax, Common 121
Toothwort 255
Touch-me-not 244, 245
Twitch see Couch-grass

Vetch, Bush 143—144, 145
   Crown 109—110, 111
   Kidney 110, 111

Tufted 143
Vetchling, Meadow 142—143
Violet, Common Dog 240, 241
   Sweet 239—240

Wall-pepper see Stonecrop, Yellow
Wall-rue 88, 89
Water-aloe see Water Soldier
Water Chestnut 16, 17
Water Crowfoot, Common 14, 15
Water Dropwort, Fine-leaved 29—30
Water-lily, Fringed 17—18
   Small 13
   White 13
   Yellow 13, 14
Water-milfoil, Spiked 16
   Whorled 16, 17
Water-plantain, 33
   Floating 34
   Lesser 34
Water Soldier 19—20
Water Violet 17
Wheat 168, 169
Whitebeam 95—97
Whortleberry see Bilberry
Willow, Crack 49
   Cricket-bat 48
   Dwarf 78
   Goat see Sallow, Great
   Weeping 47
   White 48, 49
Willow-herb, Rosebay 245
Windflower, see Wood Anemone
   Snowdrop 233
Wintergreen, Larger or Round-leaved
   249—250, 251
   One-flowered 250, 251
Winter Heliotrope 46
Wolfsbane 236, 237
   Wood Anemone, 232—233
Yellow 233
Wood or Heath Cudweed 258
Woodruff, Sweet 255—256
Woodrush, Field 125
Wood-sorrel 243—244, 245
Wormwood 200
Woundwort, Hedge 252, 253

Yarrow 124—125
Yellow-knight Fungus 220, 221
Yellow-rattle 144, 145
Yorkshire Fog 152, 153